"...a gentle story, yet poignantly profound."

Praise for *Men Shake Hands*

" Dennis Britten has shown heroic vulnerability in bringing us in to his gripping coming of age story. *Men Shake Hands* marries both the joy and pain of growing up, loss, love, and laughter in such a relatable way."

　– Lindsey Lefler, *singer/actress & private music educator*

" I did not expect to find myself stopping mid-sentence to repeat a beautifully turned phrase or savor some subtle detail that might otherwise be lost in a quick read through. Nor did I expect to be moved to tears (quite often) by memories of my own similar life experiences. This book inexorably draws the reader, chapter by chapter, ever deeper into its heart, melding equal parts of humor and pathos. It is a gentle story, yet poignantly profound. *Men Shake Hands* is a must read for any young boy who grew up to be a father and for any mother who has ever loved a son."

　– Bill Wuertz, *retired banker, dedicated musician & avid reader*

" Dennis Britten's memories in *Men Shake Hands* are full of sensory detail and emotional heft. His writing captures the cadence, the wonder, and the wisdom of Davey, as he grows to understand and maneuver the world of the arts, and of love."

　– Beth Kahlen, *performing artist & teacher*

" Growing up in a small town during the 40s and early 50s, I found Dennis Britten's book *Men Shake Hands* to be spot on. The innocence of the time but also our private struggles. No whitewash. A captivatingly honest work."

　– Sunny Graham, *public educator, & psychotherapist*

" *Men Shake Hands* is a definite page turner that moves through the ups and downs of Davey's childhood passed in a small town and into a career in music and theater that took him through Europe and to New York City. This story of Davey's adolescence will open the eyes of parents whose children want to move beyond conformity and peer pressure. As such, I wouldn't be surprised to see *Men Shake Hands* become a best seller."

　– Michael Harvey, *university writing teacher & published author*

Praise for Other Writing

Made in Oregon
New and selected poems of Dennis Britten

. " We cannot go back to a time when we and the world were young, but through poems like these we draw strength from the past and find that we have come into our own, at home in the here and now."

　– Hugh Blumenfeld, M.D., Ph.D., *University of Connecticut hospital faculty, American folk musician & singer-songwriter*

MEN SHAKE HANDS

MEN SHAKE HANDS

HANDS

A Creative Reminiscence

by

DENNIS BRITTEN

Maderlson Works
Beaverton, Oregon

Cover photo by the author

Book design and production by Lucky Valley Press
Jacksonville, Oregon www.luckyvalleypress.com

Printed on acid-free paper

CONTENTS

Part Three: *Let's Pretend*

Part Four: *Being Me*

Part Five: *Who Let You Out*

Part Six: *Changes, 1952*

For my wonderful "movie star" mom
and my dad
who did everything he could
to raise me as his own

"Things can get busy, and sometimes we fall
short, but even the smallest moments can
have the biggest impact on a child's life.
Take time to be a dad today."
– President Barack Obama

Author's Note

Realizing early on that the memory is not infallible, I decided to take gentle liberties in filling in when the memory did not.

This book is entirely based on actual events, but I have changed most of the names of the people who were still living while I wrote it to preserve their anonymity.

Those of whom were no longer with us, I did not.

PART ONE

The American Way
1944

1

Boogie Man

The new house was cold and empty except for some furniture we brought with us from the old house. This new house had a lot more rooms and an upstairs where I had my own room now. Most of the rooms were empty but I liked our new house. I liked everything there except the long hallway at the bottom of the stairs where I came down from my new bedroom. There was an opening in the wall in that hallway. It was a doorway without a door and it was always dark and real quiet in there. My brother, Scotty told me somebody bad lived there. But I already knew that.

Sometimes, after it was our house, my mom went in that door to get her fur coat. But I never went in there. And I never went by that doorway alone. I told my brother—he was nine, four years older than me—that I would never walk by that door unless he held my hand. My brother, Scotty, he was bigger than me. He had red hair and he tried to teach me things he learned in school. Other times, he would tease me though. Scotty's hand was warm and it felt good when he took my hand. He told me not to be scared. But then when we were right in front of that door, he hollered in there and ran away and I had to run too. That was fun but scary.

That hallway was a way to the kitchen. But you could go through the front room too if you went the other way at the bottom of the stairs. So when no one was there to walk with me, I went the front room way to the kitchen. I really liked going that way because the front room had a fireplace. The old house didn't have a fireplace, just a big grate in the hall floor you could look through and see the fire burning down there in the furnace. It was kinda scary and I wasn't supposed to drop any toys in there. In the new front room, there were these dark red drapes on the windows that felt really smooth when you touched them.

We spent some days at the new house before we moved there—Mom said "unpacking," but we never slept there. Not until the day we moved. The reason we moved is that my mom didn't want to live with my dad any more. My dad got pretty mad about it. They had lots of fights and then he was gone.

Before that, my dad wasn't home very much. The war came and he joined the Merchant Marines to do his duty and I didn't see him very much. Scotty said Dad was helping to fight for "truth, justice and the American way." I didn't think it was as good as Army but Scotty said it helped our boys over there.

One day in the old house when Dad was home, he said, "Davey, I have a surprise for you." He looked at me real close and his blue eyes made my tummy feel funny good. Like the times he put soap all over his hands and rubbed one of my hands between his big ones in the wash basin then the other one to make them clean.

"I'm going to take you on a bike ride." His blond hair fell in his face then from bending over. "Would you like that?"

I said, "Yup." And he put me in his bike basket and took me all the way to the top of Rocky Butte. That's about all there is to remember except when he gave me my Army doll. I like my Army doll a lot. He's kind of silly looking. A big head and a baby doll face with red cheeks. But he has an Army uniform on and an Army cap and my dad gave him to me.

The other thing I remember is how my dad smelled. He smelled like outside—when I went outside after it rained. It was clean, kind of like grass and rain. Sometimes, I would open the drawer in his dresser so I could smell that smell. One time I found some long white balloons in the drawer. I took them outside and blew them up around the neighborhood. Mom got mad about that and told me not to get in his dresser any more.

~

One night before we moved from the old house, my mom came home from work and she was really happy. I was on the floor with my brother, Scotty in front of the radio listening to *Jack Armstrong, the all American boy.* She told the lady who took care of us that she could go home. Then, when the Wheaties guy came on the radio, she said she wanted to talk to us and turned it off. She told my brother, Scotty and me that she was going to marry Mr. Brugger and we would move with him to a real nice new house in the country.

Scotty got all red and he yelled that he didn't want to move to the country. He said he wanted to stay with his friends and keep going to his school. I didn't go to school yet.

"Why can't we be with Dad anymore?" He got so red his hair looked orange.

"Yeah," I said.

"You can't even remember," he yelled at me. "You're too little."

He was right.

The Priest from our church came to the house after that to talk to my mom but he made her cry. He took off his funny hat with the fuzzy ball on the top and put it on the arm of the couch. Mom went into the kitchen to make Father Fletcher some tea. While he was walking around the front room looking at things, I took his funny hat into my mom and dad's bedroom. Father Fletcher's hat was black. The inside was shiny and smooth and on the top there was a ball. It had three sides and looked like a propeller from the top. It came down on my eyes when I put it on my head so I had to put it on the back of my head to see it in the mirror on my mom's dressing table.

I heard my mom crying in the front room. I looked out and saw her sitting on the davenport with Father Fletcher. Father Fletcher was sitting there in his black dress and being mean to her so I threw his silly hat in the toilet.

When Mom found it and gave it to him all wet, he was mad. But even when Mom told me I shouldn't have done that, I could see her smile a little bit.

~

I liked the new house. Scotty said it wasn't really a new house but it was new to me. It was bigger than our other house and it had a lot of empty rooms to play in. Scotty moved with us. That was really good. He wasn't mad anymore. The first night we stayed there, I couldn't wait to sleep in my new room upstairs. Scotty had his bedroom right next door to me and he had stars on his ceiling that glowed in the dark. That was pretty nice. I didn't mind though 'cause I had my own bedroom.

Right after dinner, I went up there. I didn't even listen to my radio programs. I just wanted to be in my new room. I washed my face and hands and brushed my teeth in the bathroom upstairs that was just for Scotty and me. Then I went into my room and put my pajamas on. I got in bed and just listened to my new room.

After a while my mom came up to tuck me in and say my prayers with me like always. She smelled good like her powder. She looked real nice too. She had on her special dress with the red flowers on it and the red cherries necklace I liked. There was the little thing she called a mole in the V at the bottom of her throat. I knew it was there since I was a baby when I used to play with those cherries. She always made her lips real red with lipstick when she wore that dress and those cherries. I liked the way she looked like a movie star. Her hair was puffy on her shoulders.

She sat down on the bed and looked at me funny. Her head on one side and her eyebrow up.

"What?" I said.

"Well, aren't you going to give Mr. Brugger a good night kiss."

"How come?" I said.

"Well, honey," she said and turned her hanky in her fingers with her red fingernails, "Mr. Brugger is your new daddy now and you should give him a good night kiss."

Her gray blue eyes, blue like a blue cloud sky, looked at me then the way that made me feel like I was special to her. I always wanted to do what she wanted then.

"Oh, okay," I said. "If you think I should."

"Yes, I do," she said. She smiled at me and sat up straight like my Army doll sitting up there on top of the dresser.

Truth, justice and the American way.

I missed having a dad.

~

I followed her down the stairs. Slow because she had to turn kind of sideways to go down with her high heels. It made the seams on the back of her legs go squiggly. We went through the front room past the fireplace and the red drapes to where Mr. Brugger was sitting at the kitchen table. He was just sitting there looking at his own face in the big, dark kitchen window behind the table. His face was real bright in the window and his big nose looked bigger there. His black hair didn't show except the shiny part.

My mom said, "Dear…Davey wants to give you a good night kiss."

I guess he didn't know she was there because Mr. Brugger jumped up from the table real fast and his long legs almost knocked over the chair. His black hair in front came down to a point my mom called a widow's peak and his eyes were almost as black as his hair. He just stared down at me.

Then he put his hand out. "Men shake hands."

His hand was cold and kind of wet. My mom had her mouth open and my chest hurt awful. My throat burned like I was going to cry, so I ran out of the kitchen into the hallway. I bumped into some of the unpacking and almost stopped. I forgot about that dark doorway until I was right in front of it. Then I got cold all over and I didn't stop running until I was in my bed upstairs.

My new daddy now? What happened to my old one? The one I loved?

There was like sand in my throat and it made me cry.

Then the crying made me sleepy.

2

Everyday Name

I was born David Williams. But everybody called me Davey. My mom told me she didn't give me a middle name because no one ever liked their name anyway. So someday I could choose a middle name and then I could maybe even use it for my everyday name. Like Michael or Timmy or even James. If I wanted.

But I think Mom had another idea.

3

Moon Squares

My bedroom in the new house was big. That's why I picked it. My brother, Scotty didn't mind. It was bigger than his but he said he wanted to have stars on his ceiling that glow in the dark. That's what his bedroom had. But my room was bigger than any room in our old house. In that old house, I was always sleeping in the bed right next to Scotty's bed and there was no upstairs.

That first night in the new house, in my new bedroom, by myself, upstairs, in that big room, when I was five, I felt awful small. I had Teddy beside me and he was little. That made me feel bigger but I couldn't sleep.

The wall that my bed was on had two windows in the middle of it and the moon was shining in. Two big sideways squares of moon on the bedroom floor. If I got out of bed, I would have to step on them. I couldn't do that. I never stepped on moon before. The old house downtown in Portland never let moon in the house. It didn't keep me awake at night. But the moon came in this house, this house in the country—in Multnomah. We called it "Mudnomah" because the rain ran down Spring Garden hill into the road by our house and made lots of mud.

I wanted to get up and get my Army Doll off my dresser but I would have to step on that moon. Maybe if I stepped there, I would fall through to the downstairs. I had bumps all over my skin and I felt cold. I hugged Teddy.

Teddy was my friend. When I was a baby, I pulled his eyes off and my mom sewed two blue buttons there. His eyes were always wide open. He had long legs but not as long as mine, not like they used to be. Mine were longer than his now that I was five.

I pulled the quilt around us. My gramma's quilt. My dad's mom, she made it with her sisters and her little girls and some other ladies before they came to Oregon. It had big colored snowflake stars on it and each lady put her name in the middle of the snowflake star they made.

Behind the wall on the other side of the room was a closet that was really the attic. That's what my step-dad, Mr. Brugger called it. He said he put a light in there for me to see with and some hooks for clothes but it was dark past the light and I didn't want to go in there. So I put my clothes on the chair my mom gave me. It was my favorite chair from our old house. It had long animal claws where you put your hands at the end of the chair arms. They looked like lion feet and felt good under your fingers. It had swirly wood all around the legs and on the back of the chair. There was soft fuzzy cloth in the middle of the back and where you sit down. I liked to sit in that chair.

From my bed, I could see something in back of that chair. It stayed down close to the floor in part of the moon there. I couldn't sleep and I wanted my Army doll.

"Mom," I said. "Mommy!"

Nobody answered.

Mom and Mr. Brugger—she told me to call him John if I didn't want to say Dad—their bedroom was at the bottom of the stairs across from the front room at the start of the long hallway I didn't like.

That thing behind the chair moved.

"Mommy!"

Then I heard Mom, "Davey?"

"Yeah."

"What's the matter, honey?"

"I can't sleep."

Pretty soon, the flap, flap sound of her slippers came across the wood floor at the top of the stairs. Then quiet on the rug in my bedroom. The light came on. I squeezed my eyes shut.

"What is it, honey?" she said.

I opened my eyes a little bit.

She had a hair net on over her pin curls and her pink bathrobe with the puckery rows of fuzz. Her slippers stuck out underneath. Mom bent over in back of the chair and picked my jeans up off the floor.

I wasn't so scared then.

"I just wanted my Army doll."

Mom made a big yawn and wiped her eyes.

"Well, why didn't you get up and get him?"

She was still standing over by the door. Most of her lipstick was off and her face looked kind of white.

"I don't know," I said.

She walked over slow to my dresser and picked up my Army doll.

Then she brought it over to the bed. She breathed out a big breath and handed him to me.

"Well, you shouldn't wake us up for such things."

She sat down and looked at me after I put him under my other arm from Teddy. He was just the same size as Teddy. Mom's face was shiny up close and kind of greasy with cold cream. She pulled the top of the sheet over the quilt and bent down and kissed me.

"Now go to sleep, macushla."

"What's that mean?" I said.

"Macushla? That's Irish for sweetheart. It's what my mama used to call me when I was little." She started to get up but she didn't. She said, "Do you want to say your prayers again?"

"Okay," I said and I looked my eyes at the little mole at the bottom of her throat. "Now I lay me down to sleep. I pray the Lord my soul to keep. If I should die before I wake, I pray the Lord my soul to take."

Mom smiled at me with her eyes the way that made me feel special, "Good boy."

"What does that mean?"

"What does what mean?"

"My soul to take."

She reached her hand out and smoothed it slow over Aunt Pearl Williams' name on my quilt. She watched her hand move slow and then her gray blue eyes looked at me.

"Well, it means that you want to be with God."

I got bumps again. "But I don't. I want to be with you."

Mom took a big breath. "I know you do, honey." Then she yawned and said, "Now, go to sleep and we'll talk about it in the morning."

"Okay," I said.

Mom turned off the light by the doorway. "Sleep tight."

"Tight?"

"Go to sleep, honey."

The light switch glowed in the dark. And the moon came back.

"Mom!" I yelled.

"What, Davey."

"I'm gonna fall downstairs."

"What?"

"The upstairs is gonna fall down!"

The light came back on. Squeeze eyes shut.

"What?" Mom said.

"Well, what's gonna keep my bedroom up here?"

Mom's eyebrows wrinkled down, "What do you mean?"

"If I step on moon, will I fall down to the down stairs?"

Mom was looking at me from the doorway with her mouth open. "What?"

I was breathing fast. There was a brown spot on my bedroom ceiling over her head near the door.

Mom stood in the doorway for a long time. She looked up at the ceiling like she was looking at the spot. She took a big breath again and let her air out real slow. Then she came over to the bed. She picked up the glass of water that was sitting on the table by my bed next to the radio with the wooden flowers on the front and gave it to me. The radio made me think of my favorite radio program. The funny one, *Baby Snooks*.

"Sit up honey and have some water."

I put my fists under me and pushed myself up to take the glass. Teddy fell over. Mom sat on the bed and waited for me to drink the water.

"Now," she said. "Tell me again what you're afraid of."

"There's moon in my bedroom and I'm way up in the air. How come the bedroom won't fall? I don't want to die before I wake."

Mom's eyebrows wrinkled down again like they did. "Oh, honey," she said and started to laugh. "Oh, I'm sorry. I know it's not funny. But you're not going to die. You're a healthy, dear little boy and nothing's going to happen to you."

She reached out and touched my cheek. I smelled the Jergen's Lotion smell on her hand.

"Lie down, Davey and let me teach you another part of that prayer." She lifted the covers and I scooted down in the warm and got my Army doll and Teddy back under my arms. "When I was a little girl this was my favorite part and I never wanted to say the prayer until I learned this part."

"It's the same prayer?" I said.

"The first part is the same. Then you say: 'But I will live for other days and pray the Lord to guide my ways.' Isn't that better?" and then she made a little laugh.

Then I said it. "But I will live for other days and pray the Lord to guide my ways."

Mom put her hand on my forehead. Her hand was cool and nice. It was soft on my face. Then she scooted down next to me on the bed. "I'm going to stay right here with you until you fall asleep and you'll see in the morning, you'll still be here—upstairs."

When I woke up in the morning, I was still there, and I could smell the bacon Mom was cooking downstairs…then the front door opened and I heard Mr. Bugger yell, "Look out world. Here comes Brew!" The door closed and he was gone to work. Mom was laughing in the kitchen. I scooted down in bed. Mr. Brugger was really scary.

4

Rule Days

My mom wet her comb under the faucet in the kitchen sink and parted my hair with it. "Now I want you to be a perfect gentleman today," she said and combed my hair to the side. She licked her fingers and pressed the hairs on the back of my head down—the ones that always stood up. "We're going to Multnomah Grade School to see about getting you into kindergarten."

I was really excited that maybe I could go to school now like Scotty. My brother, Scotty was in fourth grade there 'cause he was older than me.

I followed Mom through the front room by the fireplace and the smooth red drapes. She looked in the mirror by the front door and put her little pink feathers hat on. She pulled the veil down just under her nose and then twisted around and reached down the back of her leg to straighten the seam in her stocking. She pulled her pink gloves onto her hands, took my hand and out we went through the front door, down the big hill and through our little town of Multnomah to the school.

~

The lady in the office at school told us to have a seat while we waited for Mrs. Rheinlander, the kindergarten teacher to come to the office.

Mom pulled her skirt down over her knees, then looked kind of mad at me—her eyebrows wrinkled down. "Davey, why do you insist on touching everything along the way? You always get your hands dirty." She pulled off one of her gloves, then took her hanky out of her purse and said, "Now you have dirt on your face. Stick out your tongue."

I stuck my tongue out and she wet her hanky on it. I could smell perfume and her hanky tasted like powder. Then she rubbed the hanky on my cheek. Her pretty ruby ring sparkled in the corner of my eye. The engagement ring from John, my step dad. John said, "eight carrot, French cut."

Mrs. Rheinlander was a big lady. She had a big tummy and an apron on with different colored paint on it.

"There are so many war babies today, we have to limit the class. I'm sure you understand, Mrs. Brugger. We schedule the children to attend four days a week." She had lots of fuzzy hair and her cheeks were red. She bent over and her big eyes looked at me. "You'll have one school day every week as a day off. Isn't that great, Davey?" She clapped her hands and laughed and she didn't wait for me to answer.

~

So I started Kindergarten after New Years the first year we moved to the new house with John, my step-dad. The first days, my brother, Scotty walked me to school in the morning and my mom met me half way when I came home. After we moved into the new house, I didn't see Scotty very much except when he walked me to school. He had his own room now, like me, and he had new friends to play with. He walked ahead of me now though when we walked to school, like he didn't want to hold my hand anymore 'cause he was older than me and he got mad when I was pokey.

One time, when it was cold out and I was walking behind him 'cause he was acting like I wasn't even there, I stopped at a puddle and picked up a leaf to sail like a boat. It was an old brown leaf that was smooth on the edges. Kind of like a little canoe. Scotty turned around and came back. He kicked some mud at me and some little rocks from the road. I was down by the puddle and when I looked up, his face was red and he stamped his foot so hard he almost dropped his books.

"C'mon, Davey. You're gonna make me late for school again."

He was so mean I didn't say anything but I got right up and started walking with him. He wasn't pretending I wasn't there now.

"You know," he said, "Brew is a pretty nice guy."

Scotty called our step-dad Brew like a lot of people did. He was looking at me real serious, his blue green eyes looking at me hard.

"And you're lucky to have him as a step-dad but if you don't start acting more grown up pretty soon, he may change his mind."

"What do you mean," I said, "change his mind?"

Scotty looked away from me then and clicked his tongue like I should know what he meant.

"Well, he might just not want to be your step-dad."

I never thought about that before.

~

I liked kindergarten a lot. We did fun things. Projects, Mrs. Rheinlander called them. With big blocks of wood we built walls and towers we could get in like a fort and my favorite thing was when we painted with poster paints. The smell was neat, almost like something to eat. It always made me hungry and mixing the paint up was fun. I painted lots of things Mrs. Rheinlander said were good too. She let me take them home to my mom. Most of them were hand prints but then I painted the dog I wanted to have and then I painted the cat we did have. The black cat Mom brought home from the bakery in Multnomah that kept running in and out of the door and nobody wanted. Kitty.

I thought about painting something for John, my step-dad but he didn't look at the things I painted for Mom. Like he wasn't interested in things like that. Like he wished I wouldn't bring stuff home. I made one for my dad though and I asked Mom to mail it. John made hand-made watch crystals for all the jewelry stores. I guess they were a lot better than my art. Or maybe he was just busy with his work and fixing things around our new house…

He wasn't so scary now.

Sometimes he made me laugh when he was fixing things. He would pound some nails and then stop and take his pipe out of his mouth. The sweet smell of tobacco smoke was all around. Then he would stand up straight and tall. He'd put his hand through his wavy, black hair and sing real loud for a minute. "Open up those pearly gates; here comes Brew on his roller skates." Then pound some more nails. Sometimes pounding up on his ladder he slipped and hit his thumb and he would yell, "GOD!" then sing, "bless America."

I laughed then and he would smile down at me like he didn't mind I was there.

I liked being with him while he worked. I liked watching him do things. Singing that, "GOD! bless America." That's all he did too, when he was cutting up the big old maple tree that lightning split in the front of the house and the saw slipped. I was standing right there, maybe in the way, watching and there was blood all over him and on the saw like in a horror movie. He looked at me really mean, like I made him do it. Scary again. But then all he did was walk jerky into the house singing, "God Bless America."

Sometimes he let me use his tools. Let me turn some screws for him. He told me, "You have to hold your tongue just right." I would hand him nails too, when he was nailing something. Show him he could like me.

One time he looked up at me right in my eyes watching when he was making a bolt tight with a wrench. His deep brown eyes dark under his black eyebrows. He told me, "It's okay if you use my tools when I'm here but be sure you don't touch them when I'm not."

He said that because one time I was in the basement alone and went into his "workshop" there, where he had all his tools hanging in rows over his work bench. I was looking for something to clean up some paste I spilled on the basement floor when I was doing a project. His workshop was real neat. There were rows of shiny silver screw drivers and rows of pliers, shelves and drawers with little signs on them filled with jars and bottles with hooks and screws and bolts and nails and all kinds of neat things in them. On the floor near his bench was a can of turpentine. I didn't know what that was, turpentine, but I wanted to see if there was anything in the can. I couldn't see in it. It was dark in there. So I picked it up and put it up to my eye. This stuff poured into my eye and mom had to take me to the doctor. After that there was a rule not to go in there by myself. But I really liked to look at John's shiny tools. So I guess I forgot sometimes.

5

Poster Paints

I was in the basement one time on a Friday, it was my day off from school, and didn't have anything to do. I looked at John's tools for a while and then I sat down in my play area under the water pipes that were in the basement ceiling. I wished I could watch the clothes washing some more. But Mom was finished washing the clothes in the new Bendix we got that made the clothes go around and around behind a window in front.

Then I started thinking about Kindergarten and poster paints. I looked out the basement door. Mom was out by the big old cherry tree hanging the clothes on the clothes line. She had on her wide stretchy belt with her big skirt that came down almost to her white bobby socks and her white blouse with the short puffy sleeves she called her peasant blouse.

She was kind of dancing with the clothes in the grass that came up over her shoes and singing, "You are my sunshine, my only sunshine."

I sneaked out the basement door and through the front yard and ran down the moo-cow hill road by our house. It was fun to put my arms out and pretend I was flying. Like I could sail up through the telephone wires, up through the clouds and over the muddy hills and land, plop, right in the school yard. All the kids with their eyes open wide because I could fly.

When I got to the school, all the kids were painting with the poster paints. The nice smell I liked. Like something good to eat. My friend, Sunny Lea, was painting real fast, putting on lots of red under the blue sky. She had lots of different colors on her apron and a little bit of blue in her brown hair. Sunny Lea lived by me. Her dad owned the cow on our moo-cow hill. Michael, he was a bully and I didn't like him, he stopped painting and looked at me mean. His little eyes squinty in his fat face.

"What're you doing here?" he said.

"Visiting," I said.

"Visiting? What you mean, visiting?"

Sunny Lea looked at me quick. Pretty blue eyes. "Hi Davey," she said and started painting again.

Then Mrs. Rheinlander saw me, her eyebrows up high. "Well, hello Davey. What a surprise."

"I'm visiting," I said.

"Oh, I see. Does your mother know you're here?"

"No," I said. "She's hanging clothes."

"I see. Well now, let's go to the office and give her a call."

Sunny Lea said, "Bye Davey." Then she smiled at me.

Mrs. Rheinlander and me, we went to the office and called my mom. "Yes, he's here visiting," she said to Mom. "Bus-driver's holiday, I guess."

Then we walked back to kindergarten to wait for my mom to come. Mrs. Rheinlander had her poster paint apron on with all the colors. She rubbed the back of her big neck with her hand and said, "Davey, I'm curious. Why did you want to come and visit us today? Did you miss us?"

"I missed the painting," I said.

"Oh, you like the painting, do you?"

"Yup. I like to paint."

"Well, you do very well. I'm glad you like it but, you know, we don't have enough room for everybody all the time. So you have to give other children a chance to paint too. That's why it's important to stay at home on your day off. We would love to have you every day but there just isn't enough room."

She bent down and put her face real close to mine. Her cheeks were really red and her breath smelled like macaroni and cheese.

"Will you promise me to stay home on your day off if I give a little talk about painting to the class while we wait for your mother?"

I said, "Okay."

Mrs. Rheinlander liked to talk about Art. She liked Art so much that it made us all like it too. Some pictures she showed us she said were famous paintings. Pictures in magazines like the magazines my friend, Mrs. Baldwin, had for me to look at.

"Painting like our poster painting is only one kind of Art," she said. "Does anyone here know what else we do in class is a kind of Art?"

Sunny Lea yelled out right away, "Blocks."

"That's right Sunny Lea. Blocks. Building with blocks like we do is another kind of Art." It was neat that Sunny Lea knew that.

Mrs. Rheinlander told us that building with blocks is a way to learn how to make buildings. She showed us pictures of our Oregon capitol in Salem and a tower she said was in France.

Then she showed us something really great. She told us that later we would make things out of clay too, and showed us pictures of statues. She said people made them out of clay and that some were made out of stone. There were pictures of people carving statues with a thing called a chisel like in John's workshop. The pictures of the statues they carved were so real looking they made the skin on my arms all tingly. I wished I could do that. I never saw anything like it before. One statue was a big naked man named David, like me, and one was another naked man thinking.

I told my Mom about it on the way home. I told her I went because I missed the painting but I promised Mrs. Rheinlander that I wouldn't come again on my day off. I didn't tell Mom how much I wanted to make statues like the ones in the pictures though.

Mom pulled on my hand tight and looked in my face real serious. Her eyebrows wrinkled down like she did. "You should never leave the house without telling me," she said. "Do you understand?"

I looked at the little mole at the bottom of her throat that moved when she talked.

"But Mom, the painting…"

"I don't care about the painting." Then she pulled on my arm again. Her face all red. "Do you understand?"

"Yes," I said.

"Good," Mom said.

I guessed Mom didn't care about painting so much. She was really mad. I didn't want to make her mad like Scotty did or my dad. We walked slow through Multnomah looking in all the windows and I tried to keep from touching the stores and stuff.

I was thinking about poster paints though. Then I said, "Mom, why does Mrs. Rheinlander think I drive a bus?"

6

Statues

The next day when I woke up, it was Saturday so I still couldn't do poster paints. So I did my next favorite thing. I took my pillow into the "spare room." I liked that room. It's where my secret place was. One time, before we moved there, the "spare room" was a kitchen. The whole upstairs was a place for somebody to live. There was the bathroom that's now for Scotty and me. There was Scotty's room and John said probably my room was somebody's front room. Then there was this kitchen. It still had a drain board with cupboards under there and John put a bed in the place where somebody used to have a stove and refrigerator. I liked to get in the cupboard on the end, the last one, with my pillow and close the door. It was my secret place.

So that day, I crawled in there, in my secret place in the old-kitchen-spare-room. I pulled my pillow in and went back to sleep.

When I woke up and came out of my secret place, out of the old-kitchen-spare-room, Scotty was in the bathroom combing his hair. He had his Scout shirt on. I liked to watch him comb his red hair and he looked real nice in his Scout shirt. So I watched him. He had a neat red and yellow scarf and an Indian beaded thing to hold it on. He had a new tenderfoot pin. It was gold and it was pinned on his shirt now. The shirt was Army color like my Army doll. I wondered if Scotty was helping to fight for truth, justice and the American way like our Dad.

"How come you got your Scout shirt on?" I said.

Scotty wrinkled his eyebrows at me.

"Because, Stupid, I'm going to a Scout meeting."

"I'm not stupid," I said.

"You are too. Why else would I have my Scout shirt on?"

"It's too early for a Scout meeting."

"We're going to plan a camping trip," he said.

"Oh," I said and went to eat breakfast.

After I ate breakfast, Mom said she was going next door to have a cup of coffee with Mrs. Herman. "Be good while I'm gone," she said, "and don't play with matches." She always said that.

I didn't have anything to do again so I went down the basement stairs from the kitchen to look at John's tools.

Behind the Bendix, the sun was coming in the basement windows from the back yard. I walked into the workshop and stood in the doorway. All the tools were lined up there above the bench, all shiny and neat. Next to the long row of screw drivers and pliers was a row of chisels—little ones, medium size ones and big ones. They had clear gold colored handles you could see through and silver blades that shined in the kind of dark basement. They looked like the chisels that people made statues with in the pictures Mrs. Rheinlander showed us.

I thought that would be fun. More fun than poster paints. I would like to try that.

The turpentine can was there beside the bench. Real quiet, I sneaked up to it. I put it on the wooden grate that was on the floor in front of the bench and climbed up on it. Then I was up on the top of the bench. I guess I forgot about the rule. The chisels were right in front of me. I took one out of the holder on the wall and just felt it. Through the clear gold handle you could see metal in the middle. The curves were smooth in my hand and it looked real sharp on the end. Sharp enough to cut stone. I took down a hammer from the wall and put it under my arm and got back down.

I would just try it and then put it back.

I took the hammer and chisel over to the cement floor and got down on my knees. Then I turned the chisel so it touched the cement and hit it with the hammer. Nothing. It didn't do anything. I hit it again but nothing happened. I hit it again, this time real hard. Something happened. Uh oh, little pieces broke out of the blade. That wasn't right. It was supposed to cut stone.

There was something behind me. A sound. Then a smell. That sweet smoke smell. I looked up from the floor. *John.* His pipe was in his mouth smoking and the sun was in his eyes. They were red. His black hair in the widow's peak came down all the way to his eyes. I couldn't breathe. He took the pipe out of his mouth. Then a low sound like thunder.

I heard the pipe go crack on the basement floor somewhere behind me when I ran to the basement stairs. I fell on the first step but I jumped up again and ran up the basement stairs to our kitchen. My knee was stinging where I fell. I turned into the long hallway with the scary doorway. There was a drum booming in my head, but I could hear him coming after me up the basement stairs. Something like a big hand grabbed my inside and squeezed. I wanted to hide. But not in the scary doorway. Somebody bad lives in there.

He's coming. I run upstairs. My knee stinging. The drum booming. I hear his shoes clomp in the hallway downstairs then up the stairway behind me. I'm in the doorway of the old-kitchen-spare-room running. Headed for my secret place. Then I can't move. His big hand grabs the back of my pants and lifts me up. There's air all around me. I'm flying through the air in the upstairs old-kitchen-spare-room. Like going down too fast in the elevator. Not the moo-cow hill pretend flying. The sandy wall hits me. I can't breathe. It scrapes my arm. Then I land on the bed, eyes closed tight.

John, my step-dad, he just threw me across the room!

I can hear him breathing.

Nothing else.

After a long time, I open my eyes. John is standing in the doorway. His face is red. I watch him. My knee stings. And my arm. Then his face is not red anymore and he turns around and walks away.

~

I hope he doesn't change his mind about being my step-dad.

7

Radio Guys

My brother, Scotty, he didn't like phonies. That's what he called them—phonies. Like radio guys.

On one of his favorite radio programs he listened to in the afternoon when he got home from school—me still out playing with the neighbor kids—they talked about Wonder Bread. Builds strong bodies eight ways. Scotty, he heard that every day and he said that's what he wanted—a strong body. Every day, he's asking my mom to buy him some Wonder Bread so he can have a strong body.

One night when Mom got home from her job at the bank, she was unpacking the groceries she bought and Scotty came walking slow to the kitchen door from the last one of his radio programs—The Green Hornet. There on the drain board was a loaf of bread, bright white with red and yellow and blue balloons all over it.

Scotty's eyes get so big. I never see him get so excited. Most of the time, he acts real cool. Doesn't get excited about stuff. This time his eyes get big and he jumps through the doorway into the kitchen and runs crazy arms in the air up to the drain board and grabs the loaf of bread. Hugs it in his arms.

"Wow," he says. "You got Wonder Bread."

Mom looks down at him and kind of shakes her head.

"I don't know why you want that instead of the nice fresh bread from the bakery."

Scotty's eyebrows go up, surprised. Like he can't believe she would say that.

"Mom," he says. "This builds bodies eight ways. I told you that. Can I have some now?"

Her lips go together and pucker out like she's thinking.

"Scott, it's almost dinner time. I don't want you to spoil your appetite."

Scotty's voice goes high and his eyebrows wrinkle down.

"Ah geez, Mom," he says.

"Well, okay," she says. "But only one slice."

His face changes right away into a big smile. His freckles bouncing around.

"Wow. Thanks, Mom."

So then Scotty, he opens the red, yellow and blue balloon wrapper and takes a slice and folds the wrapper real neat again, like it's really precious stuff. He takes it over to the table and sits down next to me where I'm coloring in my coloring book. And then he takes a bite. His eyebrows come down and his eyes almost close and he nods his head up and down like he's thinking about what's in his mouth.

"Doesn't taste like much," he says.

Then he thinks some more.

"Kind of 'tuck to the roof of my mout' and it tate like paper," he says, talking funny.

Mom turns around and looks at him through her glasses that are slided down her nose. "Well, you're going to have to eat this bread. We can't afford to buy something you don't eat."

Right away, he swallows and looks up at her with big eyes.

"Oh, sure Mom. I don't really care what it tastes like. I just want a strong body."

Well, he did eat that whole loaf—Mom made him sandwiches for school every day with it—and he was on his third red, yellow and blue balloon loaf when things started to happen. But not the things Scotty wanted to happen.

Scotty always listened to people he thought were smart and acted like they cared about him. As long as it wasn't Mom. Ever since his third grade teacher Mrs. Long got him interested in school. After that, he was interested in learning most everything and always tried to get me excited 'bout things too. Always trying to teach me stuff.

One day, when Scotty was on his third loaf of Wonder Bread, he was at lunch in school after gym class. That day, gym class was wrestling and Scotty, he got smashed by this big kid. He was real steamed up about it. So he was telling his buddy, Jack, that he couldn't figure out why his body wasn't getting stronger like the radio guy said it would.

Well, Jack thought that was real funny—that Scotty was trying to get a strong body with Wonder Bread. He grabbed a slice of Scotty's bread off his sandwich and before Scotty could grab it back, Jack had it rolled into a nothing little ball of dough. Then he slung it in the air over the lunch table and it hit the ceiling up there. It just went plop and stuck up there in those white squares with all the little holes in them.

Kids saw it up there and started laughing. Pretty soon, everybody that was there was pointing and laughing.

After Scotty told me about it, I saw it still hanging up there in the cafeteria.

Well so, this really got Scotty embarrassed. He thought they were laughing at him but I think they were really laughing at that silly Wonder Bread stuck up there.

On his way home from school that day, he stopped by the little grocery store in Multnomah, where he always stopped. Mom called it the Mama and Papa store. Scotty stopped there every day to talk to the guy he said was his friend—I guess the guy was the Papa. Scotty said the guy was real smart and Scotty liked to talk to him. Anyway, he told the guy why he was upset.

The Papa guy said, "Why do you eat that crap?"

Well, 'course, Scotty, he said, "It builds bodies eight ways."

And the Papa guy, he said, "Bull shit."

That's what Scotty told Mom and me and John that night while we were waiting for Mom to put our dinner on the table. Then Scotty said that the Papa guy said he just needed to eat vegetables. He said that would make Scotty strong. But Scotty said he didn't like vegetables. So the guy told him that when he was little, he learned to like vegetables because he ate them first while they were still hot and he was still hungry and didn't leave 'em until last when they were cold.

So, Scotty told Mom that's what he was going to do and he wasn't gonna eat that crap, Wonder Bread anymore.

Mom didn't say anything when she put our food on the table, but I saw her smile and wink her eye at John when Scotty wasn't watching. Kind of like a game. Like she was on John's team now. Against us.

I couldn't believe Scotty though. Scotty and me, we always hated vegetables and now as soon as Mom puts his plate down, he's eating his broccoli like it was the best stuff he ever tasted.

"It's yucky," I said.

Scotty looked up from his plate his eyebrows up like he couldn't believe I would say that.

"Davey, try it while it's hot," he said. "It's really good."

He was always trying to teach me something. Something he learned. Most of the time, I didn't understand but I guessed I could take a bite of that green stuff. So I did.

"Yeah," I said. "It's hot but it still tastes yucky. I don't care if it makes strong bodies. Who wants a strong body if that stuff tastes yucky?"

That taste made me shiver all over.

Well, Scotty didn't give up when he wanted to teach me something. And this was something he was really excited about. He looked around the table and saw the Ketchup bottle that was always on our table at dinner time. I loved Ketchup.

"How about you put some ketchup on it?" he said.

"Ketchup on the green stuff?"

"Sure," he said. "Why not? Right, Mom?"

Mom was smiling at John again and John was shaking his head slow like they knew something we didn't. Then she smiled at Scotty. A different smile. Like she was happy with Scotty but her eyes sparkling like she was going to laugh.

"If it'll help, sure. Why not?" she said.

John smiled at me. His white teeth showing, like the whole thing was really funny. Like he finally got Mom away from me. The first time he even looked at me since I used his chisel. Most of the time it was like I wasn't even there. But now he smiled and he pushed me the bottle of ketchup across the table.

"Go ahead, it'll put hair on your teeth."

"What?" I said.

Mom made a face, quick at John.

"Don't mind John, honey," she said. "He's just teasing."

Teasing—I didn't know if he was still mad at me or what. He still kind of scared me.

He didn't scare Scotty though. So he wasn't gonna scare me. And now it was like he was laughing at me. I slow unscrewed the top off and pointed the bottle at the green stuff. Then I pounded my hand on the bottom of the bottle like you do. A slow glob of red landed on my broccoli. Looked like Christmas. Then I tasted it.

It was pretty good. I loved ketchup.

"Pretty good," I said.

Scotty grinned at me across the table. His freckles spread out over his cheeks. His gray green eyes bright. Like he was just happy he taught me something. I was really glad he didn't have to roll his eyes around and this time I didn't feel stupid.

~

The first day I saw the blob of Wonder Bread at school up in those white squares on the ceiling hanging there between all the little white dots, I came in the house early before dinner and went in my room to get my coloring book. I thought Scotty was in his room listening to his radio but I could hear him talking. I looked in his room and he was sitting in front of the radio in his chair that was most of the time by his desk. The Wonder Bread guy was talking and Scotty was talking loud back to him.

"Oh yeah?" he said. "I tried that crap."

"builds bodies," the radio guy said.

"Bull shit," Scotty said.

"eight ways," the guy said.

"Liar," Scotty said and stood up with his fists on his hips.

Then he sees me standing in his doorway.

"I hate phonies," he said.

8

More Changes

On our way to school, my brother Scotty and me, we both liked to run down the moo-cow hill by our house with our arms out—pretend we were flying. You could stand at the top and just let yourself run. It was kind of like falling except you had to look out for the mud holes. But this day was different. It was Spring and school was almost over. There were all these daffodils in the field where Sunny Lea's cow, Betsy was. And buttercups too.

Scott ran down the hill in front of me but at the bottom, he just stopped and looked at the field. When I got up to him, he just said, "Wow!" and kept looking. From one side of the hill to the other side, the field was full of yellow. There were a gazillion flowers there and they were all yellow.

After that, we walked slow and Scotty reached down and took my hand like he used to. Scotty was getting taller pretty fast. Now, he was a lot bigger than me. I liked walking with my big brother. It was neat him holding my hand too but I knew he probably thought I was just this little kid. So when a bird landed on a fence post by the road, I said, "Look the Robins are back. Must be spring." I learned in school they're the first sign of spring.

Scotty just looked down at me and said, "Blue Jay."

He was pretty smart. He knew about outdoor stuff.

Scotty got real quiet then and when I looked up at him, he closed his eyes for a minute. His face got kind of red, like it did sometimes. Mom said because he had red hair. When he opened his eyes they were all watery.

That's when he told me about moving away.

"Davey, I'm gonna go live with Dad," he says. "I know I told you I wouldn't right away but it's gonna be summer pretty soon and school'll be out."

It's silly, but I want to say, "Who's gonna walk with me by the scary doorway?" but I don't.

Scotty kept talking but his face went away from me.

"Dad said that maybe I could stay with Aunt Pearl and Uncle Herb on their dairy farm for some of the summer."

Then my heart is in my ears like that drum pounding and my feet don't want to work right. Scotty's older than me. I can't yell at him, "don't go."

I don't care about all those stupid daffodils now. I want to run at Scotty and push him down in the mud and yell NO at him. But I just hold his hand tight so I won't fall down.

"What did I do?" I said.

His eyes looked quick at me and he let go of my hand. "What?"

"Did I make you mad or something?"

Scotty looked up at the big clouds over us then and let all his air out, "No."

"But why do you want to go away?" I said.

He looked down at me again. Then his eyes kind of rolled up like they did when he was trying to teach me something from school and I didn't understand. Like he'd say it one more time was all.

"Aunt Pearl has horses I can ride, Davey. And. Well, you know, Mom and me, we yell at each other all the time."

"Why do you do that?" I almost holler at him.

"I don't know Davey," he said and let his air out with a sound like it hurt. "Maybe because I miss Dad. And Mom, she just makes me mad."

People always said that Scotty is like Dad and I'm like Mom. Maybe that's why she gets mad at him so much. Maybe that's why he wants to be with Dad. 'Cause he's like him. But I know it's me. I do stuff people don't like.

First my dad left. Now my brother. And since I chiseled the basement floor John doesn't talk to me very much. Like he doesn't even want me around.

My chest felt real tight and my throat hurt like I was gonna cry. I didn't want Scotty to know that so I didn't say anything and we just walked slow to school. I didn't want to go to school. I just wanted to run away from Scotty so my chest wouldn't feel like he was sitting on it but it was almost the end of Kindergarten so I just thought about the fairy tale book Mrs. Rheinlander was reading to us. I liked the pictures of ladies with tall cones on their heads sitting on horses that a young prince was leading. That made me forget about crying a little bit.

I came home from school by myself. Scotty always stayed late at school so I went home before he did. Sometimes I walked with other kids from our neighborhood. I liked to walk with Sunny Lea the most but she went a different way sometimes. Like today.

It was better to have someone to walk with by Mrs. Allen's house. Mrs. Allen had this mean old dog that was always waiting behind the fence in her front yard. It was a big ugly dog. Most of his hair was gone and he got real close to the ground looking up at you with his gold yellow eyes and growled low. If you got too close to the fence he would spring up and bark real loud. He looked like he wanted to jump over the fence and get you with his mean old teeth. Sometimes I would forget and be thinking about something else. He would scare me bad. Sometimes if I had to go to the bathroom anyway, that stupid old dog would make me pee my pants. Stupid dog.

So I walked home alone way on the other side of the road from Mrs. Allen's and went down the little hill on the other side of our house to see my friend Mrs. Baldwin. She lived down the hill behind our house. When I felt bad she could make me feel good. I went to see her most days but today I really wanted her to make me feel good like she always did.

I didn't tell her about Scotty going away but she could tell when there was something. She always really looked at me. Not like other big people that looked at you but didn't see. She came out of her garden with a handful of sweet peas—all different colors, red and blue, purple and pink—and got out some cookies she made. She gave me a glass of milk and took off her apron. Then we went in and sat down in her front room. She was a really old lady. She had gray hair with braids over the top of her head and real pink cheeks. She smiled all the time. She was always happy.

Mr. Baldwin was sitting in the front room in his suit and vest. He had on a white shirt with a striped tie that looked nice with his white hair. But he looked kind of weird too sitting there all dressed up. He was always real quiet and looked kind of sad. I felt bad for Mr. Baldwin always sitting in their front room all dressed up. Waiting. He used to be a school principal. Now he just had students come to his house—his study. He was waiting for a student like he did all the time.

Sometimes Mrs. Baldwin would read to me out of magazines and Mr. Baldwin would listen too. Or we would just look at all the colors in the pages of the magazine. Mrs. Baldwin would say, "Oh Davey, look at that red rose. Isn't that a beautiful color?" or "My, my, what a wonderful sunny color that room is." We would sit right next to each other with the magazine on our laps. She would turn a page and then I would turn a page. She would show me something and then it was my turn to show her something.

Today, we sat on her davenport and just talked though, while I drank my milk and ate the cookies. Mrs. Baldwin always talked to me like I was a big person. She really listened to me and I could tell her anything. I didn't want to tell her about Scotty though. It would make my chest tight again. I just looked at the sun coming through her colored glass things on the shelves in her sun porch windows while we talked. Those things were beautiful, especially the dark purple vase and the red bowl. It was red like rubies. Like Mom's ruby ring. Eight carrot, French cut. Only more. There was glass animals too, a gold giraffe and a pale blue fish. She loved colors. So do I.

Mr. Baldwin, Arthur she called him, crossed his legs and aimed the toe of his shoe in the air at the designs in the rug. He closed one eye while he watched the tip of his toe trace the design. Then he fell asleep.

He jumped when his student rang their doorbell. That made me and Mrs. Baldwin laugh and Arthur laughed too. He went to the door to let his student in and made a stinky on the way kind of loud and I tried not to laugh.

Mrs. Baldwin said we had to stop for today. She went to the kitchen and put her apron on. I went to the kitchen too. She took some of her loose hair in her fingers and put it back under her braids. Then she smiled at me big.

"I want you to take these sweet peas home for you and your mama."

She got wax paper and put it around the stems.

"Aren't the colors just wonderful? They smell good too."

She was right. Real sweet. I thanked her for the flowers and went down her front steps. I was happy.

"Say hello to your mama for me," she said.

"Okay," I said.

Mrs. Baldwin liked my mom a lot. She told me once that she thought my mom had a beautiful voice. She loved to hear her call me. Mom would stand on the back porch and call, "Daaavey." It sounded like singing.

~

It was real warm and sunny out and my mom wouldn't be home from her job at the bank for a while. I decided to put on my play clothes and play outside when I got home.

We didn't have to lock our door now that we lived in Multnomah. It was out in the country and people didn't lock their doors. That was nice. There was an empty fruit jar in the kitchen, so I put some water in it and the sweet peas. I went upstairs to my room but Scotty's door was open and I could see inside. He wasn't home yet. I went in and looked at the stars on his ceiling, the ones that glow in the dark. In the daytime they were the same color as the ceiling. Hard to see.

Scotty doesn't like me to go in his room but I wanted to anyway. There was a picture in there—on his wall—of a girl from a long, long time ago. She had a dress on from the olden days. Mom brought the picture from our old house. She said it was a famous picture. The girl had braids curled in circles over her ears and she was sitting on a bench outside. The bench looked like one from church. There were trees all around her and the bottom part of the trees was white. She was listening to a little brown bird in one of the trees. I liked that picture. I wondered what the bird sounded like, what the girl was thinking about. She was alone—like me.

I picked up Scotty's scout shirt that was over the back of his chair by the desk. I smelled it. It smelled like smoke from a fire. It smelled like Scotty too. My throat hurt and my eyes started to burn. Truth, justice and the American way.

There was Scotty sitting on my chest again. Like when we rassled. I didn't want it to be that way. I threw the scout shirt on the floor. Scotty could go ride the stupid horses for all I cared.

I looked out the window into the backyard. We had a tent out there. Scotty was teaching me how to put up a tent. "Pitch the tent," Scotty called it. It was a pup tent. I looked down at the shirt on the floor for a long time. Then I picked the shirt back up and put it over the back of his chair. Tried to make it look like it was before.

I looked out the window again. I could see the top of Mrs. Baldwin's house down the hill. Scotty told me he climbs out the window sometimes and goes up on the roof. That would be fun.

I could tell Scotty I did it too.

I opened the window. There was roof under the window and going up beside the window. It looked easy so I climbed out and crawled up the roof beside the window but the roof was really hot. I didn't think it would be hot. I guess the sun made it that way. It starts burning my hands so I turned around and sat down. I look down and I'm scared. I'm up so high. On top of the attic that's on top of Scotty's room that's on top of our kitchen that's on top of our basement that's underneath our kitchen. I wanted to go back in but to go in I have to crawl head first and I'd be upside down. The roof is steep and it's hot and I might fall off. I didn't know what to do. I looked down in the yard where the tent is. It's way down there in the backyard. It's hard to breathe. I could see Mrs. Baldwin, tiny in her garden, down the hill. Bending over.

I hollered, "Mrs. Baldwin" real loud.

She stood up and turned around. Put her hand up over her eyes because of the sun. Then her mouth opened.

"Davey?" her little voice way down there says.

"I'm on the roof and I can't get down," I yell.

"Davey, don't move. Just stay there." She runs into her house.

I'm really scared. When I hollered to Mrs. Baldwin, I started to slide down on the roof. I put my hands down to stop but the roof was still hot on my hands. So I put my arms around my knees and didn't holler again. Scotty wouldn't be scared. Scotty's always like Jack Armstrong, the all American boy.

I sat real still. Our phone rang downstairs. Someone ran fast up the stairs. Then I heard Mom.

"Davey?" The top of her head came out the window down under me and looked around.

"Yeah, I'm up here," I said up above her.

Her head turned around and looked up at me sitting with my arms around my knees tight.

"What are you doing?" she says. Her breath going in and out fast from running up the stairs.

"I'm on the roof and I can't get down," I say.

"Can you reach my hand?" she said, her voice real sweet.

I love my mom.

Then she put her arm out the window and up by me.

"Yeah," I say.

"Well, take my hand and come down to the window," says her real pretty voice.

So I did that and I could smell the Jergen's Lotion smell. When I hold her hand and the top of the window, it's easy. I start to slip. But Mom helps me in the window.

When I got inside, her eyebrows were really wrinkled down, like she does and she grabbed me by the shoulder hard.

"Why on earth were you out there up on the roof?" she said real loud, her voice different.

"Well, uh, Scotty told me-"

Then Mom made a sound like a growl she's so mad.

"Scotty has no business being out there either. You scared me half to death."

After that, we're going down the stairs slow because she had her high heels on from work and she's wobbly. Then her legs go and she just sits down hard on the stairs. She had her gray dress on with the big shoulders and my favorite red dangly cherries around her neck. She put her hands over her face—ruby ring, eight carrot, French cut, sparkling—and starts to cry.

Wow. I never saw her cry before.

So I sit down beside her, "What's the matter, Mommy?"

She doesn't look at me, just puts her arm around me and squeezed me to her tight.

9

Broken Toys

My favorite car was really not our car, it was Jacky's. Jacky was a friend of John's, my step-dad, who had to be in the war. So he asked John to take care of it for him because John didn't go to the war. John was in the Civil Defense. So, we had two cars. Mom said it was good to have two cars because we got more gas rations with two cars. Everything needed to have rations because of the war. That meant you could only get so many of things like food, shoes and gas. But if you had two cars, they gave you two times as many ration stamps for gas.

That summer after kindergarten—after Scotty, my real bother, went to live with our dad—John, my step-dad, said Robby was going to come and stay with us for a while. John, my step-dad, had two kids. There was Robert who was six months older than me. John called him Robby. Then there was Joey who was a baby. He was not even two years old. Robby and Joey, they lived with their mom, Olive. I called her Olive Oil 'cause she looked like Popeye's wife. They lived in a town called The Dalles. It was far away up the Columbia River and we had to go get Robby in one of our cars.

Jacky's car was called a coupe. It had only two doors and it had a shelf under the back window where I just fit. So I would go up there and go to sleep so I wouldn't get sick going around all the curves on the way to The Dalles. But this time was the first time going there and I didn't know about that, so I got sick. Made John mad.

But anyway, John and my mom and me, we drove to The Dalles to get Robby and he came to stay with us for a while that summer. He was real quiet and acted mad most of the time. I don't know why he was so mad. He got to stay in the old-kitchen-spare-room where my secret place was. He had a nice tan face that I wished I had instead of my white skin, freckle one but he didn't smile and his brown eyes were closed off, like he didn't want me in there to see what he was thinking. He didn't talk to me except when I asked him questions. Then he just said, "yes" or sometimes he said, "no." He had real nice clothes, nicer than me. They were always ironed nice and real clean. Like he never went outside to play. When John was home, Robby wouldn't come out to play with me and my friend, Sunny Lea. He was always with John when John was at home. He would hang on to John's pants or sit in his lap. John liked being with Robby. He liked him a lot better than me. But I never saw Robby give John a good night kiss. *Men shake hands.*

The summer Robby came to stay, I started being friends with Craig. Craig lived next door and was just four years old. He had real black hair that was cut so short there was hardly any there. He had something my mom called cowlicks. That made me laugh 'cause it looked like a cow licked his hair in places and made it go the wrong way. Cow licks. Craig and me, we played in our front yard because there was a little hill on the side of our yard that went down to the road. The little hill on the side by the road was dirt. We dug into the hill and made roads and tunnels for our toy cars. Craig and me, we had lots of toy cars. Some were old ones made out of metal. They didn't make them out of metal any more. Mom said they needed all the metal for the war. So I had a truck made of wood and we had some wooden cars too. Craig had a special one made of some new stuff called plastic.

One Monday, Sunny Lea came over and said she was waiting for the ice man. I didn't know about the ice man but Sunny Lea said he came every Monday to bring ice to the man who lived across the road from our house on 37th Street. Her blue eyes were real happy when she told us. She said he let kids have pieces of ice that fell off his truck. So Sunny Lea, Craig and me, we waited for the ice man.

Craig and me, we showed her our little hill then and our roads and tunnels. She said they were great. She asked if she could play with us sometime. I didn't think she really would want to since she was a girl. But she said honest she would like that. We were both six.

Then the ice man came in a big truck. He stopped real fast and jumped out. He told Sunny Lea, "Hi" and lifted the back door of his truck up. It was lots of loud scraping. There was a big metal thing with two handles in the back that looked like big scissors. He opened it up and stuck the pointy ends into a big block of ice and pulled it out of the truck. More loud scraping. Then he carried it up the man's walk to his house. Big slivers and chunks of ice fell out on the ground when he pulled the block out. Sunny Lea picked up one. It looked like a big piece of glass. She put it in her mouth and said to Craig and me, "Get some." So Craig and me, we got some. It was cold and tasted clean. The sun made it sparkle and drip in our hands.

Sunny Lea said, "Like diamonds. And he comes every Monday."

When I told Robby that night about the ice man, he just looked at me —eyes closed off—and said, "So what!"

~

The next day I was playing cars with Craig again and Sunny Lea came with her neighbor, Gary. He had hair that looked like straw and water gray eyes. His eyes were red around the edges like they were sore. I saw him sometimes walking home from school 'cause he lived by Sunny Lea. Sunny Lea had on her jeans and a red and white checkered shirt. Not a dress like usual. She smiled big at me.

"We brought some cars with us," she said. "Can we play on your little hill?"

The way she was, it made giggles in me.

I said, "Sure."

Sunny Lea said, "This is Gary. He's a Mormon."

I thought that wasn't very nice to call him names.

I said, "Sunny Lea, you shouldn't call him a moron."

Gary's face got all red under his straw hair.

"Not moron, silly. He's a Mormon," she said. "That's the church he goes to."

I said, "Oh."

I didn't know about that church.

~

Robby, he must of heard us all playing in the front yard because he came out to see what we were doing. He just stood there in the grass like he didn't want to get in the dirt. He had on the nice green sweater that Mom said his grandmother made for him over a white shirt and ironed pants we called "suntans." His brown hair was combed neat like he was going to school or something. He picked up the pointy end of his white shirt collar in his fingers and put it in his mouth. Then he started chewing on it. That was just something Robby did. Chewed on his shirt collars. Finally, he came up close and squatted down just watching us with his dark brown eyes. Chewing on his shirt collar.

Sunny Lea looked her blue eyes up at me and said, "Who's that?"

I said, "Oh, that's my step-brother, Robby."

Craig was running his yellow plastic car around our little hill road making car noises. Just the top of his head. Cow licks. Ha.

Craig said, "Yeah his mom and dad are divorced."

Sunny Lea looked at me quick and her eyes went big.

"I never knew anyone whose parents are divorced," she said.

We were all looking at our toy cars and didn't see Robby stand up. But then his shoe came down real hard right on top of Craig's yellow plastic car. Craig hollered and when Robby picked his foot back up, Craig's plastic car was all pieces laying in the dirt. Robby just grunted and walked away. We all looked at the pieces of plastic in the dirt.

~

Nobody talked. Then Sunny Lea stood up and breathed in and let her air out in a "humph." She wiped the dirt that was on her hands on her jeans. Her eyes were real big and blue like the sky.

She said to me, "Why did he do that?" like I should know.

I shrugged my shoulders then.

"I don't know," I said. "He's just always mad."

Craig stood up. His face was red and he made his hands into fists on his hips.

"Well, he makes me mad. Your step-brother is mean."

"I'm sorry, Craig," I said.

Gary looked up from under his straw hair.

"Next time, you can all come up to my house and play. But not Robby," he said.

"Oh that would be great," Sunny Lea said. "Gary has a neat toy garage. You can drive your car into it and an elevator takes them up to roof parking and everything."

"Wow," I said.

~

The day I went up to Gary's to play cars was kind of cold like it was in Oregon in the spring sometimes. It wasn't rainy but just cold so Mom said I should wear a jacket and a stocking cap.

Sunny Lea came down the hill to our house and asked if I wanted to play at Gary's but she whispered not to tell Robby. Sunny Lea had on her stocking cap too. We went next door to Craig's to see if he wanted to go and he said he did but he didn't want to go if Robby was coming. So we all went up to Gary's and didn't tell Robby.

The house that Gary lived in was real old and kind of funny. The paint was off in places and the sidewalk from the road into the backyard was all broken pieces. Gary was in his backyard. He didn't have on a cap. Just his straw hair. He had the sniffles. He said that his mom wanted to meet us all. That was kind of funny. I didn't know why she wanted to meet us but we went in the back door through the old screen door that slammed and he yelled, "Mom."

We followed Gary through the dining room. The floor squeaked. His mom was in the front room by a big piano with a high back, sewing. She was an old lady with grey hair and a baggy house dress. Her face was real pink and she didn't smile. I didn't know, maybe Mormons are not supposed to smile. His house smelled funny. Like old cooking or something bad in the fridge. His mom said she was "pleased to meet us" and then we went out to play cars.

We played on his sidewalk that was inside his yard and went all the way around his house. It wasn't broken where we played.

Gary's toy garage was real neat. It was made of metal so he could take it outside. I had one something like it but mine was made of cardboard because of the war and I couldn't take it outside because it might get wet.

Gary had a new plastic car that was like Craig's that got broken but Gary's was red. It was neat to have Gary's filling station garage because Craig and Sunny Lea and me, we made our own houses and yards and then took our cars to be fixed where Gary lived at the gas station. I was turning the crank for the elevator to take my car up to roof parking and making elevator noise and everything got real quiet. I didn't know what was happening. I looked up and everybody wasn't playing. They were real still, like when we play statue, just looking at Robby. He was in Gary's yard. He had his aviator helmet on. The leather kind with the sheep skin inside. Like the one I had. He was chewing on the chin strap. Not his collar this time. My stomach was kind of sick like I could taste it. He was looking at me. His eyebrows were scrunched together and he looked mad. Then he walked over to Gary's red car. His foot came up. Then it stomped on it. Gary's pale eyes got all watery and the red edges got redder. His nose was running.

"Hey," he yelled. "Why'd you do that for?"

Gary jumped up and ran at Robby and hit him in the shoulder with his fist. Robby jerked around and the wet, yucky chin strap from his helmet hit Gary in the face.

"Ow," Gary yelled.

Then Robby just turned around and walked out of Gary's yard.

"Hey, come back here," Gary yelled.

Gary's mom came out on the front porch and looked around the side. Her face was white and she looked scared. Her eyebrows up and her gray eyes wide open.

"What's going on, Gary? Why are you shouting?"

~

That night Mrs. Hoagland, Gary's mom, called on the telephone and talked with Mom. Then Mom talked real quiet to John. After that, they called Robby downstairs to the kitchen. He was up in the old-kitchen-spare-room where he was staying with us for a while. I went into the front room and stood touching the red drapes that were so smooth. I could hear what they were saying in the kitchen a little bit.

I heard John say, "Son, why did you do that?"

And Robby said, "I don't know." Then something real quiet.

Mom said, "People won't like you if you do things like that."

Then a kitchen chair scooted on the floor.

"I don't care," Robby said louder.

Mom's voice was high and she said, "Of course you do. Everyone wants friends."

Something dropped in the kitchen. It made me jump.

"They're not my friends," Robby said. This time real loud.

I felt bad for Robby. The red drapes were real smooth in my hands. I went behind the drapes and it was dark in there. The drapes felt good on my face. It was like my secret place in there.

~

The next day, I was playing in the hall outside the old-kitchen-spare-room. The hallway went around the stairs. At the back end of the stairs were some windows and a place to play. There was a railing in front of the high part over the stairs and all along the hall beside the old-kitchen-spare-room. It was a great place to play at the back end of the stairs by those windows where you could see down into the front yard. I was playing with Teddy and my Army doll that my dad gave me and some toy cars.

Robby came out of the old-kitchen-spare-room and looked at me.

Right away, I grabbed my cars up off the floor and tried to find a place to hide them. I turned to the windows and put the cars in my toy box.

"What are you doing?" Robby said.

I turned around and he was smiling. He never smiled at me. Then I saw he had my Army doll. I reached long for it. But Robby ran half way down the hall and leaned on the railing over the stairs. He was still smiling.

"Give that to me," I yelled.

"Come and get it," he said and started to laugh.

My chest went tight.

"That's my Army doll," I said.

"Well, it's mine now," he said kind of mad. Then he laughed again.

"You can't have it," I yelled. "My real dad gave that to me."

Robby stopped laughing and his face started getting red.

"Oh, yeah?" he said.

He never looked like that before. I shouldn't of said that about my dad. He looked like a statue. Like the pictures Mrs. Rheinlander showed us in Kindergarten. Except he was getting red. I always make people mad. Then his hand with my Army doll went up and I ran. I almost got it before Robby's hand came down again over the railing.

My heart jumped into my ears and I got dizzy.

My Army doll crashed on the bottom step of the stairs. His big baby doll head broke open in pieces and fell onto the floor by the front door. His arms and legs spread out all funny in his uniform.

~

Peace, justice and the American way.

10

Blowing Taps

After my Army doll got broken, Robby was different. Like he knew he did something he shouldn't of.

John, my step-dad, and Mom had a talk with him. It was real serious. Robby came up to my room and told me he was sorry about the Army doll. But I knew that anyway. When it broke, Robby's face got all white. He looked ascared too but he didn't say anything.

When he told me he was sorry, I told him it didn't matter—it was just a silly old doll anyway. I didn't tell him again that my dad gave it to me. My dad who I didn't see any more. My dad who was helping the boys over there to fight for truth, justice and the American way.

Robby said that my Army doll died with his uniform on and we should have a soldier's burial and bury him the way the army would. I thought that was a good idea.

John, my step-dad looked real sad when he told me that my Army doll couldn't be fixed. I believed him. I knew he would fix him if he could. He was being real nice. I think because he felt bad Robby did that. John, my step-dad was real good at fixing things. I was sad that the present my dad gave me when I was little was gone now. Scotty was gone. My dad was gone. But maybe John would still be my step-dad and Robby said he was sorry. That made me feel better. So Robby and me, we planned a funeral.

~

At last Christmas, I got a toy horn. Mom said bugle but it didn't sound like a bugle. It had 5 keys. Each one sounded like a kind of harmonica. Mom was real good at blowing it. In the morning, she would blow the Army wake-up tune at the bottom of the stairway. "You gotta get up, you gotta get up, you gotta get up in the morning."

Mom taught me to blow the slow one that she said the Army blows at funerals called Taps. She said that one always made her sad because my real dad's little brother, Harold that she liked a lot, was killed in Germany and the Army would have played that one at his funeral.

John, my step-dad, and Mom told Robby that he had to tell Craig and Gary that he was sorry. A course John didn't get mad at him and throw him across the room like he did me when I used his chisel. Robby had to save money out of his allowance too and buy them both a new toy car for the ones he smashed.

When he went to tell Craig and Gary he was sorry, Robby asked me to go with him. So I did. Then I told them about our soldier's burial. And when Sunny Lea came down on Monday for the ice man, we told her. They all thought it was neat and wanted to come too. Sunny Lea said she had a funeral for a bird one time so she knew about funerals. She said that she had a little flag she could bring to cover the real nice shoe box John, my step-dad found for us to bury the army doll in.

The day we had the funeral it was real dark out. The sky was full of grey clouds. Like Oregon had a lot. Robby said we should wear our aviator helmets 'cause it might rain and they were the one thing we had that looked like Army. After breakfast, we went out in the backyard with John, my step-dad's, garden shovel. We were going to dig the grave in the flower bed between the basement door and the platform on the back of the house over the septic tank.

First, I dug a little bit. Then Robby said he would dig for a while. The dirt was hard old clay dirt. Pretty soon Robby stopped though and just stood there and held onto the shovel that was stuck in the ground. He closed his eyes and sweat was running down his face. And maybe tears. I couldn't tell. I think it was tears.

"You know," he said, "Dad told me I might have to go back up to The Dalles, if I didn't make friends down here."

"Oh," I said. I didn't know what to say. Then I said, "Don't you like The Dalles?"

"The Dalles is okay," he said. Then his face kind of scrunched. "But I want to be with my dad. For a little bit anyway."

My throat started to hurt and it was hard to swallow. Robby looked down at the little hole we dug and put the aviator chin strap in his mouth and chewed.

I opened my mouth but it was hard to make words come out. Then I heard my words say, "We can be friends."

Robby looked up at me. He stopped chewing on his aviator chin strap. It looked yucky again. Then he dug some more and the grave was finished.

When Sunny Lea came in the backyard, she had a black veil she got from her mom over the top of her head and on her face. She looked scary.

The shoe box with my dead army doll was sitting on the platform over the septic tank and she put a little American flag over it. She didn't say anything. Just put her hands together like a prayer and walked over to Robby and me with her head down.

My mom, up on the back porch above us, told Gary and Craig that we were in the backyard. Craig came running down the back stairs and jumped on the platform over the septic tank and hollered, "Hi" 'cause he was only four. Gary came down kinda slow. He had on a necktie. His face that was usually the same color as his straw hair was red and he didn't smile.

"My mom said I should wear a tie," he said.

"Oh it's okay," I said. It was probly a Mormon thing.

Sunny Lea and Gary stood real quiet by the hole that Robby and me dug in the flower bed. Craig scratched his face and then his head. Cow licks. Then Robby and me, we brought over the shoe box with the flag on it and put it in the hole. I got my bugle out and started blowing Taps. I made a mistake twice and had to start again but then it was over. Sunny Lea said "Amen" when I was finished and Robby covered the shoe box and the flag with dirt. Then we all put some rocks and shells on top.

Mom, she watched from the windows on the porch up above us. She said it was quite a theatrical event.

After that, Robby wasn't so mad all the time and he played with us while he stayed for a while that summer when we were six.

~

But that wasn't the end of it.

11

Six Stitches

John, my step dad cut little pieces of glass and made them into the glass part over watches. Hand-made watch crystals. After he cut the pieces of glass and shaped them into squares and rounds, he put them in this real neat little stove he called a furnace so they would get all curved and smooth. He would put on his goggles and with one hand, he opened the little door with the window in it. Then with long tweezers in the other hand he would put the pieces of glass in the opening that was fiery hot. After they were curved and smooth, he would grind the edges on a wet stone wheel that went around and around and smelled like rain in clay dirt so they fit on top of the watches all the jewelry stores sent him.

He went to work real early in the morning at his watch crystal shop in down town Portland, so the house always smelled like breakfast when I woke up. Toast smell. Robby and me, we woke up about the same time. I would always try to get down to the kitchen first and put the pea green Fiesta Ware bowl out for him because we both hated it. Looked like pea soup. Ick. Mom's Fiesta Ware was plates and bowls and mugs in all different colors. The real ugly color was the pea soup color. We never wanted that one. So I would put it at Robby's place. Robby was real mad at me when I did that.

Mom stopped work at the bank when school ended so she could be home with me and then Robby, when he came to stay for a while that Summer. Mom said that we couldn't fight over the dishes. What was on the table stayed there. We couldn't be getting them down and then putting them back in the cupboard. So I always tried to get there first to put the pea soup dish at Robby's place. Sometimes he beat me to the table though, so I had to eat out of that one.

This day I got there first so Robby was mad. He threw little Kix breakfast cereals at me when Mom wasn't looking. But I got him good with my last bite of toast when Mom was at the sink cleaning the frying pan from John's egg. Robby jumped up real mad when I did that, but I was closest to the basement. So I ran down the stairs. He was yelling at me and chased me down the steps and through the play area in the basement.

The basement door was open so I ran through it to go outside.

When you go out there, there's a step up. My one foot ran up the step out of the basement but the other foot tripped on that step. I fell down and my eye went right down on the corner of the little cement wall that was there. All I heard was Robby behind me suck in air. Then my insides were coming out of my eye.

I rolled over and sat up on the little bit of sidewalk but I couldn't see. My eye stung. Then I could only see red. Then I saw a lot of white light coming from inside of me.

Robby was real quiet. Then he said, "Marian," kind of quiet. Then I heard him run and yell, "Marian." Then "Marian," again and "Davey's hurt."

Quiet.

Then Robby, "Yeah, real bad."

That's when I saw lots of black from the inside. Then nothing.

~

Mom was bending over me. Her face all blurry. No make-up. No lipstick. White scarf tight around her head. Tied up in front over pin curls. Like our Aunt Jemima cookie jar. Eyebrows wrinkled down.

"How do you feel, honey?" she said.

My hand felt a bed under it. Pillow under my head.

I don't know," I said. Then my eye hurt awful. "Ow," I said and my stomach turned upside down. "I think I'm gonna throw up."

"Take a deep breath," Mom said.

So I did and then I felt okay. A little better.

"Just lie still for a minute," she said and straightened up. She was standing beside her bed and I was on it. She still had on her pink bathrobe with the puckery rows of fuzz. She took a deep breath and let it out all at once. Tried to smile but didn't really.

"I'm just going to put some clothes on and then we can go to Dr. Foster in Multnomah. Okay?" she said. "He knows we're coming. Do you think you can walk that far?"

I turned my head. The little square windows in the front door were through the bedroom door that was open and I could see outside. Robby was standing by the bedroom door. Stiff like a statue and white.

"I guess," I said.

~

It was okay with Dr. Foster. The only yucky part was when he stuck a needle in my cheek to make it numb. He said to Mom it was a wonder I didn't lose my eye. It was so close. He told me he made six stitches under my eye and that I'd have a black eye for a while. I didn't get to see it though 'cause he put a big puffy bandage over it that made me look bug eyed. Like those Kamikaze pilots in the comics with their teeth grinning and goggles on. But with me only one eye.

Robby said I looked freaky. He was right but Dr. Foster gave me a neat little empty brown medicine bottle with a red rubber stopper to take home and play with. Robby didn't have one of those.

When John got home from his watch crystal shop, he was pretty mad. He looked down at us both with those black eyes of his. Not blinking. His widow's peak coming down. Face red.

"Why do you two have to be such goddamned hooligans?"

That's what John called us, hooligans. And he cussed a lot.

He said, "If I ever catch you again acting like that, I'll rip off your arm and beat you with the bloody end of it!" He was looking at me.

He sure was scary. Why didn't he feel a little bad about my eye?

~

After dinner, Mom went to the bathroom and Robby and me and John were just sitting at the table. John wasn't so upset then and his face wasn't red anymore. He got up from the table and stood behind his chair. He put his hands on the back of the chair. No smile.

"I think I better take Robby back to The Dalles tomorrow," he said.

Robby's eyes got all tears right away and he said, "Dad, I'm really sorry. I won't be a hooligan anymore."

My eye hurt and then my throat started to burn and I couldn't swallow.

John sat down in Mom's chair next to Robby and put his arm around him.

"Son, that really has nothing to do with me taking you back to The Dalles."

Robby looked down at his plate on the table, his tan face all red. Three little peas left on his plate.

"Yes it does," Robby said. "I know it does."

"Son," John said. "Your mom says it's time for you to come back and tomorrow's Saturday. I usually only work a couple hours on Saturday so I can take the time off and run you home."

Robby had tears coming down from his brown eyes. They were really open like holes where you could see deep inside him.

"But I want to stay here," he said.

John's widow's peak came down like it did. His forehead got all wrinkles and his eyes were red like he was gonna cry too.

"Come on Son," he said. "We've talked about this. You know you can't do that. I'd have to take you back sooner or later. If not tomorrow, then Sunday or a week from then."

Robby really started to cry then. He got out of his chair and looked at me like he wanted to kick me. Then he ran out of the kitchen and I heard him go up the stairs and into the old-kitchen-spare-room and slam the door.

John's long legs went out in front of him. He took a big breath and blew air out of his mouth. Made a funny farting sound with the air. Then he got up and looked at me. His eyebrows pulled together in the middle and his eyes all watery. He shrugged his shoulders. Then he put his hand up in front of his face like he didn't want me to see and went into the front room. I heard him talking on the phone.

"Yeah, Bill?" I heard him say to his partner at work. He said something quiet. Then, "I'm going to take my son back to The Dalles."

I sat at the table by myself. Looked at the red ketchup bottle there. Read Heinz. It had some dried up ketchup around the top and the lid was on the table upside down. Yucky inside. *Come on, Son. I'm taking my Son back to The Dalles. Son, son, son…Me, I'm nobody's Son. I'm just Davey.*

When John came back in the kitchen with that old maple-tree-limp of his, he just stood behind his chair. Hanging on again for a minute. Gone somewhere. Looking at himself in the dark window behind the table. Looking at his widow's peak. Light shining on his tanned, handsome face. Like he was trying to see inside himself.

When Mom came back in the kitchen, his face changed. Saw I was sitting there. Like he didn't want me sitting there. He said, "Davey, go help Robby pack up his things, would you?"

I didn't say anything. I just got up and went upstairs. Robby was sitting on his bed when I opened the door. His face was all red. Not crying anymore. He had that closed up look in his eyes that he used to have.

He kind of looked at me like he didn't see me but he said, "Davey, I'm sorry."

"Sorry for what?" I said.

"I'm sorry I hurt your eye."

I didn't know what he meant. I sat down by him on his bed.

"You didn't hurt my eye," I said. "I fell down."

He looked at me real serious then. Brown eyes wide open.

"Yeah, but I was chasing you," he said.

"We were playing," I said. "We were just playing."

He looked away from me then.

"I guess."

He looked down at his hands on his legs. "Maybe," he said.

Then he was quiet.

I thought about when he first came and how he broke Craig and Gary's toy cars and how he broke my Army doll.

Then we were both quiet sitting on his bed.

"John said I should help you pack your stuff," I said.

Robby's face scrunched up and he got tears, but he didn't say anything.

Then he said, "I'm gonna miss playing. I don't have any friends up there and Joey's a baby."

I just nodded. I liked playing with Robby. But he wouldn't of chased me and he wouldn't have to go home if I hadn't of put that pea soup Fiesta bowl on the table. If it wasn't for me. It made my throat hurt. I liked fighting over the pea soup dishes and things too but I had lots of kids to play with. I felt bad for Robby. But playing with Robby wasn't like having Scotty around. I missed how Scotty tried to teach me things. I missed his Scout shirt camp-fire smell. I really loved Scotty. A lot of times he made me feel stupid but I think that was just because I was little and he was a big kid. I guess the difference was that Scotty was my real brother.

~

The next morning John put Robby's things in Jacky's blue coup and they both got in and went to The Dalles. John said he didn't want to take a chance on me getting car sick. He said the reason was, throwing up with stitches under my eye could be dangerous. So Mom and me, we stayed home. And John took Robby, *his son*, back to The Dalles.

I didn't have anything to do and Mom said I should play outside so she could clean house. I went next door to see Craig but nobody came to the door. Then I started down the little hill behind us to see Mrs. Baldwin. On the other side of the road going down the hill, at the top of the field there, there were blackberries and Craig and his mom and some other people were picking them.

I waved at Craig when he looked up and he yelled to me, "Come and get some blackberries. They're really good."

Barbara who lived across the road was there with her Collie dog and she came out of the berries and handed me a little box made out of pieces of wood like a basket. She was real pretty. She smiled her white teeth at me too, big, like she was trying not to see my bug eye. "Help yourself. There's lots of 'em," she said.

I got over to Craig. His fingers and his mouth were all over blue with berry juice. He looked at me and grinned. Berry seeds in his teeth.

"They're really good," he said again.

So I picked two fat ones and put them in my mouth. They just kind of got all sweet and slid down my throat.

Craig was staring at me then. His mouth open, all berry juice.

"What happened to your eye?" he said.

"Oh, I fell down."

"Oh," he said. Then he shrugged and ate some more berries.

"You think I could pick some for my mom?" I said to Craig.

"Sure," he said. "My mom's gonna make a pie."

So I started filling up my basket. Berry juice on my fingers. Little rough black things not berries sticking to my fingers got in my mouth when I licked the juice off.

Craig was right. They were really good. It was hard not to eat all the ones I picked. But I wanted to take some home to Mom. It was hard to see with only one eye. I kept tripping on the long blackberry branches all over the ground. I had about half of my little basket full when I tripped and almost dropped the basket. But this time it wasn't blackberries that made me trip. I stepped on that Collie dog's foot. I didn't see him beside me because of my bug eye. When I started to fall, I felt his breath. He was as tall as me and that big mouth with all the teeth, it was right at my eye. He just opened his big ol' mouth and bit me. His teeth scraped the skin on my forehead and pulled my puffy bandage down on my cheek.

Craig just stared at my eye and said, "Oh, wow."

Barbara yelled, "No, Pal."

But it was too late. The Collie dog jumped over some blackberries and went to Barbara. She grabbed his collar and said, "Stay," real loud to the dog. She came over to me then and got down low. She looked close at my eye. "Are you all right?"

That made me feel weird, her so pretty looking at my ugly eye like that.

"Yeah. I guess so," I said. I still had my berries.

"You better have your mom look at that," she said.

"Okay," I said. I was glad to get away from Barbara looking at me like that and her dumb dog.

~

After Mom put some iodine on my forehead where the dog's teeth scraped me, she told me to go out and just sit still in the back yard so I wouldn't get into any more trouble.

I went out past the septic tank cover and sat in the grass with my back up against the big old cherry tree. The grass was long and soft. I was so tired. I was tired from my eye. I was tired from the dog bite. Tired from Robby going back to The Dalles. Tired from John calling him son. I was tired and I just fell asleep.

~

When I woke up, it was like I was still asleep and dreaming. It was beautiful music. When I opened my eye and looked around, I could still only see out of one eye. I was there in our backyard, sitting in the grass by the cherry tree but I could hear music. Then a big voice singing.

My head hurt but I got up and went over to the fence. It was a wire fence with big square holes made by the wire. There were shrubs planted on the other side so I couldn't see through everywhere. And I only had one eye to see with. I just put my fingers around the wire and held on for a while.

I remembered it was Saturday. Mr. Herman, Craig's dad, who lived next door, he was a soldier. He got wounded in the war and he was sent home. On Saturday and Sunday, he worked outside in his garden next door. On Saturdays he always had his radio on and listened to the opera that came all the way from New York City. On Sundays he listened to the ball game but on Saturday it was opera.

Then I saw Craig's dad, Mr. Herman, sitting on the grass part of the yard behind their house. The grass was cut real neat and short. He was holding their new baby, Dale between his arm and his big chest. Mr. Herman was tickling him and talking quiet little sounds to him. Craig came in the backyard through the gate that was in their white fence. Still berry stains all over him. He was carrying one of the little wooden baskets and he showed it to his dad. Mr. Herman put his other arm around Craig and pulled him up close. He said something to Craig and then he kissed him. He held him tight and smiled at him.

Men shake hands.

I held on to the wire fence. My throat hurt awful. There was never a dad around like that for me. Tears came out of my eye. I was so tired of trying not to cry. So I just let them come out. No one could see me. It felt better than the burning in my throat and my chest being tight. So I just held on to the fence real tight and cried. I listened to those big opera voices from Mr. Herman's radio next door. Some boomed like drums. Some went high like tiny whistles. Pretty.

John said "screeching." He didn't want to listen to that in our house.

Maybe the difference between being a step-dad and a real dad is like the difference of being a real brother from being a step-brother.

Anyway, the summer wasn't over yet and there was still a lot of time for surprising things to happen, even without Scotty or Robby…or a dad that wants to hug you.

12

Teeter Totter

After Robby came to stay with us for a while and went back home to The Dalles, the summer just kind of kept going. Not much happened. It just got warmer. I started to miss kindergarten. I missed doing projects. I missed poster paints and making things out of clay. Then one day I learned that when things don't seem to be happening, they do and your life gets real different.

I went to visit my friend, Mrs. Baldwin like I did most days. I went down to her house after lunch and we looked at her new magazine that the mailman brought. It had real nice pictures—pretty colors. Mrs. Baldwin told me about her daughter, Lucile who lived in Seattle. How when Lucile was a little girl they used to sit together on this same davenport and look at magazines too.

Everybody in the neighborhood had their windows open because it was warm out. While Mrs. Baldwin and me were sitting on her davenport, we could hear the slisch, slisch of the lawn mower Arthur was pushing in the little bit of grass they had by the garden in their backyard. The smell from the grass he cut was nice. There was the sound of Jane, the college girl next door, practicing her cello too and Mrs. Baldwin said she always loved to hear Jane play. Her cello had some low sounds I could feel in my tummy. They made my toes tingle.

Pretty soon, Arthur came in and got dressed in his suit because a student was coming. So I said good bye and went down their front steps.

~

I didn't have anybody to play with. Craig and his baby brother, Dale were gone to their cabin on Mt. Hood with their mom and dad. Gary was at a religious camp and Sunny Lea was down at Rockaway—at the beach. Scotty wrote me and Mom a letter and said how much fun he was having at Aunt Pearl's dairy farm riding horses. I wished I had some exciting place to go to. But I was glad there was Mrs. Baldwin. It was always fun to visit her.

There was an empty field on the other side of the road in front of Mr. and Mrs. Baldwin's house and when I came down their yard to the road, there was a boy just coming out of that field onto the road. I said Hi and he said Hi. He told me his name was Billy, Billy Rogers, and that he lived on the hill right on the other side of the field. Then he pointed at his house. It was a big white house just peeking out of the woods on the hill. He asked me if I wanted to come over and play in his woods. That sounded fun, so we started over the field to his house.

In the field, he told me that he was going to be in second grade pretty soon. I told him I was going to be in the first grade. He said that first grade was pretty easy.

Billy's front yard was like a picture in one of Mrs. Baldwin's magazines and so was his house. There were lots of big shrubs and flowers in front where we went in. It didn't look like he played there very much. It was too nice. The front room was right there inside the door. It was so clean and pretty, I was ascared to walk in there with dirty shoes from the field. He told me not to worry, his parents weren't home.

We went into the kitchen and Billy asked if I wanted anything to eat. I told him I had lunch already. He said he was going to make a peanut butter sandwich 'cause he was hungry. He got out the Wonder Bread and a jar of Skippy. He poured a glass of milk and asked me again wouldn't I like just a half a sandwich. I told him okay. So he made a whole one for him and a half for me. Really grown up like. I never made my own.

Then he poured me a glass of milk and we went out the back door with our sandwiches and milk.

Billy's backyard had two walls made out of big rocks. Like the walls in a castle. They were about as tall as me those walls on the hill going up behind his house like steps. It was level on top of the walls with flowers growing there. We went up some stone stairs in the middle past both walls and we were on top of the hill.

In the middle of big fir trees all around up there, there was a big chicken coup—a house really—and a big garden shed with a garden in between where his mom and dad grew lots of vegetables. Not like our back yard that only had a septic tank and really tall grass. They had tomatoes and green peppers, corn stalks and some green beans hanging down on a fence. There were some purple things he said were egg plants. But they didn't look like eggs. The other side of the garden shed he said was berries. It was all woods though on the side of the chicken house, with a trail leading in there.

At the big garden shed, we sat down on the steps of the porch to eat our sandwiches. Billy had freckles on his cheeks and all over his nose.

His hair was lots of little blond springs. When he moved his head they would fall down on his forehead just above his eyes. Then he would push them back. His blue eyes looked like he was laughing. Those eyes looked at me for a minute, then Billy, he pinched some of his Wonder Bread and peanut butter together between his thumb and finger.

"How long have you lived around here?" he said. "I've never seen you here."

His eyes made me want to laugh, like something was funny.

I just looked down and said, "We moved here in November."

"Well," he said, "I never go over on the other side of the field. I guess that's why I never saw you. I have a lot of kids to play with over here but today they're all gone away."

"My friends too," I said.

Then Billy said, "We have a teeter totter in the woods. Would you like to see it?"

I said, "Sure."

So we finished our sandwiches and milk. Billy took my glass and put his and mine in the garden shed and said, "Come on, I'll show you."

It was warm even in the woods. It made the tall fir trees smell real strong. The path through the ferns was thick needles and there was a piney smell everywhere. You could see little bits of blue sky through the trees when you looked up. It was real quiet here. It was kind of like my secret place in the kitchen-spare room cupboard—kind of dark and quiet—but it was outside. And there were no big people around.

Right in the middle of Billy's little woods was a clear place and there was a teeter totter there. It was one long, long board with handles made of pipe, like the water pipes under our house on the basement ceiling. They came up through the board and crossed to hold on to. The board looked old, gray like some of the trees and kind of green on the edges with a little bit of moss. The light came down dim through the trees right on that spot. There was dust in the light and it shimmered, thousands of little stars. Glow-in-the-dark stars but it was day time. Like it was a special spot and that teeter totter was just waiting there for us. Like it was waiting a real long time for us.

I just stood there and looked at the teeter totter.

Then Billy next to me said, "You want a cigarette?"

"What?" I said.

"I said, did you want a cigarette."

"I don't know," I said.

I never smoked a cigarette. My mom smoked cigarettes after dinner sometimes. I was just six. I just got out of kindergarten.

"You have cigarettes?" I said.

He looked at me with his laughing eyes.

"Yeah," he said. "I keep 'em covered up over there by that tree. It's fun to smoke a cigarette when you teeter totter."

"Where'd you get cigarettes?" I say.

Billy kind of laughed through his nose.

"Oh, I get 'em from my dad's dresser. He never misses 'em. I just take one or two at a time and put 'em in an old empty Camel pack I found."

Billy goes over to the trunk of a big fir tree and I follow him. He moves some little branches away from two roots shaped like a "Y" and there is a Camel pack squeezed down in the "Y." He pulls it out and puts the little branches back. Blond curls fall over his forehead. He grins and his eyes laugh.

"Do you know where the hidden camel, the secret camel is?" he says.

He's so smart and I'm so dumb. I don't know what he's talking about.

"What do you mean?" I say.

He leans in real close and holds the pack up to my eyes. Nice tobacco smell.

"On the pack. There's a hidden camel on the pack. Can you tell me where it is?"

I take the pack. The cellophane feels slick in my hand. I look at the line of buildings and palm trees on the pack. Like somewhere I've never seen. I try to see if part of a camel is sticking out from behind something, if a camel is trying to hide somewhere. I want to find it. I don't want to be so dumb. Stupid, Scotty says. I can't see the camel.

Billy looks at me with his laughing eyes and takes the pack. He slips it out of the cellophane and turns it over. He pulls the flap up at the paper seam in the back. There under the flap of paper is the hidden camel. Billy laughs. Billy's laugh makes me laugh.

"That's neat." I say. He's really smart. Like Scotty.

Billy looks at me with a grin kind of crooked.

"Well, you want one?"

"I don't know. I never smoked before."

His eyebrows go up.

"Oh, it's easy," he says.

"Okay," I say.

Billy takes two cigarettes out and puts them both in his mouth. He takes a wooden match he has in the cellophane wrapper part and snaps his thumb nail over the top of the match. The flame jumps up and I jump. When I jump, Billy almost burns his fingers. He laughs with the cigarettes in his mouth and lights both of them. Then he hands one to me.

"Just suck on it," he says.

So I do and then I can't stop coughing. I've got tears in my eyes and my throat hurts. It tastes bad too.

"Ugh, this is awful."

"Just try once more." Billy says. "Take the smoke in your mouth and blow it out."

So I try once more and I don't cough. Then I guess I'm not so dumb.

"Come on, let's teeter totter," he says.

I get on one end and he gets on the other. We're about the same size so it works good.

There I am smoking on a teeter totter with my new friend. This is funny. Billy laughs and I laugh and there are no big people to say we're not supposed to smoke and teeter totter. This is really fun.

~

That night under Gramma's name quilt with the colored snowflake stars, I was happy. I was happier than I can ever remember. When Mom came up to tuck me in and hear me say my prayers like always, she asked me what I did that day. That's something else Mom always did, ask me what I did that day. I told her about the teeter totter and how I met Billy Rogers. Mom smiled at me with her eyes that way that made me feel special. Then her gray blue eyes went deep inside, far away from me—remembering. She said that when she was a little girl her favorite thing was to play outside. She said she loved to swing in a swing.

That surprised me.

"They had swings in the olden days?" I said.

Mom's head went back in a big laugh, the little mole at the bottom of her throat moving up and down.

"The olden days?" she said. "It wasn't *that* long ago. Of course, we had swings. But what I loved the most was to play with my little brother in the woods by our house."

It was hard to think about Uncle Bob as a little boy that she played with in the woods. Harder than thinking of my mom as a little girl playing in the woods. Then I told Mom about Billy's woods.

I told her about his nice house and his wonderful, really big backyard. I told her about the chicken house and the big garden and garden shed. But I didn't tell her the other stuff, about the cigarettes and the hidden camel or how we smoked the cigarettes on the teeter totter or how Billy's eyes laughed. I didn't tell her how neat it was to smoke cigarettes and do stuff I knew I wasn't supposed to do. How good it was that no big people were there to tell me not to. That'd probly make her mad. I kept that secret. It was really good to have secrets and to have a friend to have secrets with.

~

Next morning, after breakfast, I went to Billy's house. He had his friend, Frank there. Frank was a little bit older than Billy, almost eight and he had a crew cut. That's real short hair that sticks up like Army guys. Frank didn't have cowlicks like Craig so his hair went straight up.

We sat on the steps of Billy's big garden shed and talked. Me on the bottom step-them on the top step. Billy and Frank talked about being in the second grade pretty soon and how they didn't like Mrs. Anderson who was going to be their teacher.

Frank looked down at me. Made me feel little. His brown eyes quiet. Kind of golden like syrup on pancakes. But they didn't laugh like Billy's.

"You gonna be in second grade?"

"No," I said. "First."

"Oh, first grade ain't nothing," he said. "'Specially if you get Miss Wright."

Billy laughed.

"Oh yeah," he said. "Frank has a crush on Miss Wright."

"Have not," Frank said and punched Billy in the arm.

"Have too," Billy said. His head nodded and the blond springs came down all squiggly. Blue eyes laughing.

Then Frank got up and walked a little bit away. Looked up at the sky. No clouds. He turned back to us. Little smile.

"Pretty warm already," he said. "Let's go in the woods."

"Okay," Billy said and we got up and followed Frank to the path.

When we got to the special spot where the light came down through the little sparkles, Frank unbuttoned his shirt and hung it on a bush on the edge of the clear place around the teeter totter. He took a pack of cigarettes out of his shirt pocket. Then he took a cigarette out and lit it with a match. He breathed in smoke and it came out his nose. That was neat. I never saw that before.

Billy saw me watching and he laughed when he said to me, "Frank taught me how to smoke. His mom and dad, they both smoke."

"Ain't shit," Frank said. "No big deal." He kicked the toe of his penny loafer in the needles on the ground.

I didn't know what to say then—him cussing like that. We all just stood there for a minute.

Then Frank, he looked at me and said, "Well, I wanna get on the teeter totter but I wanna be naked."

He kicked off his shoes and pulled his socks off. Then he just unbuttoned his pants and pulled them off. He threw them on top of his shoes. He didn't have any shorts on and he just stood there looking at us. Waiting.

Waiting. Looking kind of scary like Mrs. Allen's dog—the dog with the golden eyes that always waited inside her fence and growled low. Frank just standing there—golden eyes. Waiting. His thing hanging there for everyone to see.

Billy laughed and pulled his tee shirt up over his curly hair. He twirled it around and snapped Frank in his fanny with it. Then he ran to the other side of the teeter totter laughing so hard he bent over. Then he unbuttoned his pants and yanked them off. Just like that he was naked too.

I never saw anybody naked before except my brother, Scotty. I couldn't breathe.

When I was little, about three, before we moved to our new house in "Mudnomah," my mom and me, we used to visit her best friend, Edith who had two little girls, Maryann and Sissy. Maryann was oldest. She was about six. One time, when we were outside playing, Maryann and Sissy took me into the bushes and took my clothes off. I didn't know why they did that. They looked at my wee wee and touched it and laughed. I didn't like that very much.

Another time, Maryann and Sissy and me, we were playing in their backyard. Maryann said we were playing doctor. She laid down on her back on the grass. She pulled her shirt up and told me to be the doctor. I didn't know what to do so I got down on the grass and just kind of poked her in the tummy. Then I saw a smooth gray rock there. Like from the bottom of a creek. It was kind of heavy. I could just lift it with one hand though and I put it on her tummy. Then I heard a loud scraping noise by the house.

It was her mom, Edith. She pushed open the window in the back of the house.

She stuck her head out and yelled, "What are you kids doing?"

Maryann jumped up quick and pulled her shirt down.

"Nothing," she said.

The gray creek rock fell and hit me in the head.

By the teeter totter that day, it felt like a rock hit me in the head. I was kind of dizzy. Didn't have any air.

Billy danced over to me, naked, eyes laughing, blond springs all curly and bouncing.

"Come on, Davey. Take your clothes off."

"Is it okay?" I say. I could see out to the road through the trees. "What if someone sees us?"

"Come on, we do it all the time," Billy says.

"Looks like your little friend's a scaredy cat," Frank says and his eyes go up like Scotty's and it makes me feel stupid.

I can hear my heart in my ears like it does. Someone might see. Kind of scary but fun scary. So I pull my tee shirt out of my jeans and up over my face. I can hardly lift my arms. Eyes shut. Dark in there. Then light and trees all around me. It's like turning around and around and when you stop everything is still turning. I know I should never take all my clothes off outside. But I'm not gonna be a "scaredy cat." I drop my shirt and bend over to take my shoes off. Almost fall down. Taste dust and pine needles. Shoes off. I unbutton my jeans and let them drop to the ground. Stand there in my shorts. Pants around my feet.

"Well, come on," Billy yells, dancing naked around the teeter totter.

Frank just standing by it smoking. Golden syrup eyes. Waiting.

I bend over again. Still dizzy. Stand on one leg and tug the bottom of one leg of my jeans. Almost fall down. Hop. Get it off. Then the other one. I stand up and drop my pants on the ground. I take a big breath and let it out. Then I yank my shorts off. Step out of them.

Billy yells, "Whooee." Runs behind me and snaps my fanny with his tee shirt.

So I run to the other side of the teeter totter. Wow. That feels so good, running naked. So I run around the teeter totter the other way and slap Billy on the butt. He laughs and runs away. I'm not dizzy anymore, just happy. Free. No big people here to get mad.

Then Billy runs over to me and says, "You want a camel?"

"Sure," I say.

"You gotta show me where the hidden camel is though."

So he gets the pack by the tree and I take it out of the cellophane and say, "here" when I pull up the flap.

"Okay," he says and lights two cigarettes. Then he says, "Let's teeter totter."

Frank is already sitting on one end on the ground.

"It won't work with three," I say.

Billy's eyes laugh and his eyebrows go up.

"Sure it will. Let me show you."

Frank stands up and pulls the board up by the handle. Then the board is between his legs.

Billy pats the board on the other end and says, "You just have to sit here in front of the handle."

"Okay," I say and climb on.

Just then Frank sits down on his end of the board and it hits the dirt with a clunk. I fly up off the board and come down hard. The smooth old board hits my fanny and between my legs.

"Ow," I yell and almost lose my cigarette when it falls out of my mouth onto the board.

"Gotcha," Frank says and laughs kind of quiet.

I think that's kind of mean.

"Hey," Billy says, "that's not fair."

"Sorry," Frank says.

Then he stands up and pulls the board level again. Billy gets on in front of me and hangs on to the board with both hands.

"Okay. Now," he says.

Frank sits on his end and Billy and me, we go up. There's no handle for me to hang on to and no room to hang on to the board so I grab Billy around the middle. His smooth skin makes something inside of me feel funny, kind of like going down fast in an elevator, but nice. Then we start teeter tottering. And I forget about that and that Frank is kind of mean.

Wow. This is really fun. I'm playing with no clothes on. That's something I know I'm really not supposed to do and it's fun. Not making anybody mad. Just fun.

Playing naked in a secret place. Now I have another secret, a really big one.

13

Ration Stamps

It was a Wednesday afternoon in August and Craig and me, we were playing cars in our little hill by the road in front of the house. It was real hot out 'cause it was August. But I could smell this cool dirt smell from my dump truck full of dirt and the tunnel I just dug up under the shade of our hill where I parked my new car. I had a new plastic car that was blue like Jacky's coupe that John, my step-dad drove while his friend Jacky was away in the war. My new toy car had a pretend rumble seat in the back-end, though, instead of a trunk. Jacky's coupe didn't have one of those but I wished it did. It would be fun to sit back there.

That day was a day I wanted to go play with Billy Rogers in our secret place but when I got up that morning, Mom said I had to stay home and clean up my room. She said since it's August, summer is almost over and it will be time for school pretty soon. She said I have to start first grade with a clean room. I don't want summer to end, though. I'm having so much fun playing in Billy's woods and cleaning up my room was boring.

In the afternoon, after I cleaned up my room, I get tired of playing cars with Craig, crawling in the dirt, sweat on my face. So I get up and put my arms out like airplane wings and start my airplane engines. Errum, errum. When Craig hears my engines start, he looks up, dirt on his nose and in his black hair, his shoe untied and sees me starting to fly. Craig quick ties up his tennis shoe and starts his engines then, errum, errum, even before he gets up or puts his wings out to fly.

I took off making engine noises, then machine gun noises. *Errum, errum, kuh kuh kuh.* My wings spread out and tipped to one side of the road and then to the other side flying over the dust down the moo-cow hill. I looked back over my wings. Craig was right behind me, his little short legs running fast. His cowlick made him look like he was flying really fast, like the wind was blowing his hair flat. But he couldn't fly as fast as me 'cause he was only four. I swooped down low and dodged his machine gun shots and flew back up the hill to shoot at him. Flew by him fast, *errarow, kuh kuh kuh.* We did a dog fight back and forth across the road all the way down the hill. Craig, he was so short he couldn't bend down much lower, so he dodged my bullets leaning out of the way on one leg as he flew by me shooting, *errarow, kuh kuh kuh.*

At the bottom of the hill, the dust from the clay dirt was deep and dry that summer. It was soft and smooth like Mom's face powder. I dove down and grabbed a handful of dust. I threw it in the hot dry air and made bomb sounds deep in my throat. Then Craig did it. Playing war was almost as much fun as playing naked in the woods.

The wild sweet pea vines beside the road were all dried up in the heat and their little pea pods were gun shots when they popped open. The Scotch Broom was doing it too. Pops and rattles, snaps and bangs. Craig and me, we bombed the enemies shooting at us from beside the road and then flew back up the hill.

Just when we were coming back up the hill, I see Jacky's coupe speeding down Spring Garden hill into our driveway. It's only afternoon and John, my step-dad is home. He never comes home from his watch crystal shop until night time. I don't know why he's home.

The coupe stops fast and a cloud of dust comes right behind it into the driveway. John jumps out and sees Craig and me standing in the yard looking at him. He's still wearing his dirty white cords from work. His black hair is sticking out and his dark eyes are kind of wild—looking at us and not looking at us. Craig grabs my arm like he's scared. John is scary a lot a times but this time he's even scary to Craig.

John, he jumps in the air with his arms out like he's flying too and yells, "The war is over." Then his long legs run into the house like they're running faster than John can. No limp at all.

I don't know what he means. Craig and me, we look at each other. We don't know what he means.

Then John comes out of the house again. He jumps over the steps there down into the front yard. He's pulling Mom by the hand. Mom trips on the doorstep. Almost falls down. They are both yelling and laughing. "It's over. It's over. It's finally over."

I've never seen 'em act like that before. They look like little kids. Like us. Jumping and twirling, John's arms flapping. Mom is spinning around in the front yard. There are tears coming down her face. Her long brown, Rita Hayworth movie star hair is flying out in the air behind her. Her striped skirt floating up like a big bell over her saddle shoes and bobby socks. John is jumping up and down like a giant jack-in-the-box. His head back howling like I heard wolves do on my radio programs.

"Craig," he yells, "go tell your mom. The war is over."

Then all there is of Craig is little puffs of dust from his heels running out into the road and around the fence into his yard next door.

Mom runs over to me laughing. Her hand out.

"Come on, Davey," she says. "We're going down town."

She takes my hand and John grabs the other one and they swing me between them to the car. Mom on one side, John on the other and it feels like a ride at the Oaks Amusement Park, swinging. They're yelling, "Wheee." The air goes by my ears and that's what it feels like—Wheee.

Fun. Kind of like the teeter-totter. But something else too. Like family. John's big hand holding mine, strong. Not strange like before and scary. And Mom's soft hand, warm. Those two hands made me feel like I belonged right there with them. Both of them. That was really different.

Then we're in Jacky's coupe—me in the middle—and we're driving up Spring Garden hill making dust behind us on our way to Portland.

~

Everything's different. There's been war since I can remember. Now there's no war.

~

Portland looks like it's snowing. It's summer. It's August. And it looks like it's snowing. There are flakes falling everywhere outside the car windows.

John says it would be best to find a place to park on the west side of town nearest to where we live instead of going all the way down town. So we park by the Guild Theatre. I can hardly hear John when he says we should start walking down to the big public library. Everyone is blowing car horns. Some long sounds—people holding their horns down—some short sounds—honks and toots, some really high, whiney sounds and some are big, low ones. So many horns you can't hear anything else.

As soon as we get out of the car, I see the snowflakes are not snow but paper. Most of them are ration stamps.

I pick up a handful and yell to Mom, "Why are they throwing these away?"

Mom is laughing and grabbing at them falling around her, slapping at the stamps and knocking them to the ground.

"Because we don't need them anymore," she yells back. "Hooray."

I can't believe it. They were what everybody wanted yesterday.

I yell, "Hooray" like Mom and toss the handful of stamps into the air like I did the dry dust on the moo-cow hill. No bomb sounds this time.

Then I pick some up and lick the backs and stick them on my hands, then on my tee shirt. We're all laughing so I lick more and stick them on the car wind shields parked on the street. Nobody even tells me not to. Other people see me and start sticking them on themselves and the people they're with. Stamps are fluttering down from all the windows of the buildings above us. Mom's hair is full of them and John's too.

There are people everywhere. We can hardly move on the sidewalk now. People are squeezing by me and pushing me into Mom and John's legs and the streets are filling up too. Even some colored people and Chinese. You don't see many of them in Portland most of the time. I can hear people laughing and some singing. "Over there, over there." I'm too little to see much but I hear a radio playing jitterbug real loud and through people's legs I can see some ladies and men are dancing out in the street.

We are trying to get down to Broadway on the sidewalk through all the people. Then John sees a customer of his standing by the curb in front of his Jewelry store. Rothstein's Jewelry. He's kind of bent over with his bald head in his hands. His shoulders are shaking. He looks like he's crying. John says we should wait by the store and he goes up to the man and says something. The man answers and John puts an arm over the man's shoulders, hugs him to his side. I don't know why but I feel really bad for the man. Crying and everybody else is so happy.

Just then a woman with gray hair comes out of the front of the jewelry store and locks the door. She goes over to John and the man at the curb and John puts his other arm around the woman like he knows her too. She opens her purse for a hanky and is wiping her eyes.

Mom and me, we walk over to the doorway of Rothstein's now real close in the doorway and I pull on her hand. Feel her rings press into my fingers. Jergen's Lotion smell.

"Mom," I say, "why are they crying when everybody else is so happy?"

Mom leans down close. Her eyebrows are really pulled down and her eyes are full of tears. "Well honey, it's probably like your uncle Harold." She can hardly get his name out. Her voice sounds like it got stuck somewhere in her throat. "You remember your grandma Williams told you he died over in Germany?"

~

I never knew my uncle Harold. He was my real dad's little brother. I didn't know about him until I stayed at my gramma's one weekend last year. My Gramma Williams and her family came to Oregon from Arkansas.

That's where she made my snowflake star quilt with all her lady friends and relatives.

I was playing on the hill beside their house the first day I stayed over with them on the east side of Portland. I didn't know my Gramma Williams very well and her husband didn't ever talk. Old Grampa Williams, he didn't have any hair left and just sat around and made loud noises sometimes. Like a kind of short yell. Gramma Williams just said to me, "He ain't well." So I played outside so I didn't have to talk to them. When the sun was going down, I came in.

Gramma Williams was in the kitchen where she was most of the time. When I came in the kitchen door from outside, she looked up from the sink where she was peeling potatoes. Her long skinny face looked tired. She pushed some loose hair to her bun in the back with her arm. She didn't smile. She never smiled.

"Been up yonder?" she said.

I guessed that was the name of the hill where I was so I said, "Yup."

"Harold used to love to go up yonder," she said.

I didn't know who that was.

She stopped peeling potatoes again and looked at me close with her gray eyes that looked like dish water. Her lips were so thin and white. It was like she didn't have any.

"You know about Harold?"

"No?" I said.

"Lord Jesus help us."

Gramma Williams always said things like that. She belonged to the Apostolic Faith. They had a big neon sign right down town in Portland that said, "Jesus the Light of the World." They didn't believe in movies or card playing or dancing. Gramma Williams thought my mom was a sinner because Mom was a Catholic.

"Don't they teach you nothin' child? Harold was your daddy Earl's brother. 'Course your daddy, he didn't much care for Harold. Lord forgive him and bless my children. Sin of Cain and Abel. That's what it is."

I didn't know what to say. I didn't know who "they" was. Or Cain or Abel. Or anything Gramma Williams was talking about. Just then Grampa Williams, who was at the kitchen table eating broken up corn bread with a spoon out of a glass of buttermilk with salt and pepper yelled, "Amen!" real loud and scared me.

Gramma Williams saw me jump and she said, "Com'ere child, let me show you somethin.'"

She went upstairs to her bedroom and I followed behind her wrinkled stockings. They looked like loose skin on her long, skinny legs. She went to the other side of the big bed with the quilt on it, the one that was made by the ladies in Gramma Williams' church. Then she opened the closet door. The room smelled funny. Kind of like bad breath. It smelled more when she opened the closet door. She pulled out a stool from under the big bed and put it in the closet so she could reach the top shelf in there. Then she pulled down a fancy box from the shelf that was peachy pink. It was a little smaller than the cigar box that John kept his special things in. Gramma Williams sat down on the big bed with the box and patted her hand on the quilt beside her.

"Come here child," she said.

I climbed up on the big bed beside her and said, "What is that?"

She opened the peachy pink box and there, on some soft velvet cloth like Mom's fancy dress, was a beautiful purple ribbon. There was a shiny gold heart hanging from it with a smooth purple colored heart inside the gold edge. A gold picture of George Washington was on the purple part. My brother, Scotty told me once that George Washington had wooden teeth. But I think he was just kidding me.

Gramma Williams' face was really wrinkled up when I asked her about the heart and there was water filling up her eyes. "This here's your uncle Harold's purple heart," she said. "They sent it to me instead of sending my boy home."

She was still wearing her kitchen apron and she took a plain hanky out of the pocket and pushed it real hard in her eyes. Then she blew her nose on it. Her tired, dishwater eyes were all red and so was her nose. "He was killed over there in Germany," she said.

~

When I asked Mom about Harold after I stayed with Gramma Williams that time, she got lots of tears too. "Poor Harold," she said, little sparkles on her eye lashes, her pretty mouth soft in a smile, remembering. "He was a sweetheart. But your dad and he didn't get along. Probably because Harold didn't go along with that damn religion of theirs."

~

"It's probably like your uncle Harold," Mom says in that doorway of Rothstein's jewelry store. "They probably lost somebody too."

The bald man and the gray haired lady step into the street—into all the people there and John comes back over to us. His eyes look down, wrinkles in his forehead.

"Rothstein and his wife," John says. "The rest of their family was over there."

I didn't know what he meant but I didn't say anything.

Then John looks down at me from way up there and says, "It's getting really crowded, Davey. Would you like to ride on my shoulders?"

I don't know what to say. I never did that before. John, my step-dad, he's hardly never touched me before, except sometimes he takes my hand. I don't think he even likes me very much. But this day seems so different. And then before I can say anything his big hands just pick me up and put me on his shoulders. My whole body is shaking. I look down at his thick black hair—his widow's peak upside down—and smell his smell of pipe tobacco and something else really nice. It makes me feel really funny. It's kind of scary too. Like that time on the roof. I have to put my hands on his forehead to stay up there, it's so high. His tanned skin under my white fingers. I take a breath, make myself stop shaking.

It's kind of fun. Up there I can see everything. Big people everywhere acting like kids. Laughing and whooping. Dancing and yelling. Sitting on cars, on stairways, on fire escapes. Throwing ration stamps and catching long strips of them coming out of windows up above.

And Mr. Rothstein is not the only one I see crying that day.

I see a girl dressed pretty in a silky dress—belt in the middle, seams in her stockings. Probably coming from work. She's got a little summer hat kind of down on her forehead with a veil and she's turning sideways to get down the sidewalk. Two sailors are coming at her through all the people there. One of 'em salutes real nice when they go past her. Her white gloves open her purse and get a hanky. Then she kind of falls sideways against a tree in front of the library and cries into her hanky.

On the other side of the street, I see a man sitting on top of his car over the windshield, feet on the hood, with his head in his hands. Like he doesn't hear the music or the people dancing.

From up there I see a Negro man. He's holding a big colored lady who has her head on his chest. His head back looking at the sky. Tears on his face. His big white teeth bright like he's smiling.

Did all those people lose somebody too?

~

I guess Scotty would've thought I was stupid, but that day I wondered what that meant—what he always said "peace, justice and the American way." That day the war ended. That day the newspaper called VJ Day. Wednesday, August 15, 1945.

PART TWO

Somewhere Else

14

Winter Days

Big people, they say one thing but they mean something else. Or they say one thing but it really *is* something else. And sometimes, I think they say they believe in something just because they don't want anyone to know they don't know what it means.

Like peace, justice and the American way. That's something I started to learn about big people even before that next year when I got to be seven.

~

When first grade started up, I didn't see Billy Rogers so much. He was in second grade and he had a lot of friends from his neighborhood to play with. It started raining on Halloween. Mom says, in Oregon it always starts to rain on Halloween and doesn't stop 'til summer. And it was too cold out before that to play naked in his woods anyway.

One afternoon though, after school when I went down the little hill behind us to visit Mrs. Baldwin, I saw Billy alone out on the road in front of his house across the field. He waved at me and I waved back. Then he made a wave like I should come over, so I made the same wave back. We both just stood there looking across the field. That made me laugh. Then we both started across the field.

No more high grass. Just little soggy weeds.

Billy was laughing. His laughing eyes, just slits. His hair kind of wet from the wet in the air.

"So now you're in first grade, you don't wanna come over anymore?" he said when we got to the middle.

When I stood still, I started to sink. I pulled one foot up and it made a sucking sound.

"No, I'll come over," I said down at my muddy shoe.

"Okay," he said. "We better move or we'll get sucked in. I'll race you to my side."

So we both ran up to the road in front of his house. We made lots of sucking sounds—thwap, thwap—and blobs of mud went flying all over. I won. But hunks of muddy ol' grass were stuck to my jeans. And my shoes were all over muddy. So were his.

Billy thought it was funny though. He started dancing around in the street. His wet wool coat arms flapping.

"Mud people, mud people," he was singing.

"Come on up to the garden shed," he said when he stopped dancing, out of breath. "We can clean 'em off."

After we cleaned the mud off our shoes, we went in his back door and Billy made us peanut butter sandwiches. Then we got some milk and sat down at his kitchen table.

Billy took a bite of his sandwich and a great big gulp of his milk that came out his nose. He was coughing. Yucky white snot running down his lip. It made me spit mine all the way over the table from laughing. He was laughing at that and coughing and so was I. Finally, we stopped laughing and he stopped coughing, face all red, and pushed his wet hair back out of his eyes. Blue.

"Tomorrow is the Cinnamon Bear," he said, when he could talk.

"The what?" I said.

"The Cinnamon Bear. Don't you know about the Cinnamon Bear?"

"No," I said. "What's the Cinnamon Bear?"

"It's this great program on the radio." He moved his glass of milk and scooted his chair closer. His arms on the table. Eyes big. "It's about Paddy O'Cinnamon, the Cinnamon Bear and how he takes these two twin kids, Judy and Jimmy, to Maybeland through the little end of a telescope, chasing the Crazy Quilt Dragon who stole their silver star that they keep in their attic for the top of the Christmas tree."

Billy stopped quick and took a big breath.

"And there's a witch in it, Witch Wintergreen and some pirates and everything. Even Santa."

He stopped and took another gulp of milk. It didn't come out his nose this time, though.

Then he said, "It's only on at Christmas time for a while. It's really neat. You missed the first one but it's on the radio every day until Christmas. Well, weekdays. You wanna come over and listen?"

"Sure," I said and banged my fist on the table. I wanted to be as excited as he was. "What time?"

Billy laughed and said, "Four o'clock." Then banged his fist on the table too.

"Okay, I'll come over," I said when we stopped laughing.

"You can come over right after school and we can play until it comes on," he said. "You know, you can even go to Lipman's department store downtown and meet the Cinnamon Bear before Christmas. He meets kids there."

"Wow, that's neat," I said.

Billy's pretty smart. Maybe Scotty didn't know about the Cinnamon Bear. He never told me. Mom just had to let me go see him.

~

The next day at school, I couldn't think about anything else except the Cinnamon Bear. All the other kids knew about it too. When I got out of school, it was raining and that mean old dog was waiting for me behind Mrs. Allan's picket fence. When I saw that old dog out there, I thought of Billy's know-it-all friend, Frank. I hoped he wouldn't be at Billy's today. He was mean. Frank was, I mean.

I went behind some people's houses so I wouldn't have to walk in front of Mrs. Allen's house but I had to climb over a wire fence when I went that way. So it was almost time for the Cinnamon Bear when I got to Billy's. I was glad Frank wasn't there. We went right up to his room and Billy, he went over to his radio and turned it on. Billy called it his Philco. It didn't have wooden flowers on it like mine. It was little and smooth and white. Something like plastic. It looked like the bread box in the kitchen at our house. Real new. Not big and clunky like my old wooden radio. The guy from Lipman's was talking.

Billy took my wet jacket and put it over the back of the chair by his desk. Then we layed down on his big bed. His bed was bigger than mine and he had a bedspread with puckery fuz like Mom's bathrobe. I could feel Billy breathing next to me and he had a nice warm smell. I closed my eyes 'cause the Cinnamon Bear started.

It was really neat. Up in their attic, when the Cinnamon bear told Jimmy and Judy to look at themselves in the mirror through the wrong end of the telescope so they would get smaller, I could see it all happening in my head with my eyes closed. I opened my eyes and looked over at Billy. He had his eyes shut too. It was good to be there beside Billy. Smell his smell. And listen to The Cinnamon Bear with my friend. It made that place in my chest all warm feeling. When Judy and Jimmy were only four inches tall, they went through a hole in the wall to chase the Crazy Quilt Dragon up Lollypop Mountain. It was better than Baby Snooks or

The Life of Riley or even Fibber McGee and Molly. But it was only fifteen minutes. I could hardly wait for the next one. Billy said I could come back every day and listen.

~

That night under my colored snowflake quilt, I hugged Teddy's brown face and gold cheeks close and thought about how maybe Teddy could take me on an adventure like Jimmy and Judy. I asked him, could he shrink me to be little like them. His big wide-open blue button eyes laughed like Billy's.

When Mom came up to tuck me in and hear my prayers, I told her about the radio program. She sat on my bed and smoothed her hand over the names on my colored snowflake quilt and listened. Her eyes looked real deep in mine like she could see it all happening in my head like I did. Her gray blue eyes soft like wispy sky clouds. Her eyebrows up now and little half-moons at the corners of her pretty red mouth like the story was special, like I was.

When I told it all to her, she said. "We could visit him when we go downtown to visit Santa."

My heart almost made my quilt jump, it started to beat so much.

"The Cinnamon Bear?" I said.

"Yup," Mom said.

"And Santa?" I said.

"Yup," Mom said again. "When we bring Robby down for Christmas, we'll have Scott over and all four of us can take the bus down to Portland. We'll go to Lipman's," she said.

When she turned my light out, I kissed Teddy real hard. I could feel his bear nose smoosh into his face. Then I put him under my arm so he could go to sleep. I didn't think I could go to sleep. But I did. I knew Mom never said anything she didn't mean.

15

Lipman's

I never visited Santa before. Last year Mom helped me write him a letter. Now we were going to see Santa and The Cinnamon Bear too. And best of all my brother Scotty was coming too.

'Cause I listened when Mom told Scotty on the telephone that we were going downtown to see Santa and The Cinnamon Bear, I could tell he didn't want to go. She told him Robby was coming down from The Dalles so we could all go together and she wanted him to come too. He still didn't want to and then Mom said he should care more about his brothers. Then he said something that made her mad at him and she yelled at him on the phone. They always got mad at each other. I wished they didn't. It made a yucky feeling in my stomach. After that though, he said he would come. My feet did a tap dance in the kitchen where Mom couldn't see.

So then, the Sunday before we went to see Santa and The Cinnamon Bear, we drove up to The Dalles to get Robby. When John's friend, Jacky came back from the war, he took the coupe, so we had to take our big Oldsmobile to The Dalles. I didn't like it like I did the coupe but it did have a window shelf in the back for me to ride on so I could sleep and not get car sick. 'Course I was almost too big for the shelf now. I had to pull my knees up and there wasn't any room for my pillow. The shelf was covered with this fuzzy stuff too, not smooth like the seats. It was bristly. Not too good to sleep on. But the Oldsmobile had more room in the back seat for me and Robby to play on the way back. I didn't like it so much, though. Not like the coupe. The coupe made me feel like we were a family. Little and close.

It was hard rainy that day. It sounded like it would come right through the car roof and you couldn't see outside. Robby and me, we got John to sing a song, the old song about the beer bottle. When we asked him, John got a real sad look on his face in the mirror over the swish-clunk, swish-clunk of the window wipers. His dark eyes sad like he was going to cry. Then he started to sing slow and soft like he did when he sang that song.

"Just an old beer bottle floating on the foam.

Only an empty bottle, many a mile from home."

John reached a hand up then and wiped a pretend tear away from his eyes.

"Inside was a piece of paper, with this message on:"

Then he sniffed real loud.

"whoever finds this bottle will find the beer all gone."

After that, he kind of laughed deep in his throat and his eyes crinkled up. Then we asked him to sing it again. It was our favorite part of driving back from The Dalles. Except for Mom's faces.

Mom wore her glasses most of the time now. She used to take them off when she went some place but she said she was tired of not seeing things. After John sang again, Robby and me yelled that it was Mom's time to make faces.

Her forehead wrinkled like she was thinking hard. Her lips puckered up.

"Oh, I don't know," she said. "That's a hard act to follow."

"C'mon, Mom. C'mon," we said.

It wouldn't be any fun without her faces.

Then she pulled her glasses to the end of her nose, crossed her eyes and out came her tongue, her pretty movie star face gone. Then Robby and me, we rolled around the back seat laughing. When we rolled into each other, it made it funnier and we laughed harder. When I looked up, Mom was still looking over the front seat. Face all funny. I laughed until I had tears and my stomach hurt.

~

When Scotty came over the next day, he looked mad. The muscle in the back of his jaw stuck out and moved up and down like he was chewing with his mouth closed tight. He just stood around with his arms folded and his chin down on his chest. It was strange to see him. It seemed like I never saw him. Not hardly since he went to live with our dad last spring. It was like he didn't want to be my brother anymore. Like he didn't want to be there. It made my throat all burny. But I tried not to think about it. I thought about Paddy O'Cinnamon and Maybeland and the Lollypop Mountain and that finally the day to go see Santa and The Cinnamon Bear was here. Every time Scotty saw how excited I was though, he would just roll his eyes around and breathe out air. My feet didn't feel like tap dancing about Scotty anymore. But when he saw Santa, I knew he'd be different.

Robby was excited too. His brown eyes got real big when he told me he knew about The Cinnamon Bear from the radio up in The Dalles. He said he already saw Santa last year though. Robby was always saying how he was older than me. Six months.

I was ready to go before anybody else and had to wait. It was like they wouldn't ever be ready to go. When Mom and Scotty, and me and Robby went out the front door, it wasn't raining and Mom said it was okay for me and Robby to race each other up Spring Garden hill to the bus stop on Capitol Highway. We both wanted to be the first one to see The Cinnamon Bear. When we got to the bus stop, though, we had to wait for Mom and Scotty.

"How big do you think he is," Robby said, "The Cinnamon Bear?"

Robby was panting from running up the hill and he bent over with one hand on his knee. With the other one he stuck his clean white shirt collar in his mouth and started to chew. His long brown eye lashes blinking up and down.

"I don't know," I said.

I never thought about that. I guess I just thought he was about as big as Teddy. That's what I saw in my head.

"Well, you know, he hangs on their Christmas tree himself. He must be small."

"Oh," I said. "I thought he was more like a teddy bear."

Then I remembered how he got Judy and Jimmy real small to follow the Crazy Quilt Dragon.

"I never thought about that," I said. "I guess he must be really small since he made Jimmy and Judy little."

Robby was really chewing now, like it helped him think. His collar looked really yucky with teeth marks and spit on it. I didn't like to look at it. When I looked away, I saw Mom and Scotty coming up to the bus stop. I guess they were arguing again 'cause Scotty's arms and legs were stiff walking and his face was all red and Mom was leaning over him talking loud. Her eyebrows wrinkled down.

I heard her say, "You just be quiet about it."

I didn't want them to be mad, so I said real happy like, "Be quiet about what?"

Scotty just growled in his throat.

And Mom said, "Never mind." She was really mad.

Robby was still chewing on his collar and wondering about The Cinnamon Bear.

So he said, "Marion, how big do you think The Cinnamon Bear is?"

Mom looked surprised. "Oh," she said. She let out a big breath and tried to smile but didn't really. Like she does after she's mad. "Well, I guess he's normal size. Uh, about yours and Davey's size."

I was over three feet now and so was Robby. John measured us every time Robby was with us. We stood up against the frame of the old-kitchen-spare-room door and John would make marks with the dates—his hand on top of my head to smoosh my hair down. His face close to mine with his pipe tobacco, leather smell.

Men shake hands.

I was glad I grew faster than Robby.

Robby, he chewed his collar faster when Mom said that and his eyes looked like they didn't believe her. His dark eyebrows way up. Brown eyes wide.

"Oh, you think he's that big?" he said. "Then how does he hang on the Christmas tree?"

Scotty crossed his arms and mumbled something and Mom looked at him quick. His mouth just closed tight and twisted to the side. Then to the other side and he tapped his foot.

"Don't chew your collar, Robby," Mom said.

Then the bus came.

~

Two bus stops, then up on the high viaduct over the old railroad tracks and we were in Multnomah. Past the bakery where Mom got our cat and John's Market, the butcher where she always got our meat and then the bus stop at the Rexall drugstore. Robby and me, we were playing a game we made up. Who could be the first to see a new model 1945 car. Who ever saw the most 1945 cars first by the time we got to Portland won.

At the Rexall the bus stopped to let people on. At first I didn't see because I was looking at cars out the window but then Robby punched me in the arm. His face was all red and his cheeks puffed out like it was gonna explode. His eyes looked in the aisle where people walk so I looked too. There was this big fat lady coming. She was wearing a great big, really hairy fur coat that looked like a bear. It made her look as big across as the aisle and she was only as tall as the bus seats. Her face was like a red balloon. And on top was a hat that looked like an upside-down flowerpot. It had a veil stretched over her balloon face and on top her flowerpot one feather sticking kind of crooked up in the air. That round lady, she was just rolling down the middle of the bus at Robby and me like a great big bowling ball.

Robby's face exploded then and he fell down to the floor between our seat and the one in front laughing. I couldn't help it. I went after him, down between the seats, laughing.

Mom was sitting with Scotty behind us. I don't think Mom knew why we were laughing, though.

"Hey, you two," she said. Mom's voice was loud mad. "Behave yourselves."

It was funnier than Mom making faces though, the fat lady with the flowerpot hat.

Robby took a breath and straightened up his face down there between the seats. Then he whispered, "Santa's wife."

That made all my air and spit fly out between my lips. But Mom's voice was sharp in my ear over the seat, "Sit back up in your seats and behave."

Both of us tried to sit up and behave but when I looked at Robby, it all started again. My sides hurt from laughing but as hard as I tried, I couldn't stop laughing.

Santa's wife.

Mom said if we didn't behave, she would take us back home, but I couldn't get that lady rolling down the aisle out of my head. I closed my eyes and there was the flowerpot hat. Then I tried to do our car game but all I could see was bowling balls. Robby would laugh and it would start all over again. *Making Mom mad. Don't laugh.* I tried to be serious and ask the serious part in my head why the lady would wear a coat that made her look like a—*a beach ball with a flowerpot on top?*

No good. There was the picture again.

~

When we got to Portland and we got off the bus, we didn't see the lady with the flowerpot again so the giggles finally went away.

Mom looked mad at us though, her forehead wrinkled down like she did. Her gray sky eyes, like rain clouds.

"I don't know what's wrong with you two today," she said.

Scotty just rolled his eyes around.

We got to ride the sliding stairs up to the third floor at Lipman and Wolfe where The Cinnamon Bear was. Mom said escalator. It was fun sliding up the stairs. I never did that before. I thought maybe it would catch my toes under the metal thing where you get off, so I jumped over it. Mom asked a man who was wearing a flower on his coat where The

Cinnamon Bear was, and he showed us the way. He wrinkled his eyes and looked sad at Robby and me though. He said he was afraid Paddy was taking a rest right then.

There was a yellow sign up in front of The Cinnamon Bear's chair that said:

"TOP OF THE MORNIN' TO YA.

I'M ON A BREAK.

BE BACK SOON.

PADDY O' CINNAMON."

Mom let out a big breath and said, "Wouldn't you know." Then, "How 'bout we go see Santa first?"

Robby stuck his collar in his mouth and said, "Ah, geez."

So, we were looking for Santa and all of a sudden Scotty started laughing. He pointed at something. I couldn't see over the thing that had shirts piled on it 'cause I was too little. So, I didn't know why he was laughing. But Mom wasn't laughing. She grabbed Robby and me by the hand and started pulling us a different way.

Her face got red and her eyebrows wrinkled down, and she hollered at Scotty, "Edward Scott Williams. What did I tell you?"

Robby and me, we didn't know what he was laughing at.

"What's funny," I said.

Mom said, "Never mind," and pulled Robby and me harder.

Robby just chewed his collar. Eye lashes up and down.

At Santa's Village, Robby and me, we had to get at the end of a line to see him. Only four kids ahead of us though. Mom and Scotty didn't get in line. They just waited over at the side.

I said to Robby, "Why do you think Scotty doesn't want to get in line?"

Robby thought about it for a minute. Chewing. Then he said, "Maybe Santa didn't bring him anything last year."

"Maybe," I said. "I wonder why Santa wouldn't bring him anything."

When Robby and me got up to Santa, Robby got really polite and said I should go first because I never met him before. But I think he was just nervous. He was chewing his collar lickity split and his tan face got red like he was embarrassed or something.

I just walked up to Santa and stood in front of him. He looked down at me from his big red chair through all that white hair—his mustache, his beard, big white eyebrows up—and said, "Well, Mr. Freckles, would you like to sit in Santa's lap?"

I didn't know if I wanted to do that. So, I just looked up at him. My face felt hot. I didn't say anything. But I didn't like him calling me Mr. Freckles. I could hear the kids in line behind me. A baby was crying, and a soft bell rang two times over a loud speaker.

So, Santa, he said, "What's your name little boy?"

I said, "Davey."

Then he put his head back and laughed. I didn't know what was funny, so I didn't laugh. But he just kept saying, Ho, Ho, Ho. It was weird.

Then he said, "Well, Davey, come up here and tell me what you'd like for Christmas." And his big arms just picked me up and put me on his lap. Just like when John put me up on his shoulders.

Santa was still looking at me through all that hair. I never saw so much hair on somebody's face. Big white eyebrows with a lot of hair and a mustache that went into his beard that I was almost sitting on. I could smell his B.O. He held onto me so I wouldn't fall off his lap and he put his big hairy face right up to mine.

I got so scared; I couldn't remember what I wanted to tell him. It felt like I had to pee and all I could think was someday I wanted a piano like my aunt Ethelyn or John's mom, Gramma Brugger who lived on a farm. So, I said I wanted a piano like Gramma's.

Santa didn't say, "Ho, Ho, Ho" then. He didn't even smile. I wasn't sure he even heard me—like he was thinking of something else—until he said, "Hunh. I'll see what I can do."

Then it was Robby's turn. I was glad it was over.

I looked down at Robby standing there. His face was still red. He looked back at me and his mouth moved with no sound. It said, *Santa's wife.*

There it was in my head again—the upside down flowerpot on the round lady's head.

We both started to laugh all over again and I didn't wait for Santa to put me down.

After that, we all went back to see The Cinnamon Bear. He was done resting, sitting in his chair. I didn't feel scared of him. He just looked like my Teddy except he was bigger. I didn't have to tell him what I wanted for Christmas or sit in his lap. He shook our hands, Robby and me, and asked us where we lived. Then he talked to both of us like we were old friends, asked us how Mom and Dad were and how we were doing in school. When he asked us if we liked his radio program, I got so excited I told him about me and Billy listening every day. He liked that so much he gave me a hug. He felt just like Teddy. His fur soft and smooth. And he didn't have B.O. like Santa.

'Cause he was big like a person, Robby asked him how he got small enough to hang on a Christmas tree. Paddy said it was fairy magic and he couldn't tell or the fairies would be angry with him. Being right there with The Cinnamon Bear and talking to him was really fun.

He gave us each a little silver star shaped pencil box that had a pencil in it that looked like a candy cane, an eraser that looked like a tiny cinnamon bear and a little pencil sharpener that was like the glass airplane Jimmy and Judy flew in. I knew the pencil box must have fairy magic in it too, it felt so good in my hand, smooth silver with sharp star points. I knew it must be worth a lot of money. I couldn't wait to show all the kids in first grade. A girl with a basket there gave us a gingerbread man cookie to eat too that looked a little bit like him and Paddy, he said he'd see us again next year. Boy, The Cinnamon Bear was sure neat.

~

That night Scotty stayed with us in his room next to mine with the stars on the ceiling that glow in the dark. I was happy he was in there. It was almost like it used to be. Like maybe he might even stay. Like maybe he did wanna be my brother after all.

After I got my pajamas on, I went in our bathroom and washed my face and brushed my teeth. Then I went by Scotty's door and saw him in bed. His room was always neat. He always hung up all his clothes like he was supposed to. Everything put away. His covers neat on the bed over him. He was reading his Boy's Life magazine. I waited in his doorway for a minute. He didn't look mad like he did before. His face quiet and handsome. He had his glasses on and looked like he was smiling at something.

Only his red hair all messed up from the pillow in back of his head.

I wished I had red hair like his instead of old nothing brown hair. Red hair was cool. It made me feel good he was here.

"Didn't Santa bring you anything last year?" I said.

He kind of jumped and said, "What?"

"I was wondering why you didn't want to meet Santa today," I said. "Didn't he bring you anything last year?"

He just looked at me a long time. I couldn't see his eyes—the bed lamp light on his glasses. Then he put his magazine down and took off his glasses. He put his fingers in his red hair and said, "I'm too old for that stuff."

"Too old?" I said.

"Well Davey, I'm gonna be eleven next month."

"Yeah, but doesn't Santa still bring you presents?"

He just looked at me again. But his gray green eyes looked like they were looking inside instead of out at me. He started biting the inside of his cheek and his eyes scrunched up. It made all his freckles come together over his nose.

"Davey, why do you let them all lie to you?" he said.

He always said things like that. Like I would know what he meant when he knew I didn't.

I leaned against the edge of his door. Tried to look like I didn't feel stupid. Like I was more interested in something outside his window. Except it was dark out. Then I really felt dumb.

"What?" I said.

His forehead winkled down like Mom's. First time I saw he looked a lot like her.

"All that stuff about The Cinnamon Bear and Santa Claus. You're not a baby anymore. Why do you let them lie to you about that stuff? It pisses me off."

Scotty liked to say those things Army guys said. Like "hubba, hubba" or "pissed off." But I knew Scotty was trying to teach me something like he did. I liked him being my big brother again and trying to teach me things. But I felt stupid. Like always. My face felt hot and I was getting mad. He really could make me feel that way. I didn't know what he was talking about.

I looked down at the floor—at the linoleum there that looked like wood boards.

"Whata you mean," I said.

I looked up then and Scotty, he just rolled his eyes around.

Then he said, "It's all pretend. It's all make believe."

I felt my chest start to get tight.

"What? You mean The Cinnamon Bear?"

Scotty's eyebrows came down and his nose bunched up.

"Yeah," he said. "Whata you think I was laughing at today? That phony Cinnamon Bear was sitting there with his fake head off so he could have a smoke on his break."

My throat hurt and it was hard to say but I said, "and Santa?"

Scotty nodded his head but all I could see through the tears in my eyes was the lamp light shiny on his red hair.

"Yup, all make believe."

I don't know why but I knew he was just being mean. Tears started running down my face. Maybe that was why Mom was always mad at him. Maybe he always just tries to make people feel stupid.

Oh, no it's not," I yelled at him. "Santa is real. Last year he brought me my play service station. And my friend, Billy, he knows better'n you. The Cinnamon Bear is real."

I ran into my room and got under my colored snowflake quilt and hugged Teddy as hard as I could. I kissed him on his nose and felt it smoosh into his face. I wiped the tears off my face with the sheet.

I knew The Cinnamon Bear was real. I knew Teddy could take me on an adventure too, if he wanted to. And I knew Santa wasn't make believe. He brought me stuff.

I don't know why Scotty is so mean. First, he moves away and won't be my brother anymore and now he comes back just to make me feel bad.

I hope he doesn't come back to stay.

It was raining again. The wind banged it against my bedroom windows. Then it was quiet. Then it banged again like it wanted to get in. I snuggled down under the covers with Teddy where it was nice and warm and quiet.

I could always ask Mom about Santa and The Cinnamon Bear. I knew she'd tell me the truth.

16

Silent Night

I didn't ask Mom about Santa or The Cinnamon Bear. I knew she'd tell me the truth but I didn't know if I really wanted to know that. I tried not to think about it. Singing was a good way not to think about bad things. My first grade teacher, Mrs. Wright played the piano. She was teaching us Christmas songs. That was fun. I loved to sing.

After the day we went to see Santa and the Cinnamon Bear, Scotty didn't stay with us. He went back to stay with Dad.

I was still mad at him for what he said to me that night but when he went back to stay with Dad, it made my stomach feel funny. Like I was hungry or something. I wished he didn't go. He should of stayed.

When Scotty was real little, when he was learning to talk, my Gramma Jones and Mom tried to get Scotty to say grandpa. It was the first time my Gramma Jones was a gramma.

They would say, "Gran pah, gran pah."

But all he could say was the last part that came out "Pop." From that time on, that was my grandpa's name. Pop. Everybody called him Pop, even the people he was a lawyer for. I guess it just fit him better than Ancel. And he told Mom and my gramma after, that he most certainly did not want to be called Grandpa anyway. So, you could say, Scotty gave Pop his name.

Pop was my favorite relative. He was the oldest too. He had those brown spots on the back of his hands and he had gray hair like my gramma. Gramma was fifty three years old. But I'm not sure how old Pop was. The reason I know how old Gramma Jones was, happened at Christmas time that year when Pop was talking to Mom and John and they didn't know I heard.

Most Sundays Pop would come out to see us. Gramma had been sick for a long time so Pop came out by himself. Pop and Gramma had a big old house in Portland but he loved to come out to our house and go for a walk in the country. Always dressed like a lawyer. His dark suit with little gray lines in it and his vest that matched, his gray hat and nice shiny shoes with the wings on the toes. They were really swell but they always made him look funny to me walking out in the country. We had a lot of mud in Mudnomah. Mom most always made me wear goulashes.

Pop always brought us chocolate covered cherries. Mom hated them but she didn't tell him. He loved to eat them and smoke his cigar. He said a cigar was never any good until you lit it about three or four times. Those cigars smelled good and bad at the same time. Like wet leaves burning or the smell of the barns on my aunt Pearl's dairy farm.

Pop, he had nick names for everybody. I guess maybe he thought if he had one, everybody should. My Mom's older sister who lived with Pop and Gramma in their big house with her two little girls, he called "Toot." Maybe because he called Gramma, "Bell." Her name was Isabelle. Toot and Bell. Like sounds from boats on the river downtown.

He called my mom, "Rascal Bear" and my name was "Old Fraternity Sister." He always laughed when he called me that, but I didn't know what it meant, or why it was funny, so it made me a little bit mad. But I loved Pop and it made him happy, I guess. So it was okay.

One Sunday, after Scotty went back to his place with Dad, Pop came out to visit us. I was outside playing with my cars in our little hill because it stopped raining. The dirt was all muddy though and I had to wear my winter coat 'cause it was cold out. The coat was getting mud on it and my jeans were all over muddy especially in the knees. Most of my cars were dirty and had mud on them 'cause I forgot and left them out there in the rain. I was wishing it was summer again.

The wet grass up in the front lawn was just right to wipe the mud off my two little cars. On the metal one, though, the paint was coming off. It wasn't good to leave them out in the rain. Then Pop stamped his shoes on the gravel at the end of our driveway like he did after he walked down Spring Garden hill from the bus stop. There were crunchy sounds and I smelled his wet-leaves-burning cigar so I left my cars in the grass and ran to meet him.

His hand came out of his overcoat pocket and took the cigar out of his mouth when he heard me holler, "Hi Pop." There was smoke around his face and hat and he sucked air through his teeth two or three times fast, like he did. Like he was trying to get the little pieces of tobacco out of there.

His eyes crinkled up and he said, "Well, hello there, Old Fraternity Sister."

I hugged him around the knees and he laughed low in his throat.

"Where's your mama?" he said.

"Oh, she's in the house. Brew's in the garage working on his car."

"Ah hah," he said like that settled everything he wanted to know.

He bent his tall body down to me. His brown eyes looking steady into my blue ones. His smell in my nose—cigar-barn smells and aftershave. That aftershave Mom called Bay Rum.

"Why don't you run and give these to your mama while I talk to your daddy?"

So I went in and gave the chocolates to Mom and told her Pop was here. Mom just kind of rolled her eyes like Scotty does when she saw the chocolate covered cherries and put them on the mantle over the fireplace.

Pretty soon, Pop came in with John and offered us all a piece of candy and we sat down in the front room a few minutes. Real soon the house smelled like Pop's cigar. Closed up, that wet leaf and barn smell wasn't as nice as it was outside.

Then Pop, he looked over at me where I was sitting on the other end of the davenport from him. His arm up on the back. He wasn't smiling like he was most of the time and a big line was coming down between his eyebrows. His big brown eyes looked more inside than out.

"Why don't you run back outside and play for a bit?" he said.

There was something that always reminded me of pictures in my school books of Abraham Lincoln about Pop when he was serious. I didn't see him serious very often but it was then I always remembered Mom told me how Pop was born in Kentucky and traveled to Illinois before he came to Oregon. Then he became a Lawyer. On his lawyer desk, he had two little people. One was a little statue of Abe Lincoln. The other one had a tall hat where you could put pencils. Mom said his name was Winston Churchill.

Pop was saying, "I have something I want to say to your mama and daddy."

So I got up and started out the front door. Pop said something behind me and Mom and John went into the kitchen with him. I waited a minute and then went slow back through the front room, past the fireplace and peeked into the kitchen. Mom and John were sitting at the table. Pop put his cigar in the ashtray on the table and started to talk.

"Bell has cancer," he said.

I heard Mom breathe in fast and John banged the table, his voice low but sharp.

"Damn it," he said.

I didn't know what Pop meant but I knew it was important. There was a chair in the front room by the kitchen doorway. So I sat down there. Out the window there by the kitchen door, there was the big bluish fir tree in Craig's yard next door. Scotty said *Blue Spruce.* The clock on the mantle over the fireplace ticked and there was no other sound.

Then I heard Pop say, "Other than that, she's healthy. She's fifty three years old. I know she can get through this. She's a fighter."

I didn't know she was that old. I knew she was old but not that old.

Then Mom said, "Does she know?"

"No," Pop said. "That's the problem. We can't tell her. She believes it's contagious."

John still sounded mad.

"Oh, for cryin' out loud," he said.

And Mom said, "But that's silly." Her voice sounded pinched in her throat like she was going to cry.

"Maybe," Pop said.

The slippery cloth on the arms of my chair felt wet under my hands.

"But you know, not a lot is known about the disease. She might be right."

"Pop," Mom said, "that's ridiculous." She spit it out like she was mad like John now.

"Perhaps," he said. And then Pop almost whispered, "but if she knew she had it, she might not want to continue. Because she believes it is."

"Where is it?" John said.

"Liver," Pop said.

One of the kitchen chairs scooted on the floor with a loud scrape and it scared me. I jumped up quick and ran tiptoe to the front door. The door opened real quiet and I slipped sideways past the screen door and closed them both as quiet as I could.

~

One of my favorite Christmas songs that Mrs. Wright was teaching us at school was Silent Night. Mrs. Wright was really good at getting us kids to see how it was. She told us Jesus was born in a country with deserts and camels. She said there is nothing like the desert at night. The sky is like black velvet and you can see millions of stars over you in the quiet of the desert where there are no cars or airplanes. I loved that song, Silent Night, then. I could close my eyes on the days I walked home alone from school and hum that song. Right away, there would be stars as far as I could see and it would be quiet. I could even walk by Mrs. Allen's mean old dog and not be scared. When I was humming or singing, I would hardly hear him growl.

On Christmas Eve after dinner, we were going over to Pop and Gramma's for a party. My aunt Ethelyn, that Pop called Toot, would be there with my two cousins. They were girls. Not much fun to play with but we could always chase each other. My Mom's brother, Bob was going to come with his wife and two boys. But they were little kids too. Robby was in The Dalles and Scotty was with our dad. So I would be the oldest kid there. Nobody to really play with.

After we finished dinner on Christmas Eve at our house, Mom told me I better get ready so I went upstairs and put on my red and green Christmas tie with my white shirt and found my red pull-over sweater and pulled it over. Then I had to comb my hair 'cause that sweater always messed up my hair.

I went into the bathroom that used to be Scotty's and my bathroom. Now it was just my bathroom. I wet my old brown hair and parted it in the mirror where I used to see Scotty comb his nice red hair that shined light back and fix his Scout shirt on meeting nights. It made me awful lonesome. My freckles were the only thing I had that looked like Scotty. I didn't like to look at myself too much in the mirror. There was always this girly looking boy there. My face was so white. It wouldn't tan. I just got sunburned in the summer. And my cheeks were always too pink. But while I was combing my hair, I saw the new scar under my eye from falling on the cement wall. That helped my face look more like a boy's. I couldn't wait to start having some whiskers to shave though, like John.

Under the mirror by the sink, there was this thing screwed to the wall for holding a glass and tooth brushes. It was then that I knew Scotty was really gone. There was only one tooth brush there. Mine. There was only one towel hanging on the towel rack. Only one washcloth. Scotty was gone. He was never coming back and I was going to grow up without my brother. Alone.

Then I looked back at myself in the mirror, at the tears coming down from my eyes and something creepy happened. I wasn't alone. There were two people—the one in the mirror and the one that was looking in the mirror. Which one was me, I couldn't tell. It felt like I was really the one in the mirror. Somebody I saw all the time. But if that was me, who was the one standing out here looking. The one that felt like somebody I didn't know. The one that was changing. It was really scary. I threw the comb down in the bathroom sink and ran downstairs to go to the party.

~

I always had fun with my cousins, Margo and Katy, even if they were pretty little. We loved to chase each other. I chased Margo and Katy around Pop's house only about two times while the big people were getting drinks in the kitchen. Then my aunt Ethelyn told us to stop running in the house.

When I was real little, my aunt Ethelyn used to be my favorite relative. She played the piano real well and used to play for me a lot. That was strange too, because my aunt Ethelyn was born with two thumbs on her right hand. Mom told me the doctors took one off but the one they left never grew right. It looked like a claw. But I guess she could reach more keys on the piano than most people with that funny thumb. That was something about Mom's family; they always did what they wanted to, whether it was easy or not.

After Ethelyn got married and had babies, though, we didn't seem to be friends anymore.

I was sorry she told us kids to stop running. I didn't know what else to do with my cousins. They were little and they were girls. What do you do with little girls except chase them?

Then Ethelyn came over to where I was sitting in the front room and sat down next to me. She looked at me like she used to. Her brown eyes soft. Big happy-to-see-you smile.

"Are you having fun, Davey?" she said.

I didn't think I should tell her I didn't know what to do with Margo and Katy if I didn't chase them, so I just said, "Yeah, I guess so." I tried to not look at her thumb. I knew I shouldn't look, but something always made me want to.

I don't know if she heard what I said, though, because right away she said, "Your mama, Marian, tells me you've been learning some Christmas songs."

Her voice sounded excited that I was learning some music so I said I was.

She leaned down to me close. Her skin was different than Mom's. Not as smooth. She had tiny little scars in her cheeks and she wore kind of thick glasses. She looked really different than Mom. Her eyebrows were up above her glasses asking a question real quiet to me.

"What if I play the piano for you and you sing for us?"

That sounded like fun. So I said, "Sure. Can I sing Silent Night?"

She smiled her smile at me that didn't make her prettier like it does some people but I felt like we were good friends again.

Just then, my uncle Bob came in with his family. So all the big people went in the kitchen for drinks. Except Pop.

All Pop needed was a good cigar and his family around him to be happy.

He came over with his cigar in his fingers and said, "Well hello there, Old Fraternity Sister. I hear you're going to favor us with a song."

Seeing Pop made me feel a lot better. I didn't know what to do with myself and there were too many people there I didn't know very well.

I said, "I guess so."

The chewed end of his little bit of cigar was yucky. Like Robby's leather aviator helmet strap after he chewed on it.

Pop let a big breath of air out and sat down in the chair next to me where Ethelyn had been. He put the yucky end in his mouth and took a big puff. Then he took it out and watched the big cloud of smoke he breathed out. He rolled the little stub between his thumb and finger and looked at it with his eyes almost shut. His wonderful Abe Lincoln face full of lines and thinking turned and smiled at me then. Smell of Bay Rum and dairy barns. A little dab of shaving cream in his ear.

"Wonderful," he said. "But don't start 'til I bring your grandmother down from upstairs."

He grabbed the arms of the chair like they might get away and made a grunt in his throat when he got up. He winked down at me. Then he turned the corner into the hall and went upstairs.

Ethelyn was already sitting on the piano bench talking to Mom. So I went over to the piano.

I heard her say, "We can't tell her how serious it is. She'd probably do away with herself."

Mom put her head in her hands and kind of rocked back and forth on the bench. Then she looked up and saw me. There were tears in her eyes.

"Hi, sweetie," she said.

~

I couldn't believe Pop could carry Gramma down the stairs. But there he was, coming down the stairs with Gramma in his arms. She had her arms around his neck and her cheek was laying on his shoulder. Pop had one arm under her legs and his other one around her little shoulders. She looked like she didn't weigh anything at all. My strong gramma who raised my mom and her two sisters and my uncle Bob and one time ran her own business looked so tiny now that Pop carried her as easy as he would the little bird Sunny Lea buried in her yard. I never thought her arms and legs could look so little.

My uncle Bob grabbed a chair and brought it over by the piano and Pop set Gramma down in it.

Gramma was fifty three but she was still beautiful. She had what Mom called "the Callahan good looks." All Gramma's Callahan brothers and sisters were good looking, Mom said. Her eyes were the same gray misty-sky-cloud blue as Mom's and her hair had turned white but it was thick like Mom's movie star hair. Her skin was smooth and pink and she had a pretty white night gown on.

When Pop carried her, it fluttered around her legs and fell smooth around the chair. No wrinkles. It scooped soft down from one shoulder and up to the other like it was made of clouds.

She smiled a sweet thin smile at every one and said, "Merry Christmas."

I was only six, almost seven, but I knew it must be really hard for her to be sick and stay at home all the time. She used to be working as much as Pop. Maybe more. She ran her own café downtown in Portland, The Magic Lantern Tea Room. The one time my mom took me there, way back when I don't think I was even five yet. my chest almost popped open it got so big watching my tall gramma with her silver hair, her high heels and movie star shoulders. How everybody at the Café said, "Yes, Madam" to her.

~

Mom took me by the hand that night when she took me to Gramma's Magic Lantern Tea Room 'cause I was still little then and we climbed up the long high stairs off the street. At the top a man in a black suit and a black bow tie that made his shirt look really white led us to a little table by the window where I could kneel on the chair and look out. See all the people and the lights on Broadway down below.

After while, in the Café, I saw my Gramma Jones. I knew it was her even from behind her. Her hair was silver white. It got that way when she was really young. It was short. Like Jane's mother in my Dick and Jane book. Mom told me they called Gamma's hair style a Marcel. It was neat little ripples that came down over her ears like tiny waves on the beach.

Her sparkly silver dress had big movie star shoulders and it came down real long almost all the way to her silver high-heeled shoes.

I heard the black suit man say to her, "Madam, your daughter is here."

Pretty soon, my gramma came real slow over to our little table. Her silver dress slippery like a snake skin. She blew out blue white smoke from her long white cigarette in a holder like in the movies.

I couldn't wait to give her the poster painting I made for her in kindergarten class. The painting of our new house in Multnomah. It had all the things in it that were great about that house. The little maple tree in front that John planted. The little dirt hill where we played cars. Even the white picket fence next door along the Herman's driveway.

She let out a big breath when she saw it and her eyebrows went up over her blue eyes that looked silvery in the light from the candles. Her hand put the cigarette down in the ashtray on our table and caught a hold of her glasses that were swinging on a string from around her neck. Then she held the picture up and the glasses with the other hand.

"Oh Davey," she said, "it's beautiful."

My face got really hot then.

"I'm going to have it framed. But first I want you to sign it."

That made me get really embarrassed. It wasn't that good. Maybe she just always liked anything I did. But then I looked at it again. Mom said Gramma owned the café. That she told everybody there what to do. So she must know about things. Maybe my painting was okay. She was sure important and she thought it was beautiful.

She put it down on the table and took a fountain pen out of her tiny silver purse that sparkled like her dress. The pen was open then and in my hand so I thought I better sign it.

Gramma put one hand on her hip and moved so her dress glittered, "Some classy doll, huh?" She leaned down to Mom then and said quiet just for us to hear, "Aren't I something? Out here being the elegant lady." Her blue eyes shimmered in the candles like she was laughing inside. "It's all an act. The dish washer quit just before the dinner hour. Temperamental little runt that he was. Now I have to run back to the kitchen every half hour and wash dishes." She let out a breath and her eyebrows went up. "Nothing I haven't done before I suppose."

"Oh Mama," my mom said, "I can help."

A big line came down in Gramma's forehead and the shimmer was gone out of her eyes. Her hand reached out and touched Mom's cheek. "Don't be silly, Macushla, if you baled me out with everything that went wrong in this joint, you'd have a full time job. I'll take care of it." She smiled at Mom with a soft smile and the shimmer was back in her blue eyes. "Besides, you brought Davey to have an evening out. I wouldn't hear of it."

Then her face turned quick to me. "Keep it up, young man," she said. You're a real artist." And she picked up the painting. Looked at it again. "I expect great things from you. You'll make your Grandma Belle proud." She quick kissed my forehead. "You're the berries." Then she picked up her pen and her cigarette holder. Her silver dress flashed through the café. And she was gone into the kitchen.

I looked at Mom.

"That means she really likes you."

~

But now she was so little and all the time sick. It was hard to remember her so strong.

Ethelyn smiled at her mama from the piano bench and said, "Mama, Little Davey is going to sing you a Christmas song."

Gramma looked over and smiled kind of tired at me and said, "How nice." Her eyes so blue in her pale face.

Then everybody got real quiet and Ethelyn started to play Silent Night. After a little bit she kind of slowed down and nodded to me and I started to sing. My legs were shaking when I started and so was my voice a little. My red and green Christmas tie was too tight, so I reached up and pulled at my collar. I didn't want to look at everybody looking at me.

There was a picture hanging on the wall behind Gramma. The picture of Jesus when he was little. He had blond curly hair like my friend Billy Rodgers in that picture. He was wearing a crown and pointed at his heart that was on fire.

At first, it was nice just to sing to Billy in the picture. I didn't know much about Jesus. But then I looked down in Gramma's eyes. They told me that I could make her proud. That's when I remembered what Mrs. Wright said. And, right away, there I was on my camel, out under the stars, singing with my wonderful Gramma. There were stars as far as you could see in the black velvet sky. It was peaceful and quiet and my voice felt like it could fly out into that night in the desert. So I just let it go. My chest really opened up. It wasn't like all the times it felt so tight. This time it felt so different I almost wanted to laugh. I looked back at all the people and it felt good. When I looked at Gramma, there were stars in her gray blue eyes that melted and came running down her cheeks. Then everybody clapped and it was over. I didn't want it to end.

Gramma reached her skinny white arms out and gave me a hug and kissed me on the cheek. She smelled soft like powder.

She looked at me with those blue sparkly tears and said, "Thank you Davey."

Mom came over to me and said I did real good.

But something made me worry.

"Mom," I said, "I'm sorry I made Gramma cry."

Mom's eyebrows went up and a little punch of air came out of her mouth.

"Honey," she said. "That's perfectly okay. Sometimes people cry because they're happy. You just made Gramma really happy."

"Really?" I said.

"Sure," she said.

Inside me something happened then. I could feel tears in my eyes too. I made Gramma happy and that made tears in my eyes. I guess big people aren't so different from kids.

It was different than when you feel bad, like Scotty made me feel about the Cinnamon Bear and Santa. I knew this was real, the singing. Nobody could tell me it wasn't. I could make people really happy with singing. That made me even happier than Santa…or the Cinnamon Bear.

17

About Babies

My friend Gary and me, we started walking home from school more times together that spring. My best friend, Billy always rode the bus 'cause his house was farther away. Gary lived near Sunny Lea on Thirty-Ninth Street. When I walked home with him, we went his way so I didn't have to walk by Mrs. Allen's mean old dog on Thirty-Seventh Street and Gary and me, we talked about lots of good things.

Those streets weren't really streets, though. They were dirt roads with lots of mud puddles. Gary liked to stop at mud puddles like I did to sail leaves and build little rock bridges. Not like my brother, Scotty who used to get mad and say I was pokey. Gary was getting kind of fat though. Starting to look like Tubby in the Little Lulu comics. Mom said too much candy. So, anyway, this day I was walking home slow with Gary and we saw something special. We came up the road to the top of Sunny's field singing loud together, "Great green gobs of gooey, gooey gopher guts."

Just then the sun came out bright and we saw the yellow. The daffodils came real early that year in Sunny Lea's field that went all the way through from Thirty-Ninth Street to our road on Thirty-Seventh—our Moo-Cow Hill. The sun was shining all over on those yellow daffodils and buttercups. You couldn't hardly see anything else but yellow, the sun so bright on it. The wind made waves like the ocean, yellow ones, that went all the way down the hill and up the other side. Little waves shifting across it on the bottom. The quiet sound of them rubbing against each other. And shadow clouds floating over those waves. It was so neat, and my throat was getting all tight and burny thinking about the first time Scotty and me saw them together that we almost didn't see the even more special thing.

It was a jittery little thing beside the road. A tiny bird in the grass by the fence on Sunny Lea's field. He looked like he fell out of the tree that was there. He didn't hardly have any feathers and there were pieces of pretty blue egg shell by him.

Gary and me, we get down by that little pink thing. His tiny mouth opening and closing, not making a sound. His little eyes squeezed shut.

And then there are birds coming down from the tree. Big birds, one with a red belly, dive bombing us.

Down by that little wiggling bird, Gary, he looks through his straw hair at me. His water gray eyes red around the edges and some brown "Sugar Daddy" in the corners of his mouth from the sucker he bought in Multnomah.

"Do you think we should do something with it?" Gary says.

"We better just leave this little Robin alone," I say. "I think we're making his momma and daddy mad."

Gary brushes his straight no-color hair out of his eyes with his hand that has some of the brown goo on it too. His mouth puckers, like he doesn't believe me.

"How do you know it's a Robin?" he says.

"My big brother, Scotty, he taught me," I say. "He knows a lot about Nature."

Since that time he made me feel awful stupid, that time I told Scotty that some Blue Jays were Robins, I always make sure before I call any bird anything.

"Wow, that's cool," he says.

Gary doesn't have a big brother.

Just then the big brown bird with his red belly—I'm sure he's a Robin—flies right between us and back up again. He's making a loud chirping, almost a squawking sound I never hear a bird make.

Gary says, "Okay. Let's go." Then he sticks his sticky sucker back in his mouth. Brown sucker stuff all over his hand.

We start away slow and I look back two or three times. I'm worried about the baby. The big Robin doesn't seem to know what to do. He's just diving down and flying around up above it.

I'm watching that daddy bird. I'm thinking he must be the daddy 'cause he seems to care so much, but he doesn't know what to do about the baby bird. Hopping around in the grass. First one way then the other. But he doesn't do anything. That's how dads are, I'm thinking. And I'm worried about the baby. I was a baby once.

"I wonder about babies," I say.

Gary says, "Huh?" He's more interested in his "Sugar Daddy."

"Well, I wonder how they get here," I say.

Up on that other side of the hill now, you can smell the daffodils in the wind. Not sweet. Not sour. Something in between that smells like spring.

That's when I just start thinking to myself and talking at the same time.

"Well, I know little birds come in eggs," I say. "I guess they lay them like chickens. My step-dad, Brew, his mom has a farm. I saw one time how the eggs just come out of them. Like they're making big doody. But people babies don't come in eggs, do they?"

Gary gets red, like he does and says, "I don't know."

Gary never wants to talk about things like that. He just gets all red. Maybe it's because he's Mormon. Maybe Mormons don't like to talk about babies.

"Oh," I say. "I guess you don't want to talk about babies."

Gary just takes the brown sticky sucker out of his mouth and looks down at the muddy road. His face all over red.

"You said 'big doody,'" he says.

I decide to talk to Mom about babies. Gary's too dumb.

~

Mom looks at me really different when I ask if people come in eggs. Her glasses slided down on her nose under some dark lines in her forehead. Her mouth open almost like she's mad.

"What?" she says.

That look makes me kind of scared. Maybe I'm not supposed to ask that.

"Well," I say, "people don't come in eggs, do they? Like chickens?"

It's Saturday at lunch time and Mom's fixing me a sandwich. The knife is stopped in the air. Mayonnaise on it.

Mom smiles then almost like she's going to laugh. But then she stops and says, "Uh hum," like she's got something stuck in her throat. "I just thought you'd be a lot older when you asked me a question like that."

"I'm seven years old," I say.

One of her eyebrows goes up without the other one.

"I know, honey," she says.

The knife is still in the air. She looks at it like she doesn't know what to do with it.

Just then our black cat Mom brought home from the bakery jumps up on the window sill outside the kitchen window and starts to thump. She learned that somebody comes to let her in the house when she scratches herself there and her elbow thumps the window.

"Thump, thump, thump" her elbow goes against the window.

Mom looks over at the window. She lets out her breath like she was holding it and puts the knife down on the drain board. She takes another big breath like she's going to do something hard.

Then she says, "Hang on a minute, Davey."

After Mom lets Kitty in, she brings my sandwich and sits down at the table across from me and looks at me with that look that usually makes me feel special. But now it's mixed up with something else like it hurts and I don't want to look back.

I look down at the little brown mole in the V of her throat. Then down at her hand on the table. The ruby ring on her finger. John says, "eight carrot—French cut."

"Davey," she says, "your father didn't want kids."

I hear what she says but I don't, 'cause of the buzz it makes in my head.

Then she is saying, "When we got married, I was nineteen and I didn't know anything about babies. My parents, like a lot of other parents at that time, didn't believe in talking about it, so Scotty was already on the way when we got married. I swore then that when my children began to ask questions, I would tell them everything."

I love my mom so much right then. Talking to me like I'm a big person. Somebody grown up like she is.

So then Mom, she told me that people's babies didn't need an egg shell to protect them because the mama's body swelled up around the baby to protect it until it was ready to be born. Then she said she would start at the beginning and told me how people babies were made. How the man uses his thing to help make the baby. How he puts it in the lady's thing.

That made me kind of dizzy when I thought about it and my tummy felt weird but then she said that what they do is only possible when two people love each other very much. That made it a little better. It sounded okay. I wondered if I would ever find somebody to feel that way about. So, when we had to do that to make a baby, it wouldn't be yucky.

After I asked her about babies and how they got here. After she told me how they did get here. After that, she told me that my brother, Scotty was an accident. Well, I thought maybe that was like falling off your bicycle. But, she explained to me what she meant was that he was a surprise.
It was then I found out why I felt special to her when she looked at me that certain way.

It was then she told me I was not an accident. I was not a surprise. I was born because I was wanted.

"Like I told you, your father didn't want kids," Mom said.

The buzz was in my head again and my face was hot. Right then I didn't like my dad very much. I don't think Mom wanted me to, either. He wasn't even as good a dad as that Robin. At least the baby Robin's dad stayed around when the baby needed him. I took a gulp of my milk 'cause my throat was burning again.

"Even after your brother was born, your dad was determined we wouldn't have any more babies. He was born poor and still didn't make very much money, so he figured we just couldn't afford them. And besides, he really didn't like kids."

I looked down at my sandwich on the plate in front of me so she wouldn't see my eyes were wet. Didn't like kids. *That's why he left. I was a kid and he didn't like kids.* I didn't like my dad right then either.

She told me that she begged and pleaded. She told him that Scotty deserved to have a brother or sister so he wouldn't be alone. Mom said she had her two sisters and her brother.

"That's what Irish Catholics do," she said, "have lots of kids."

Kitty rubbed against my leg under the table. She wanted to be petted. I didn't want to pet her.

Mom was looking out the kitchen window into the back yard but her eyes looked like they were looking far away.

She said, "Catholics don't believe in prevention."

"Prevention?" I said.

Mom looked over at me then. But like she didn't see me. Then her eyebrows went up, surprised. She took a big breath and let it out again.

Kitty walked out through the kitchen door into the front room.

"Sweetie, remember those white balloons you found in your dad's drawer before we moved here?" she said. "You blew them up around the neighborhood and I got mad at you?"

"Yeah," I said.

"Well those are called prophylactics. They're to keep people from having babies." She let a big breath out and her shoulders went down. Her hand brushed some bread crumbs off the table. "Your dad used them so we wouldn't have any babies."

Mom looked over at me. Her eyes got red. Then watery and she looked down. Her mouth closed and her teeth bit down hard.

"I tried everything. I even went so far as to poke pin holes in them. Nothing worked."

Then she told me that she threatened to leave him.
I was born after that.

~

Mom looked down at the table, at my sandwich sitting on the plate.
"Aren't you going to eat your sandwich, Davey?"
I looked down too. Like I just woke up.
"Oh, I guess I forgot about it, Mom." I said.
"I think you should eat it, honey. I want you to stay healthy."
Her eyes looked inside quick, remembering and a little smile was right then on her mouth. Half moons on the corners.
"I guess I still worry," she said.
Mom told me a story then about when I was two months old. She said that I got an ear infection. The doctor called it "upper respiratory and near fatal ear infection." That I screamed for over a week and a half. There was nothing she could do. She prayed. She cried. She pleaded and begged again—this time with God.
"Then I started to read," she said, "which is what I always did to escape. I was reading Daphne De Maurier's Rebecca. As I finished the last page, I heard you cooing in the bedroom. I closed the book and you were well." she said. "I was so relieved. You could have died."
It was kinda like she was talking to herself. But she smiled at me then. Her gray blue eyes looked right into mine. They made me warm all over.
Since I can remember, when Mom looks at me, there's a look that I'm special.

~

I never see that look from my step-dad, John though. Mom, told me that day he had an operation not to have kids. So maybe John doesn't like kids, either...except for Robby.

18

Pussy Willows

The sky was so gray it made the yellow green shoots of skunk cabbage look like they were glowing. They came straight up out of the muddy ground in the ditch on the side of the field across from Billy's house. Under my fingers, their thin wrinkled leaves were like new baby skin. They were new skunk cabbage babies. I was thinking a lot about babies after Mom told me how babies got made.

I wanted to stay looking at those skunk cabbage babies but the ground was so wet, it was almost like it was a creek and my shoes were getting too wet.

When I got to his house, Billy and me went out to the teeter totter. Out through the bushes along the path with their tiny green buds. Fog was hanging around the trees making the woods quiet and creepy. Black and gray ghost trees. All you could hear was soft dripping from the branches. There was a deep, damp woods smell of dirt and pine needles. The air was heavy to breathe but it felt good in my chest, breathing in that woods. The damp in the wood of the teeter totter board came through my cords. It made my fanny feel cool where I was sitting. Like the woods was trying to get inside you. Into my skin through my wool coat, through my thick cords, through my wet shoes, in through my hair, and through my nose, making me part of it. Like I was part of that April woods starting to come alive.

Billy and me we were talking about babies. Billy liked to talk about serious things. He wasn't like Gary who was only interested in his all-day sucker, his Sugar Daddy.

"I know the mama has the baby in her stomach," Billy said. "Frank told me how it gets there. But he didn't know how it comes out."

When I told him the baby comes out between the mama's legs, Billy stopped the teeter totter. He just put his feet on the ground with the board in between his legs. His mouth was open. He reached his hand up and scratched his forehead. Blond hair squiggles came out of his stocking cap.

"Are you sure?" he said.

"Yup, my mom told me."

"Geez, I thought maybe it comes out her mouth. That's where she puts the man's thing, right?"

"Yuck," I said. "That's disgusting." Then I almost laughed. "Did Frank tell you that?"

"Well, yeah. Isn't that right?"

Then I did laugh. Frank, the know-it-all. Here I'm the one in first grade and I'm telling second graders how it is. When I told Billy everything Mom told me, he got all red in his face and put his hand over the front of his pants. He kind of jiggled his legs back and forth like his pants got stuck up tight from the teeter totter and stepped off the board. He went over to the big old fir tree where he kept his Camels between the roots in the dirt. I thought he was gonna uncover his cigarettes but he just sat down and leaned against the tree trunk. His hand still in front of his pants.

I went over and sat down on the pine needles next to him and leaned up against the tree too.

"I thought you were gonna have a cigarette," I said.

Billy looked up into the trees.

"Naw, I don't keep 'em out here when it's so wet."

A black crow flew into the fir tree way up above us and cawed three times real quick and just sat there. A stick was poking my fanny so I moved sideways against Billy and took it out from under me. It made the pine needles smell, a smell like closed up dirt. Like the dirt floor in our shed behind the house.

"Talking this stuff about making babies gives me a boner," Billy said.

"A boner?"

"You know, makes my thing go hard."

"Oh," I said.

Talking about making babies didn't make my thing hard, but when Billy said his was, it started making mine that way.

Billy got up then and went over to a pussy willow bush that had little white fuzzy buds on it. He stood there for a minute looking down at the bush. His face still kind of red. His hand in front of him. Then he broke one of the little buds off. Even the pussy willow had its little babies. Soft and fuzzy. He ran his fingers over it. Then he saw I was watching and tossed it at me. Like he was a little mad. Like I caught him doing something.

It landed in my lap and when I looked down, it looked like a tiny little rabbit's foot. It was like the rabbit's foot John, my step-dad had in his dresser drawer.

~

One day after school, I went into Mom and John's room. Mom wasn't home from work yet and I wanted to smell the after shave that I knew John kept on his dresser. John always smelled like pipe tobacco and his own smell but sometimes he smelled really good like his after shave. It was nicer than Pop's Bay Rum. Sweeter.

It was on his dresser so I took the little white cone shaped bottle down to smell it. Old Spice it said on the bottle. It had ropes and anchors by the writing. I pulled the little pointy thing out of the top and took a big breath. It smelled really good. It smelled like John. I put it back and opened the drawer at the top. There was a cigar box in the drawer next to his hankies and socks. I opened the lid and there was lots of neat things in there.

One of those things was a rabbit's foot on a chain. Looking at his things in that box like I knew I shouldn't made my thing hard too. Just like now.

Billy looked at me sideways over by that pussy willow, I was feeling the little rabbit's foot.

"Is yours hard?" he said.

My face felt real hot. My mouth was all dry too. I could hardly talk.

"Yeah," I said.

That crow up above us jumped off the branch just then. I jumped when I heard his wings flap and he flew into the fog. *Caw, caw, caw.*

"You wanna see mine?" Billy said.

My head felt dizzy again like that first day we played naked.

"Whata you mean?" I said.

His blue eyes turned around to mine.

"I mean while it's hard."

My heart was beating loud in my chest. I didn't know why. I saw Billy's thing before when we played naked. I thought he maybe could hear my heart banging, it was so loud. But I said, "Yeah, I guess," and got up. My legs were shaky, my face felt hot and my heart was banging. My thing poked my cords out in front so I grabbed it with one hand. I got more dizzy then but the dizzy felt good. I never felt that before.

I walked over to the pussy willow bush and Billy grinned at me. Made little dents in his cheeks. His face was still red and I thought maybe mine was too. When I got over to him, he unzipped his pants and his hard little thing popped out.

I never noticed before but his looked so different than mine. It was like the skin was pulled back or there wasn't any skin at all. It looked nice but it just looked different.

The water drops on the fir tree branches were making little plopping sounds when they fell on the ground. Billy was holding his coat open and his warm smell was in my nose. I could still feel that good dizzy feeling.

Billy moved his legs from one foot to the other and I heard him make a little laugh so I looked up. But his blue eyes weren't laughing like they usually were. Inside them was somebody I never saw before.

"Can I see yours?" he said.

I swallowed but there wasn't anything to swallow.

"Mine's so different," I said.

"Yeah, I know. I've seen it," he said with another little laugh that sounded embarrassed, "but I've never seen it when it was hard. Does it make a difference?"

"Yeah, I guess."

"My skin was cut off after I was born," he said.

"Oooh, cut off. Wow, that musta hurt."

"Naw. I don't even remember it. My mom told me."

I heard the crow again, far off. *Caw, caw, caw.* I looked at the pussy willows 'cause I didn't want Billy to know I really wanted to look at his thing. Then I looked again and unzipped my cords.

"Wow," he said. "It does make a difference. It looks more like mine now."

My face felt really hot. I said, "that's because the skin is pulled back."

"Uh huh," he said.

Close up was the slow water drops in the woods and I could feel some sun was coming through the fog.

Billy's got bigger and he said, "So the man really puts it in the woman's thing, huh?"

"Yup," I said.

I never felt anything like this. If the woods wanted to get in me, I felt big enough to hold it all. I took a big breath and breathed the whole woods in—trees, crows, foggy sunshine, dirt smell and the pussy willows—all of it.

"Boy," he said, "yours is a lot bigger than mine. I wonder why. I'm older."

"Don't know," I said.

What I really wanted to do was reach out and touch Billy's. I wondered if he would touch mine. But when I thought about that I got so dizzy, it was scary. It didn't feel so good anymore. My knees got all funny and I thought I might fall down. So I put my thing back in and zipped up my pants. And, after a little bit, so did Billy.

19

Saying Goodbye

About the end of first grade that spring, Mom told me that Dad got married.

"Married?" I said. "How can he do that?"

The new paint in the kitchen was in the corners of my eyes. *Robin's Egg Blue* and *Fresh Peach*.

"What do you mean? Why couldn't he do that?"

"Well, he's married to you. He's my dad."

"Honey, he's not married to me anymore. I'm married to John. You know that."

I ran my fingers along the chrome frame that was around the edge of the Robin's Egg Blue Formica top on the new dinette-set table. Mom put the sandwich she made down in front of me on the Robin's Egg Blue Formica, but I wasn't hungry anymore.

"Anyway, he married a woman named Lou Ella who lives in California."

I watched the little tan colored mole in the V of Mom's throat that moved up and down when she talked. But for some reason, her words didn't make any sense to me. I could still see the mole move up and down and her mouth open and shut but I was somewhere where I couldn't understand her words.

She reached up and I saw a red finger-nail flick an eye lash out of the corner of her eye. And then I heard, "Scott and your dad moved down to California and they want you to spend two months with them in Nevada City this summer."

I did understand the words that said my dad and my brother wanted me to be with them but it was like hearing someone say that next week I was going to the moon. My dad left over a year and a half ago and all I ever heard from him was he sent me a Donald Duck camera for Christmas and I thought maybe I might never hear from my brother again either. Now they both wanted me to come and live in California.

Mom's wispy cloud blue sky eyes were looking into mine. Her eyebrows pulled down.

"What do you think? Would you like to spend summer with them?"

"In California?" I said.

"Yes," her mouth said, "for a couple of months this summer." The little mole bobbed up and down.

"I guess," I said.

Mom was sitting in the chair across the table from me now. Her hand with the ruby, eight-carrot-French cut, reached out and patted my hand. Jergen's Lotion smell.

"Well, you give it some thought. School's not even out yet."

~

So then everybody just thought I was going to go to California for the summer. Even me.

I really wanted to go live with Scotty. I missed him a lot. And I made up stories in my head about how it would be to have my real dad to live with. How he'd pick me up and hug me like he used to. How he would read to me like Mom does. How just me and him and Scotty could go camping together. Or to the circus. Or just the movies. But it was going to be hard to leave all my friends.

Days were so slow going by. In the mornings I would wake up and go to the calendar that I made in my first grade class just before Christmas and put on the wall of my room. There was a little picture in the squares I made for every day. Pictures I found in magazines of animals and people or buildings and flowers, anything small enough to cut out and paste in the square. In the morning, I would put an X through the square of the day that just passed and count the days left until school ended and I would go to California. Finally, it got to be the Saturday before I would leave on the Greyhound Bus. I couldn't hardly think of anything else. I was gonna go live with my real dad and my brother. But before I left I had to say goodbye.

First, I went up Spring Garden hill to 39th Street to see Sunny Lea. I passed that corner where she got us all to play kick-the-can at night after dinner. I was sure gonna miss that. Then I had to walk out in her field 'cause her mom said she was out with Petunia, their pig. There were only a few daffodils left. Most of them Sunny Lea's family already picked and sold to flower stores or they were dried up brown.

Petunia lived at the top of the moo-cow hill in a pig pen. Sunny Lea really liked Petunia, her little pink pig that looked like a ballet dancer. She walked real dainty on the tip of her toes.

"It makes me sad you won't be here all summer," Sunny Lea said. "You said we could do some play acting like they do on the radio."

"Well, it's only for two months. Maybe when I come back."

Sunny Lea's face was pretty red and she puckered her mouth up tight.

"Well, maybe I won't be here when you get back."

"Where're you going?"

She put Petunia in her little house and slammed the door. The pen smelled pretty bad. Like poo.

"Well, I might just go away too."

Sunny Lea turned away from me and walked fast through the grass and daffodil leaves to her house. When she was almost there, she looked back over her shoulder and said, "Bye."

I stood by Petunia's pen smelling pig poo. Now, I really wasn't sure I wanted to go away. But I went back up to Spring Garden to see Gary and then next door to see Craig. I wanted to say goodbye to everyone. But I wanted to say goodbye to Billy last.

When I went to say goodbye to Gary, he was busy eating a big bowl of ice cream. Chocolate. He had some on his chin. But he didn't ask me if I wanted any. He told me some people from his Ward were going to California for the summer too. Craig told me he was going to be at their cabin on Mt. Hood with his little brother Dale and his mom most of the time I was gone. So I told them both to have a good time.

The field across from Billy's house was dry now and wild mustard was blooming yellow all over the field and some purple and some white flowers that I didn't know the name for that look like mustard except for the color. The grass was getting almost up to my waist when I walked through the field and it felt good to drag my hands through it. It tickled my hand and smelled fresh. Kind of the way it tastes when you chew on the end of a piece of grass. I took a deep breath to breathe in that fresh smell of grass and the wild flowers but it made me sneeze.

I was sneezing when I came up onto the road in front of Billy's house and Frank was there in the road.

Frank looked at me with a smile that looked like he knew something that he knew I would like to know but he wouldn't tell me. He always looked like that. His one eyebrow went up in his forehead over the pancake syrup of his eyes.

"Well, if it isn't little Davey B. Did you get through first grade or did they keep you back?"

I didn't know why he always had to be mean like that.

"Yeah, I got through," I said.

Frank picked up some gravel by the road and started tossing rocks into the field.

"How come you're over in our neighborhood?"

I didn't figure it was any of his business but I told him I came to see Billy.

"Not home," he said and threw a little rock hard like it was a dart he was throwing at a target.

"Billy's not home?"

"Like I said." He threw another rock.

"Well, I came to say goodbye. I'm going to California for two months." Like if I told him, it would make Billy be home.

"When you leavin'?"

"Tomorrow morning."

Frank stopped throwing rocks and turned to me with his teeth smiling and his syrupy brown eyes glowing. Mrs. Allen's mean old dog.

"Well, Billy and his folks went away for the week-end. Guess you can't say goodbye."

My arms were dead things hanging beside me and my legs were tree stumps. Somewhere in my head I wondered if this is what it feels like to be dead.

I couldn't make my voice work. All I could hear were the little plunks as the rocks Frank was throwing again landed out somewhere in the field.

"I'll tell him you came by," he said.

I heard myself just barely say, "Okay" and I turned real slow and went back across the field. I could feel Frank looking at my back and heard him say, "Shish," soft between his teeth.

~

I came out in front of the Baldwin's house and stood looking up at their front porch but I didn't really see it. All that was in my head was I was going away and Billy wasn't home to say goodbye. Then I saw the Baldwin's house and something told me inside, I needed to say goodbye to my good friends there.

Mrs. Baldwin came to the front door in her apron. Wisps of hair were falling out from under the braids over the top of her head. Her cheeks were real pink and it made her gray eyes look almost blue. Her eyebrows went up in her forehead making all the lines there move up.

"Davey," she said. "What a surprise. I'm baking cookies. Come in and have one."

She reached out to open the screen door toward me and moved sideways so I could come in.

"Arthur is in the bedroom teaching a student. The door is closed but we'll go in the kitchen anyway."

In the kitchen, she poured me a little glass of milk and handed me a warm oatmeal cookie off the wax paper she had on the drain board.

"It must be about time for you to leave for California."

"Tomorrow sometime," I said.

"Oh, my goodness," she said.

She put down the pancake turner she was holding and looked at me with her soft gray eyes. My throat started hurting and I looked down at her linoleum floor, little gray bricks. Tears came out and I didn't know that was going to happen until they made tiny wet dots on the gray bricks. Sunny Lea was mad at me and Billy wasn't home and mean old Frank was there instead and I already missed Mrs. Baldwin and I wasn't even gone yet.

Mrs. Baldwin came over and put her arms around me and pulled me into her apron. It smelled like cookies. It smelled like Oregon. It smelled like home. And I just cried into her apron. But I started getting mad at myself for being such a cry baby. And she was pulling my head so hard into her apron, I could hardly breathe. So I started getting mad at her.

After a minute, though, she took my hand and led me back out through the front room, past the magazines on the coffee table, past all her pretty colored glass in the window and out onto the front porch. She sat down on the top step of the porch and patted the wood of the step beside her. I sat down there and we both just looked out across the field. All the colors of yellow and purple and white and green looked prettier than any of the pictures we ever looked at in her magazines.

"Sure is pretty isn't it, Davey?"

"Yup," I said. It was all I could say 'cause I thought I might start crying again.

She turned her gray eyes to me sitting there beside her and put her soft old hand over mine.

"Just remember, sweetheart, this is your home. I know it seems like a long time at your age, but two months isn't very long and you'll be back here before you know it."

Her hand felt warm over mine but some cool air blew through the trees in her yard and made me shiver and my skin bumpy.

"I know," I said.

She put her arm around my shoulders and squeezed me tight to her.

"And Arthur and me, we're not going anywhere. We'll be right here when you get back."

Then we looked out into all the flowers again.

20

Aunt Pearl's

When I woke up next morning, I all the sudden had that going down fast in an elevator feeling in my stomach. I thought about Aunt Pearl and the dairy farm. She told me I could ride horses this year, but now I was going to California. Oh poop!!

Last year, just after I met Billy Rogers, Pearl wrote Mom a letter and asked if I wanted to stay on her dairy farm out in Forest Grove for a few days. She said they had some room now that Scotty went back to spend the rest of the summer with Dad.

I knew that new things could be pretty scary but exciting too. I couldn't wait to ride the horses that Scotty always talked about. One of my favorite radio programs was The Lone Ranger. That's what I wanted to do. *Ride like the wind. Hiyo, Silver. Pin back those ears.* So last summer I went to Aunt Pearl's.

~

Aunt Pearl was really different looking than most ladies I knew. She wore pants all the time and usually a flannel shirt. Sometimes, really old cowboy boots. They always had mud on them and the high heels were worn down all slanty. Pearl's husband, Herb called 'em "shit kickers." So I guess maybe that wasn't mud on them. In the house she always just wore some thick warm socks. Gray with red tops.

She seemed so different than Dad too. He never wore just socks. He wore penny loafers and nice smooth feeling slacks with ironed creases.

No one hardly ever saw Uncle Herb, Pearl's husband. He was always out in the barns and I think he even slept out there. Pearl and my cousin, Velma, slept in the big farm house though. That's where I got to stay in a big Mom and Dad sized bed all by myself.

I told Pearl right away I wanted to ride the horses.

She looked at me with her gray eyes that were like Gramma Williams' except not so tired looking. They looked sad though. Like they didn't want to look at me. Not at my eyes anyway.

"I'm sorry Davey you're a little young this year. But I'm sure you can ride next year."

I really didn't like to hear that. I looked down at the gravel by the edge of the pasture where the horses were. My shoes were all dusty and they kicked at the little rocks.

"I'm sorry, Davey."

I kicked some more rocks into the weeds and Pearl reached down and squeezed my hand. Like she wanted me to look up. So I let my eyes look up then as far as the little wart she had on the side of her bottom lip.

"I know you probably had your heart set on riding horses, didn't you?"

I just shook my head, yes.

"Well, honey, horses are real serious business. They can be dangerous if you don't know what you're doing. They're wild horses when we bring them down out of the mountains. It's up to us to take that wild meanness out of them right here on the farm. But while you're here this year, I'll teach you what you have to know so that next year you'll be an old hand at it. Okay?"

So I said, "Okay."

Silver, the Lone Ranger's horse never seemed dangerous. I always thought you just had to be friends with a horse and then he'd let you ride him. I didn't know you had to learn stuff about him. Like school.

Pearl smiled her eyes right into mine then. That was something Pearl didn't do very often. Smile. She was like the rest of the family from Arkansas. To them life was real serious so they didn't smile much.

She let go of my hand and used her arm to brush the grayish blond wispy hairs up on her head. She always pinned her hair up but it never stayed so lots of times she wore an old pushed in cowboy hat. Like somebody sat on it.

There was lots to learn on her dairy farm but it was fun. Not like school. I learned how to milk a cow with my hands. Most of the time the cows were milked by machines but sometimes they did it by hand if a cow was skittish or something.

Uncle Herb just came up to me that first day. I was backing up from an old cow who looked like she was trying to eat my shirt.

There was a swoosh of gray red hair and the strong smell of his body that worked hard and Herb said, "Young'un, let me teach you how to milk her."

A smile spread clean across his face all white teeth like he really liked kids. Like he really liked *me*. Then he grabbed my hand in his big rough hand and a little stool with the other. My hand never felt that little as it did in his big one. Before I had time to say anything, he had me on the little stool behind her leg and my hands on her long goose bumpy teats that felt like chicken skin in my fingers. Herb's huge warm hands were over the top of mine squeezing and pulling my hands down. Pumping a stream of milk into a bucket. Zing. Zing. His big shoulders were around mine and his breath was on my neck. Like a big warm hug that made me feel happy and safe. Even behind a big old cow. But what was better, I was actually milking her. He let go and I kept pumping milk from old Mrs. Cow into that bucket. Zing, zing, zing.

It was neat to watch the milk run over the ice cold pipes in the cooling house too, where the milk got cold before they put it in huge cans and took it to a place to have it bottled.

But the best of all were the horses. There was one horse on her farm I really loved. He was my friend. His name was Chubby. Real dark brown almost black. He was older and a little bit fat but he was very patient. Aunt Pearl taught me how to curry him and keep his hair neat and clean. There was an old wooden chair I had to climb up on, to reach the top of him. I found it leaning up against the wall of his barn. It was covered with hay dust and worn down to the bare wood mostly. Carved long spokes on the back that looked like they were made from tinker toys like I loved to play with at home.

I just finished up currying Chubby when Pearl came in the barn one hot afternoon and saw what a good job I did. How Chubby nuzzled me under my arm with his nose when I was done.

She looked at me. Gray metal eyes in the dim sunlight coming through the dust in the air. Her eyebrows together.

"Let's say that Chubby is half your horse, half mine."

"Huh?" I said. My eyes on that wart on her bottom lip. It was what made Pearl look like Pearl, that wart. Like who she was.

She reached down and picked up a piece of straw and put it in her mouth. Then her eyes went kind of squinty and she took the straw out and looked at it.

"Wouldn't you like to own half a horse? Better than none, right?" Her voice flat sounding. Chubby munching hay. She tossed the straw back down under Chubby.

I was still standing on the seat of the old chair so I sat down and slid off so I was standing next to Aunt Pearl. Little puffs of straw dust up from the floor. The air in the barn was hot and sweet with the smell of hay. I was so happy I smiled like Goofy at her but I still didn't know what she meant.

Her hand reached out and I felt it rough on my bare sweaty shoulder.

"You own the back end and I own the front end. So while you're here, you clean up after him and I feed him. Okay?"

The corner of her mouth by her little wart twitched a little.

I guess it was her kind of joke but it still made me happy. 'Cause now I owned half a horse. Like she said, better than none.

~

That's the way Aunt Pearl was most of the time. The only time, in those couple of days, I saw my Aunt Pearl in a dress is when she took me to church.

That Saturday afternoon on the farm, I woke up from my nap and I could hear a different kind of music. It wasn't the radio because it sounded too close and it wasn't a record player either. I got up and went out into Aunt Pearl's front room and saw Velma, my cousin, sitting on the floor. She had a guitar laying across her knees and she was bent over it playing. Sliding her hands up and down the strings. I never saw anyone playing a guitar like that before. And this one had a real strange sound. Not just short notes but long twangy ones that held and slid up high before they ended.

I climbed up in the big chair Pearl called her "Lazy Boy" and watched Velma play.

My cousin Velma was a pretty blond girl. She was a real cowgirl. She wore jeans and plaid shirts and boots like her mom, Aunt Pearl, but she was real pretty. White teeth smile. Deep blue eyes. Her clothes new and sparkly like a rodeo queen and there was nothing sad or tired about Velma. She was 16.

The end of the song came and she looked her deep blue eyes at me and said, "Hi. You awake?"

I was listening to the music so hard, her voice surprised me. I guess I was the Lazy Boy, half dreaming.

"Oh, yeah. I guess so. That was sure pretty."

Her blue eyes got bluer and her mouth turned up. White teeth showing. Velma was different than the rest of that family, she smiled a lot. Seemed like everything she said or what anybody said to her made her eyes crinkle up and her white teeth show.

"You liked it, huh?"

"Yeah, I never heard that kind of guitar before."

She looked down at the guitar in her lap like she kind of forgot it was there. She had little metal things on her fingers and she twanged a string then slid her finger up it. It had a sharp metal sound. A sound that made my back shiver, it was so strong and clear. Someday, maybe I could make music with something like that.

"This here's a real gee-tar," she said. "A lap steel gee-tar. I love playing it. I heard it first at mama's church. I love my guitar but I don't go to that weird church anymore. I suppose she's gonna take you."

She looked up at me in the "Lazy Boy." Not smiling this time. Not at all. She shook her head and let out a big breath. "They always try to get everyone to go. Anyone they can get their hooks into."

~

Sunday morning Aunt Pearl woke me up real early and said, "Time to get up, Davey. We don't want to be late for church."

Aunt Pearl made waffles that day. Breakfast was always the biggest meal on her dairy farm and Sunday she always made waffles. I walked into the kitchen and my mouth was watering from the smell of coffee and bacon and the waffles steaming in the waffle iron. Pearl was sitting on a kitchen chair in a kind of silky dress with little no-color flowers all over it and her big brown apron. On her feet, big wooly socks with holes in the heels. She was turned out from the table with a big bowl in her lap stirring hard with a wooden spoon. She was making little grunty noises and the spoon bonked the side of the bowl. *Bonk, uhm, stir. Bonk, uh, stir.*

I sat down in the chair next to her at the table and looked into the bowl. Her face was red and the muscles in her jaw and neck were tight like the muscles in her arm and hand, stirring. Something stiff and golden yellow. *Bonk, uh, stir.* She looked up at me and her voice squeezed out of her throat.

"Fresh butter and honey," she said. "Nothing tastes better on waffles." *Bonk, uhm, stir.*

I think she was right.

Velma came in then and sat at the table. Sleepy blue eyes. She yawned. Then she grinned at me.

Uncle Herb came in just when Aunt Pearl put his waffle down on the table next to where Velma was sitting. His gray reddish hair in his eyes. A wink was all I saw of Herb that morning. A flash of bright blue-green and his white teeth, then he put his head down eating and I could only see the top of his head.

After breakfast, Uncle Herb and Velma got up and went out to the barns and Aunt Pearl took off her apron. She brought some black kind of sandal shoes over to the table and sat down in her chair again. When she bent over grunting again to take her socks off and buckle the black straps behind her ankles, her bosoms squashed up on her knees and pushed over the top of her dress. I didn't know she had such big ones before. They made me kind of embarrassed. Then she plopped a little black hat on her head with a veil over her forehead. She looked down at me. No smile.

"Ready?" she said.

And I followed her out to her dusty old pick-up.

Inside the pick-up, it smelled like cow manure. Like everything at the farm. It was a smell I kind of liked. Fresh and a little sweet. But, in the closed up truck, it was mixed with the smell of dust and the smell of Aunt Pearl. Mom said Aunt Pearl and Gramma Williams and the whole family didn't believe in deodorant, or perfume or even make-up because of their religion. Aunt Pearl didn't wear nylons even. Mom said they didn't believe in anything that modern women did. Their church didn't even let them cut their hair.

The funny thing was, though, Aunt Pearl was so much of a woman it made me kind of embarrassed. Like, even when she was in her flannel shirt, her pants and broke down cowboy boots, I was looking at her naked. Her natural smell, her big bosoms moving against each other, even the wart on her bottom lip and her messy hair pinned up was more female than all the other ladies' high heels, lipstick and perfume. I was okay when Mom looked like a movie star, but, I don't know why, being closed up in her pick-up with Aunt Pearl's smell that was so female made me kind of nervous.

Aunt Pearl turned the key and stepped on the gas pedal a couple of times and the old pick-up went bouncing down their gravel road to the highway. It sounded like a big empty tin can rolling on the gravel.

"Isn't Uncle Herb coming to church?" I said.

Aunt Pearl's face just looked at the windshield. Like maybe she didn't hear me. Her mouth tight. Little wart on her bottom lip.

Gravel crunched on the road under the truck.

"Your Uncle Herb is a sinner man," she said. "He doesn't belong to our church."

The truck hit the edge of the cement and bounced up on the highway.

"He's a good man but a sinner," she said. "As long as he doesn't belong to our church, he's a sinner man."

~

The sign in front of the church said: *Church of the Apostolic Faith – Jesus the Light of the World*. A lot of people were out in front of the church and inside too. And they all knew Aunt Pearl. They all said, "Hello, Sister Williams" or "Good morning, Saint Pearl." That was funny. All the saints in our Catholic church were dead.

I held tight to Aunt Pearl's hand so I wouldn't get lost in all the people. Her hand was rough in mine, even rougher than John, my step-dad's.

We went down the middle of the church and then we just sat down on some folding chairs. There weren't any benches or places to kneel down like the church I used to go to with Mom and this church smelled dusty, not fresh dust like the truck, but old closed up dust, and like all the smells of the people there. Like B.O. 'Cause it was already pretty warm that morning. It was noisy too. All the people talking to each other.

Morning, Pastor Andrews. Sister Janice. Saint Howard, how's your mama feelin'?

The talking stopped all at once though and then there was a lot of banging and scraping. People sitting in the folding chairs. A man in a gray suit came out and said, "Welcome," then some stuff I couldn't understand. His voice sing-songy up and down. Something like, "Lord awmitey hep is sinners thet we is" and "Dave'll drugess duh-yown." His eyes were wide open like he was scared or something and he talked real fast and kind of weird. Then he yelled, "Halleluyah!" and everybody yelled back at him, "Halleluyah!"

The man sat down then and a girl who looked a little like Velma, except she wasn't pretty like Velma, she came out holding a musical thing on her chest. It had strings that she played with her fingers. She looked real droopy. Long kind of blond hair down to her middle. Her face like she was gonna cry. Her little sad voice sang this little sad song I couldn't understand but everyone around me smiled like they liked what she was singing.

When the sad girl finished her singing, the man in the gray suit stood up again and started talking. He was excited about something. His body going up and down like he had springs in his knees. His eyes like that black man in the movies when he got scared. Then his face got all red and he started getting mad. He yelled at the people and banged his fist down on the wooden thing in front of him. People started yelling back at him and getting mad too.

I looked up at Pearl sitting next to me. Like maybe we should get out of there. Like there might be a fight or something. But Pearl just looked straight ahead like she did in the truck.

Everybody started yelling then and getting up. It was getting pretty scary. Then somebody started to play the piano and people were still yelling but clapping then to the music. Pearl too. Still not smiling. I couldn't tell if she was happy or mad or what. The music stopped and everybody was sitting down. Every once in a while a holler. Some lady yelled, "Amen!" real loud. Somebody else, a man's voice up high then down low like a dive bomber, yelled, "Jee-sus!" Then quiet.

The guy in the gray suit got up again and pointed at someone and said, "Brother James."

I heard a man's voice behind me start to talk. This man, I could understand. He talked normal, not like the guy in the gray suit, and he was saying how he used to be. How he used to be a sinner and did bad things. Real bad things. He was a gambler who lost all the pay from his job. He chased after women and he was a drunk that beat his wife 'cause she couldn't give him any babies.

Aunt Pearl reached over and took my hand and squeezed it awful tight. It kind of hurt. She pressed her eyes shut so that tears came out. One made a shiny line in the blond fuzz on her cheek all the way past the wart on her lip. It made me real sad to see her cry. To hear how the man did bad things. Then he said he found the Lord.

Somebody yelled, "Halleluyah!"

Pearl said real quiet, "Amen," and let go of my hand. She reached down in the crease between her bosoms and took out a hanky. I had that nervous feeling again.

The gray suit guy said, "Thank you, Brother James." Then he pointed again and said, "Sister Charlene."

I could only see the back of a big fat lady who was standing down in front of us talking but I could hear her telling everybody how bad she used to be.

Boy, I missed our old church. I missed the smell of incense and the little blinking candles, all the beautiful paintings and statues to look at, like the art we learned about in school, the flowers and nice music, the men singing. Father Fletcher in his long dress. All I could do here was sit and listen to all these people get up and tell how bad they used to be. Giving testimony they called it. How could they all be such bad people? My legs hurt from just sitting there and my fanny hurt from the metal chair.

It used to hurt my knees to kneel so much at our church and to sit on the wooden benches, but now I sure wished I could do all that kneeling and sitting and standing. This church was too hot and smelly and there were too many people who used to do bad things. The folding chair was worse than the stool we had to sit on in the corner at school when we were bad. It looked like every one of these people was going to stand up and talk. They should just have to sit in the corner for being bad. Pretty soon I wanted to jump up and run around the church.

I started to wiggle around and Aunt Pearl looked down at me quick with her eyebrows bunched up and raised her finger up at me. I knew what she meant. I sat still but it was awful. I thought this church was pretty exciting at first but now I knew why Velma didn't want to come here.

At last, everybody stood up to sing one more time and the gray suit guy invited all the people down to the front. Not everybody was going down front but there were a lot of them. After I stood up, I lost Pearl because my foot was asleep and I was trying to stand still but people were hurrying to get down front and this big lady couldn't get by me so I got pushed down front too.

Some people brought these things with them that looked like little kneeling benches except they were too small for big people to kneel on. I thought maybe people were going to pray. I just wanted to go outside. Too many people. Too hot.

The gray suit guy was putting a lot of the little kneeling things down on the floor and the other people put theirs down too. Then everybody got down on the floor and put their heads on the little benches. I didn't know what they were doing. They looked crazy laying on the floor with their heads on little benches. The piano was playing loud and the gray suit guy was yelling something about sin. Then the floor started to move or I thought it did 'cause all the people on the floor started rolling around.

I was afraid I might get knocked down so I got down too. There was one of the little benches on the floor by me so I put my head on it. Everybody was making groaning sounds. Like you roll around in bed when you're sick. The Gray suit guy yelled, "Halleluyah!" and people yelled "Yessir!" and "Amen!" Then everybody was groaning and yelling, "Halleluyah!" and "Yes, Lord!" Voices getting higher and louder. Rolling faster.

A man beside me rolled into me so I rolled the other way into the big lady on that side. Everybody was yelling and moaning, "Jesus!" and "Halleluyah!" real loud, so I did too. It was fun. It was better than running around the church like I thought about doing. Kind of like running naked in the woods. So I rolled and hollered and then I started to laugh.

I rolled into the big lady again and her red face and wet kind of slobbery mouth was right in front of my face. Happy tears on her cheeks. Strings of spit between her lips.

She said, "Are you saved, little boy?"

So I just laughed and said real loud, "Yeah!"

Whatever that was, I was that.

21

Bus Ride

I was sure gonna miss aunt Pearl and Herb and specially the horses. Not that church though. But, like I said, everybody just thought I was going to go to California for the summer. Even me.

So, we all got into John's big Oldsmobile after dinner that Sunday to go down to the Greyhound bus depot in Portland across from the "Y." It wasn't very far from where I saw the end of the war in August. But that seemed so long ago when I was a little kid sticking ration stamps on things. Like I was somebody else now. Somebody going to California.

"The bus leaves at seven o'clock and gets into Sacramento in the morning at seven thirty," Mom said.

She had a pretty, new hat on. It was dark-red with a veil over her face that had little dark-red fuzzy nubs some places in it. Her eyelashes brushed against it when they moved up and down.

"So that way, when you wake up in the morning you'll be there. Your dad and Scott will meet you and drive you to their place in Nevada City."

She was talking to me over the front seat. I was too big to get up on the back shelf now but I had the whole back seat for myself. Mom bought me a new shirt from J.C. Penny's with red fire trucks on it and new jeans and shoes for my trip to California. Bees were flying around in my tummy though and I couldn't sit still.

"Nevada City isn't far from Sacramento," John said to the windshield, big smile while he was driving.

Mom reached her dark-red glove up and pulled the veil out a little from her face so her eyelashes wouldn't hit it.

"Scotty told me on the phone that he is going to come back with you in two months and spend the school year with us. Won't that be nice?" Her eyes opened real wide. Eyebrows up. John quick looked at Mom. No smile now.

I was thinking about Billy and how I didn't get to say goodbye and the bees were buzzing around in my tummy about going on the bus all the way to California. At first I really wanted to go. Now I wasn't so sure.

But hearing about Scotty made me happy. Maybe going to California would be okay after all.

Just before seven o'clock the phony radio announcer voice in the depot said real loud that the bus was "now boarding for Sacramento, California and all points south." I gave my suit case to the driver who told Mom he would take good care of me. Then I said goodbye to John and Mom. John messed up my hair, like he does. I don't know why he does that. It just makes me mad. It makes my hair feel like it's growing the wrong way and it makes me feel like some dumb little kid when he does it. Maybe that's why.

Mom bent down and hugged me. Then she squatted down sideways and picked up her veil and kissed me on the cheek. Her eyelashes were all sparkly and her eyes were red. Afterward, she rubbed the lipstick off my cheek with her hanky. The smell of her perfume and powder made a lump in my throat and my eyes started to burn so I got on the bus with my cellophane bag of peppermint puffs to eat on the way and sat by a window.

Mom stood on the sidewalk outside the bus depot waving her hanky at me when the bus bumped out the driveway and swayed all the way to one side turning into the street. John next to her smiling like when he made a joke, like he was glad I was going. They got smaller until they were little black specks. One waving. Then the bus roared around a corner.

The Willamette River was outside the bus and I watched it out the window when I could see it. Flat silver glass and black shadows through the trees. Pretty but kind of spooky. There was nobody in the seat beside me. When it was too dark to see, I layed down in both seats. My tummy was real jumpy still but I ate some peppermint puff balls and after a while the bees went away. The bus was just making a humming sound now. I hummed with it but I couldn't hear my voice. After that, I fell asleep.

~

Dad's blond hair falls in his face from bending over to pick me up. Fresh grass and rain smell. His blue eyes smiling at me. Scotty's jumping up and down he's so excited to see me. I feel like singing.

Then this rough voice, "Hey Buddy, we're in Sacramento."

I opened my eyes but I feel like I'm still asleep. There's this guy I don't know looking at me. His big face that needs a shave is real close to mine.

"You awake?"

Then I see the bus driver hat—gray with a shiny badge in front—and I remember I'm on a bus going to California. I yawn and sit up in the seat and some sun that comes in the back seat window hits me in the eyes.

My eyes are blinking and I'm kind of dizzy but I say, "yeah."

"Come on and I'll get your bag from under the bus."

I followed him out and he reached in the doors that were open under the bus and got my suit case. He picked it up with one of his big hands and took my hand with his other one and we went into the depot. There was something else fluttery in my tummy then. People're looking at us. They think I'm a friend of the bus driver. Pretty neat.

"You see your people here anywhere?" he said.

I looked around. The place smelled like old cigarette smoke and something else stinky. There were some people asleep on benches and some people standing in a line. One guy was pulling handles in and out of a table and banging it with his hips making bells ring but I didn't see Dad or Scotty.

"Well come on then. Let me introduce you to Dutch. I've got to high-tale it out of here."

We walked through a door and we were back behind the ticket window. Back where only the important bus people go. The bus driver let go of my hand and set my suit case down. His big whiskery face smiled down at me.

"Have a seat," he says and pats the top edge of my suit case.

I sat down on it and he walked over and talked to a man on a stool selling tickets who looks over at me and winks. A tall skinny guy with a long nose. He points out into the depot and says something to my bus driver.

"Dutch says he'll keep an eye on you if you sit on the bench outside his window."

So out in the depot again the bus driver leaves me and my suit case on a bench to wait for Scotty and Dad. He waves. But then he just walks away and leaves me there.

I'm pretty hungry. That's when I remember I left my peppermint puff balls on the bus. I scoot off the edge of the bench. My feet don't touch the floor just sitting there. The big clock way up on the wall near the ceiling looked like the one at school except a lot bigger and this one had a really long hand that ticked in jerks around it. There were two shorter hands too like at school that say it's five minutes after eight. I looked around the depot again but I couldn't see Dad or Scotty anywhere. There were more people now but no Dad or Scotty. My chest feels tight like it did when Scotty went away to live with Dad. But I climb back up on the bench to wait.

~

I'm turned around looking over the back of the wooden bench like maybe I can see them when somebody sits down next to me. Real close. Like they know me. It scares me, 'cause it's a lady with a real dirty face and I don't know her. She's got gloves on that don't have any fingers and an old dark blue sweater with dribbles that are white and crusty down the front. She reaches up with one long dirty finger and touches the end of her nose. She smells like Petunia's pig poo.

"Mrs. Daniels said you'd be here."

"Who?" I say.

But she just goes on like she doesn't hear me.

"Last week, over tea, she suddenly said she's pregnant. How do you like them cookies?"

Then she looks right at me and laughs. She only has three teeth and her gums are black where her other teeth used to be. I think of how Witch Wintergreen looked in my head when I listened to The Cinnamon Bear on the radio. Her hat has some old roses on it and one is loose and falling on her forehead.

"Okay, Sara, why don't you move on?"

I look up and there's a policeman standing in front of us in a dark blue uniform—the color of her sweater, except it's clean. There's a neat gold badge on his chest that looks like a knight's shield in the fairytales we read in kindergarten. Only littler.

I guess he's talking to the lady 'cause she stands up quick. She stamps her foot real hard. Her old sandal almost comes off her foot and then she doubles over laughing real hard.

"Okay, okay, Sara," he says.

She stops and makes a face at him. It's all twisted up like rubber. Then she walks away.

Then the policeman sat down where she was, but not so close. He has real dark brown hair, almost black and the skin on his face where he shaves is dark too, almost blue but there aren't any whiskers. His face looks smooth and his eyes are really blue.

"You coming or going?" he says.

"I'm waiting for my dad and my brother, Scotty to come and get me. Dutch is keeping an eye on me."

"Who?" he says.

His badge flashes at me from the lights in the ceiling.

I point at the ticket window.

"That guy."

He smiles his white, white teeth at me.

"Oh, I see." Then, "Where'd you come from, uh, what's your name?"

"Davey. Portland," I say.

His dark brown eyebrows go way up.

"Portland? Why, that was more than an hour ago."

I look up at the big, ticking clock that says eight thirty and five minutes more now.

"Yup. I guess so."

His eyebrows come way back down then, and he says, "Wait here a minute, Davey. Let me talk to your friend Dutch."

When he comes back, he squats down in front of me and puts his hand on my knee. Up close, I can see all kinds of writing and pictures on his gold badge. It's really neat.

"Davey, do you have a phone number for your Dad? Maybe we could give him a call."

I unzip my zipper pocket on my jacket where Mom put the note with Dad's address and phone number, "Just in case," and give it to the policeman. I'm glad I didn't leave it on the bus with my peppermint puffs.

His white teeth smile at me again.

"Swell, Davey. You just stay put another minute and I'll give him a call."

When he comes back, he says Dad is on his way. Then he asks if I'm hungry, if I want some breakfast.

~

Jerry, the policeman, and me were sitting in the coffee shop together and I was finishing my pancakes when Dad and Scotty came in. Scotty pushed in beside me right up to the counter. His red hair almost blond and lots more freckles on his cheeks.

"Geez, Davey, we thought you were going to get here at seven thirty tonight. Not seven thirty this morning."

Then he looked his worried eyes around at Dad like "isn't that right?"

My dad just looked really "pissed."

Something went tight in my chest again.

22

Nevada City

My dad looked different than I remembered he did. And not just because he was mad. Mom told me once that my dad was one of the most dour men she ever met. I didn't know what that meant so she told me that he was always unhappy.

Her misty sky cloud eyes looked away from me and went inside.

"Oh, not before we were married, mind you. I don't think I would have married him. But then afterward, he always seemed out of sorts. Grumpy. You know?"

So, I guess I expected he'd be grumpy but other things were different. He didn't have very much of the blond wavy hair I remembered. It was just kind of wispy and his forehead went up higher than it used to. His eyes that used to be so blue were the biggest thing that changed. Now they were tired and gray like his mom, Gramma Williams.

His tired gray eyes looked at me but they didn't do like the blue eyes that used to make my insides feel funny. He reached his arm out stiff and messed up my hair. Like John. And there was sweat smell. Not rain and grass.

"Hi, Dave," he said.

No picking me up in a hug like I thought. Not even a smile. Like he might be happy to see me. And why do big people always have to mess up my hair? Makes me mad.

Scotty didn't take my hand like he used to do either, but he put his arm around my shoulders and said, "Well, let's go."

Made me feel better. Good. Older. More like Scotty. More like brothers.

Dad picked up my bag and thanked Jerry, the policeman and I said goodbye to him. Then Scotty and me, we ran out to Dad's car.

It was a car I never saw before and it had a goat made out of chrome on the hood.

The goat was running fast like the wind.

"Wow, that's neat," I said.

Scotty's blond/red hair flashed in the hot sun outside the depot and he said like it was real important that I know, "It's a Dodge."

"I meant the goat," I said. I wanted to reach up and run my hand over the smooth chrome but it was too high up to reach.

Scotty's eyes rolled up in his head like they did.

"It's a ram, dummy."

"Looks like a goat to me," I said. I was mad he made me feel stupid already.

Scotty leaned his head to the side and his voice came out softer like he was sorry he called me dummy.

"It's a kind of a goat, Davey. But it has curved horns."

Scotty teaching me again. I didn't say anything. Teaching was okay.

Out in that Greyhound parking lot, the sun was so hot it was making prickly little sweat drops on my lip and I could feel the skin on the back of my neck turning red already. I didn't get the red hair Scotty got but I got the white skin that burns almost as soon as some hot sun gets to it. And my shirt that was sticking to my back was yucky. I never felt the sun so hot before.

"Sure is hot here."

Scotty's shoulders went up and down like maybe he didn't care or something.

"Yeah, Sacramento is always hot."

I hoped that meant that Nevada City wouldn't be so hot.

Dad put my suit case in the trunk and looked at us. Eyes just slits from the sun. No smile. Little puffs under his eyes. Wearing a nice sport coat and his smooth slacks with the ironed creases and really swell saddle shoes. Scotty wrote to me that Dad liked to play golf and always dressed like a golfer. Pretty hot for a sport coat, I thought.

"Okay, Guys," Dad said. "In the car. Hubba, Hubba."

In the car with all the windows rolled down, it was better. Not so hot. At least the wind made me not feel my sweat. Everything out side the car along the road was dry, dry grass and dead brown weeds. There weren't any trees. Not like Oregon. It seemed funny not to see trees. Only one once in a while that looked brown and dried up. Growing all by itself. I thought I knew how it felt. Kind of sad and lonely. Lots of grass though. Dried up.

Pretty soon we were going along beside a lot of greenish brown water. It was moving pretty quick like it wanted to get away from this place fast.

Scotty said, "Sacramento River." Said it like he said it so many times it didn't mean anything or wasn't important. He was sitting in the middle, in the front seat, next to Dad, just looking straight ahead out the windshield. Not smiling. He looked so much like Dad. Dour.

In my head I'm watching the Willamette out of the bus window in between the fir trees, how everything along it has lots of company. How it's green and happy looking in the cool, damp air. How Mom and me, we look a lot alike. Brown hair, happy. How we both like to laugh. I'm sure Nevada City will be better than this hot dried up place.

I'm already missing our moo-cow hill and the wild flowers in the field by Billy's house, the giant, shady fir trees in his woods and the smell of Mr. Baldwin's green grass after he cuts it. My friends who smile and are happy to see me. New things can be exciting but they can be scary too. Like going to school when the summer is over. Everything is gonna be new, new teacher, the new kids you don't know and new things to learn. Exciting but scary.

When we come into Nevada City, I'm surprised it's like a city, more like a city than "Mudnomah." Yeah, it's called a city but from the letters Scotty wrote I thought it would be more like a town. But even right outside of Nevada City, everything is dried up. I'm hoping that Dad and Scotty's place is somewhere greener.

Then Dad stops the Dodge and says, "Here we are."

He just stops the car next to the curb. I don't get it.

So I say, "Where?"

Dad just puts his arm over the back of the seat and pulls himself in front of Scotty leaning at me over by the window. Tired gray eyes with little puffs under them.

"This is it," he says.

I look around but there is nothing but stores and buildings and sidewalks. Inside the car it's really sticky hot now that we're parked.

Scotty stretches his arms over his head, then starts to slide out of the car after Dad.

"Were home," he says and heads for the door of the shop there. The sign on the window says, *Earl Williams – Watch Maker*.

~

The bug eyed lady with curly brown hair behind the counter, Dad tells me, is my new step-mother, Lou Ella. She comes out from behind the counter and squats down right in front of me. Her nylons make a scrunchy sound and her bug eyes are right in front of mine. There's no place for me to look except right at her big eyes that look like they're going to pop out and she's so close my eyes can't really focus anyway. So I look up at her hair.

"Well," she says, "so this is little Davey."

All I can see when I look up is some brownish pink make-up on her forehead caked along her hair in sweat dribbles from the heat. So I look down. All I can see there are her knees coming out from her skirt. They're a shiny white color from the nylons stretched over them. She smells hot and really sweet from her perfume. My stomach is kind of sick like going down in an elevator.

'Cause I don't say anything, she reaches up and messes up my hair.

"Well, welcome to our home, Davey."

Dad's hand is on my shoulder then, his strong fingers pressing my shoulder and I know right then how much I always wanted my dad to be around to touch me like that. Then he says down to me, "Aren't you going to say thank you to Lou Ella?"

So I real quick say, "Thank you."

She says, "Your welcome," and starts to stand back up but she kind of wobbles and Dad reaches out to help her.

There is sweat sliding down my front under my shirt. Dad's hand is gone from my shoulder. And it feels like my shirt is stuck to my back forever.

23

Fox Tails

In his watch maker shop in Nevada City that first day, I watched Dad help Lou Ella stand back up on her high heels and I thought about Aunt Pearl. Dad looked so different than he did when I was little. Back when I was a baby. Back when he put me in his bike basket and took me to the top of Rocky Butte. I looked at him when he helped Lou Ella on her wobbly high heels and he looked like his sister, Pearl. Except for the wart on her lip. I never thought that before.

Pearl was his twin sister, but I always wondered why they called Dad and Pearl twins because they didn't look like the same people, like twins do. I guess something around his eyes looked the same as Aunt Pearl. Same kinda gray tired. Maybe something around his mouth too. The way it was a little pretty. Turned up at the corners. But they were sure different people. Dad was a golfer and Aunt Pearl was a dairy farmer.

We were all standing there, Dad, Lou Ella, me and Scotty, like we kinda went to sleep or something. There wasn't hardly any air in Dad's shop and it was hard to breathe in all that heat. Ever since I got to California, there was sweat on my lip under my nose it was so hot.

Then Scotty said, "Come on, I'll show you where you're gonna stay."

We went through some curtains in a doorway at the back of the shop. Gray curtains with big red and pink flowers on them. Peonies or something. In the back behind them there was a big room with gray linoleum on the floor, linoleum that looked like gray bricks, same as Mrs. Baldwin's, and a kind of kitchen over on one side. Drain board with a sink. An old stove with funny looking burners.

Scotty walked up to it kind of important like. Being a big shot. Being Jack Armstrong, the all American boy from our radio program. Chest out, arms swinging. No smile on his face. Just his freckles. And his new round glasses with gold frames. He turned a knob on the front of the stove. It started to click. Then slow like, he took a box of matches off the shelf over the stove, scraped a match on the box. It smelled like Billy lighting cigarettes Then he put it over the burner. Blue fire jumped up under the match.

"Wow," I said.

I never saw that before. We always had regular electric burners. Not real fire. Blue fire.

Scotty smiled at me like it was nothing new. Something he saw all the time. He was still being the big shot. Still being Jack Armstrong. He turned the switch and the fire went out.

There was a little old refrigerator with legs on it that Scotty called an ice box. But it didn't have ice in it like the guy brought to our street in Multnomah. It was real dim in the room. The only window was on the ceiling. I never saw that before either. You could see the sky up above there.

Scotty showed me where I was gonna sleep. It was over on the other side of the room from the kitchen. No bedroom. Just a folding wooden bed, legs that made an X at both ends, canvas on the top so I wouldn't fall through—no mattress or anything—and some blankets piled on the end. I never saw a bed like that before either. At the other end of the same room was a davenport, an old red one, a coffee table and a big brown stuffed chair.

"Dad and Lou Ella sleep in the back room past the davenport," Scotty said, "Next to my room."

I didn't say anything to Scotty but this seemed like a pretty funny house to me.

Then Scotty's eyes got bigger behind his round glasses and his eyebrows went up.

"Wanna see something neat?"

"Sure," I said.

Scotty made his fingers say, "Com'ere" to me and he went quick to the middle of the room. He got down on the linoleum on his knees and said, "This is really neat." He stuck his finger in a hole there on the floor and pulled up a trap door with a little ring. You couldn't tell there was a door there because there was gray brick linoleum on it and it looked like floor. I could hear a gurgling sound, and there was a smell like the woods at home. Wet dirt after it rains.

It made me think of Billy's woods in the fog. Water dripping from the big fir trees.

I got down on my knees and looked down in the hole. I felt cool air blow against my face. Something tight in my chest, that came that morning when I first saw Dad and Scotty at the bus depot, went away. The air coming up felt so cool and good in that hot dry room—in that hot dry

Nevada City. Then I saw water rushing, bubbling by under the hole in the floor.

"What is it?" I said.

"It's a creek."

Scotty was looking up at me. A big smile in his freckles. His glasses slipped down on his nose.

"It runs under the house. Isn't that neat?"

"Yeah… It runs under the house?"

"Yup."

"That seems like a funny place for a creek," I said.

"Yeah, I guess." Then he sat back on his heels and pushed his glasses back up on his nose. "The rule is though we can't throw anything in it. Dad and Lou Ella do but we're not supposed to. Okay?"

"Okay," I said.

~

Dad brought my suit case in after that and put it under my bed. He had his jacket off and his white shirt rolled up to his elbows. Suspenders up over his shoulders. He carried the suit case in like it didn't weigh anything and slid it smooth on the linoleum under the bed like he did everything. One slick move with his long fingers. Like a piece from the inside of a watch slipped into place.

"I hope the cot will be okay, Dave. We're all just kind of camping out here."

It was real quiet in the room then and I could just barely hear the creek running under the floor. Dad was looking at me like I should say something so I said, "Yeah." But I didn't know what he meant, camping out. We weren't outside, we were inside in the funny place where he lived with a bug eyed woman that wasn't Mom.

Dad looked around the room quick like he didn't know where to put his eyes. They stopped and looked at me for a minute. Then down at his saddle shoes. He took a big breath and his suspenders went a lot longer. Then they went shorter again slow when he let the breath out.

"Well, I have to work. Lou Ella and I will be out front. Maybe Scott'll show you a little bit of the town."

"Sure, Dad." Then Scotty turned to the curtains in the doorway. Not very much of the Peonies on this side. Some of their color came through from the other side. Mostly gray. "C'mon," he said without ever looking back at me.

~

Out in front of the store, Scotty led me between Dad's building and the building next door to the back. It was all dirt out in back, dirt that was all over black and smelled like car oil. There were some old banged up cars with the paint wearing off from the heat parked out there on the black dirt. The sun coming real bright in my eyes and hot off their windows. Some old tires were there too and old engine parts in the dry weeds by the road. And garbage cans. And dust. And it was hot.

My new jeans from J. C. Penny's were damp on my legs and sweat came down trickly behind my ears.

"I know a short cut," Scotty said. His eyes big again behind his glasses.

"To where?"

"The bakery. It's my favorite place. They have swell butterhorns."

"What's that?"

"Wait and see," he said. Jack Armstrong again.

We walked a little ways down the black dirt road and pretty soon along the side past the gravel you could see the creek running in the ditch.

"That the same creek?"

"Yeah," Scotty said. "Going to the Sacramento."

Behind a store that smelled like good things baking—cinnamon and chocolate chip cookies and fresh bread—we walked through some dry grass and weeds and I got little stickery arrow things stuck in my pants and socks.

"Fox tails," Scotty said. "They're all over California."

Scotty always knows stuff like that.

~

Inside the bakery it was like in Multnomah only more. They had pies—black berry with crisscross crust on top and lemon with high white stuff—and cakes with chocolate frosting and lemony yellow and pink too and cookies that were almost as big as pies and little peanut butter ones with fork marks on top and all kinds of things I never saw before. They had all kind of donuts—some with see-through frosting and maple bars too. Maple bars were my favorite thing at the Multnomah bakery. Inside the screen door, under the fan up on the ceiling that was turning slow in the hot day, I just closed my eyes and let my nose have a party. All the smells together into one big smell that made my mouth water.

By the fresh bread and rolls, Scotty showed me what he called butterhorns.

"They're good for breakfast when they're warm with butter on 'em," he said and moved his tongue around on his lips. "But I think they're good anytime."

There were some round ones with a circle of orange in the middle Scotty said was apricot and some with yellow that Scotty said was custard. Even something called a bear claw. I told him I wanted to try the custard one. Scotty got the apricot.

He reached down deep in his jeans pocket and gave the lady some money and we went out the screen door holding our butterhorns. Outside, I kept my eyes shut for a minute so I could keep the smell inside me.

"Let's go sit by the creek and eat these," Scotty said.

"Okay," I said. Then I had to open my eyes.

We walked out back again behind the building and back through the fox tails. We crossed the black dirt road and the hot smell of car oil came in my nose and spoiled the good smell. The back of my neck was all wet with sweat and it was running down my face too. The red fire trucks on my new J.C. Penny shirt were all wrinkled and wet from sweat and my socks and pants cuffs were full of stickery fox tails. Scratchy on my ankles.

When we got to the edge of the black dirt, in the gravel and dry weeds beside the road, we sat down with our legs down the bank of the ditch where the water gurgled fast through the rocks. The sun was hot but there were some dusty bushes there that kept it off of us a little bit. I took a bite of my butterhorn and even though it was hot and the car oil smell was bad and the little stickery arrow things were scratching my ankles, it tasted really good. It was even better than my favorite Multnomah maple bars. I ate real slow and watched the water. Tasted the smooth custard. The water gurgling through the rocks and by the dusty bushes.

After I finished, I just sat quiet for a minute then tried to pull some of the fox tails out of my socks. It was hard because the little arrow things wanted to go in but didn't want to come back out again.

"You have to push 'em all the way through," Scotty said. "Then pull them out the other side."

When I tried that, it worked.

"Do you get to come here a lot?" I said.

Scotty looked over at me with squinty eyes, his freckles all bunched up.

"All the time," he said.

Scotty was a lot like Billy. I guess he didn't need big people around to tell him what to do.

"So Dad just gives you the money for the bakery?"

"Oh, that," Scotty said. "Yeah, for here and the café. Lou Ella hates to cook. So we eat at the café restaurant across the street from the shop all the time."

Scotty looked down at the water and rolled a piece of his butterhorn around between his fingers. Apricot stuff sticky on his fingers and dirty from all the dirt there.

"I never eat with them. They're always fighting."

"Always fighting?"

Scotty looked over at me and the hot blue sky flashed in his round glasses.

"Yeah, they really don't like each other very much."

He looked down the bank and dug his tennis shoe heel into the gravel and dirt.

"They don't do anything but yell at each other."

"But, how come?" I said. "Why is he with her then and not Mom?"

"Why? Why do you think? Mom kicked him out and married Brew. That's why."

Scotty's face was all red and he stuffed the last bite of his butterhorn into his mouth. A hot wind blew the dusty bush a little bit and sun flashed on his blond red hair. Blew the hot yucky car oil smell in my nose.

There was a pounding in my ears and that tight sharp feeling in my chest again. It felt like a great big fox tail that would have to be pushed all the way through and pulled out the other side.

24

Janie's Café

Back in the shop before dinner was the second time I saw Lou Ella, my new step-mom. She was at the other end of the shop bent down under the work light on Dad's bench. The fan there blowing her hair so it stuck out funny in bunches of curly cues. Black against the light. She was writing something on little tags on the watches Dad had to work on, so she didn't see me watching her at first.

I was trying to see if there was something special about her that maybe I missed, because I couldn't understand why Dad would want to marry her instead of Mom. I didn't believe Scotty that Mom "kicked Dad out." Mom wouldn't do that.

She looked up at me when she knew I was watching and real quick smiled. Too big. Lips way up over her teeth. Then looked down again writing. The smile gone. There was something kinda screwy about her. Not just her big brown bug eyes and stuck out curly hair that made her look like a clown but something more. Like she's all the time nervous.

Up come the eyes again and up go the lips. Big smile. Nervous. Like she was afraid I'd see her not smiling.

~

Dad and Lou Ella had to work at the shop until seven o'clock. So Dad gave Scotty some money and told him to take me across the street to Janie's Café. That's when I saw Janie the first time.

Janie was standing behind her big horse-shoe shaped counter up front talking to a man who was sitting there eating. There were only two people eating—a lady or girl, not very old, and the man. The man had strings of hair combed up over his bald head from the side like he put each string just in that place on purpose. He was looking down at his food so I could see the top of his head real good. Janie was wearing a waitress uniform, pink dress with a short skirt, a white apron down over her skirt and ruffles up over her shoulders, a little ruffled cap on her head. Her hair was combed up from her forehead and movie star hair down to her shoulders covered with a hair net like Mom wore to bed sometimes. She had a cigarette in one hand kind of waving it around while she talked and she was sucking on a tooth pick in her other hand and chewing gum all at the same time. She waved at Scotty and yelled, "Hi Hun."

There were tables in the back but they were all empty. Scotty sat on a stool at the horse-shoe counter so I sat next to him. A big fan over us on the ceiling was blowing the hot air around but there was still sweat on my lip.

Janie put her cigarette down careful in her ash tray next to a glass of ice tea and put her tooth pick next to it. Then she came over to us and said, "Who's your little friend?"

Scotty just jerked his head sideways at me Jack Armstrong-like again and said, "Oh this is my little brother, Davey. Remember, I told you he was coming from Portland."

Janie smiled real big. One of her front teeth was gold. It looked like it was a solid piece of gold. Like it was worth a lot of money.

"Oh, yeah. Hi Hun." Then she reached out her hand to shake mine.

Funny, in my head I thought, men shake hands.

I guess what John said to me that first night never went out of my head. I hardly ever saw men shake hands. No one ever shook mine. This was the first time. And it's Janie. But she didn't really shake it. Just held on to it for a minute.

"Any brother of Scott's is a friend of mine." Then she laughed like it was a joke or something.

I was kind of surprised but I took a hold of her hand and then I shook it. It felt real hot and kind of rough like Aunt Pearl's. I looked down and it was red and had flaky skin. Being a waitress must be hard work like on a dairy farm.

"Well, you're a cutie," she said.

She looked at Scott then and said, "The special tonight is liver and onions with mashed potatoes and broccoli. How does that sound, Hun?"

"Yum," Scotty said. "How about it, Davey? They have ketchup for your broccoli."

Janie's little thin eyebrows went up, "for the broccoli?"

"Yeah, he likes it on broccoli," Scotty said.

The hot air blowing around us made me kind of dizzy and my stomach felt yucky. I looked down at the counter that had little marbley lines in it and said, "Uch, it's too hot."

"I know what you mean," Janie said. Then to Scotty, "He's probably not used to the heat here yet." She pulled a paper napkin out of the silver holder there and patted her face. "Maybe you'd like a milk shake instead."

I looked at Scott and he said, "Is that what you'd like?"

"Can I?"

"Sure," he said. Still being Jack.

"How about a black walnut one?" Janie said.

Black Walnut ice cream milkshakes were Janie's specialty. The one I had that first day in Nevada City was really good. Creamy like vanilla but not so sweet. A little bit sharp. Lemony from the little dark specks of walnut. And cold. Most of all it was cold. That was the best part in that hot town. The metal thing she made it in was all frosty on the outside and drops of cold water were sliding down onto the horse-shoe counter where she set it beside my tall cone shaped glass. A little glass stand on the bottom of the milkshake glass held it up and it had glass ruffles on the top where you drink. After Janie poured the milkshake in my glass the metal can was still half full. Yum. And even the little cold drops on it looked good enough to lick off. But Janie poured a cold glass of water and put it down on the counter too.

25

Somewhere Else

It was always hot while I was in Nevada City. When I woke up in the morning, it was hot. When I played outside with Scotty during the day, it was hot. Because it was so hot, we didn't do much, just went to the bakery or sat by the creek. Sometimes I played in Dad's shop if he didn't have a customer. By dinner time, it was even hotter and I never felt like eating anything but a black walnut milkshake.

I guess Dad didn't care what I ate so I had a black walnut ice cream milkshake every night after that for my dinner.

Scotty and I fixed ourselves some cereal and milk in the morning after Dad and Lou Ella had their coffee and went out front to work in the shop. Sometimes, Scotty and I talked. Scotty knew lots about things outside. Birds and plants and trees and how to hike and camp out and make a fire with no matches but he didn't know everything.

Because I lived with Mom, I was sure he didn't really know about Mom and Dad like he said he did. And I didn't think he knew about Dad and Lou Ella either. They never yelled at each other like Scotty said. They didn't even talk to each other. Oh, sometimes real soft. Two or three words. Through their teeth, not even moving their lips.

Then sometimes after breakfast, Scotty would go play with his friend, Larry. Larry was even older than Scotty. He was all muscley and had sandy hair and freckles. Hiking and camping-out were what he did most of the time and he wore tight tee shirts to show off his muscles. The first time he saw me he said, "Does the runt have to tag along?" I didn't like Larry very much. He thought he was such hot stuff. So I stayed in the dim, hot room behind the shop when Scotty played with Larry.

I never had anything to do then, so I would lie down on my bed that dad called a camp cot and look up at the sky above the window in the ceiling. Sometimes there'd be a cloud and I'd try to see the picture in it. Like Scotty and me used to do when I was little. A clown face and some-times a dog. Sometimes a bird would zip by on his way someplace and I wished I could fly so I could fly back to Oregon. Mostly, it was only blank blue sky I could see 'cause it was hot and dry outside. So then I would just think about Oregon. Think about my friend, Billy and dream about playing in his cool, shady woods. Dream about the teeter totter and about the camel behind the flap on the cigarette pack.

I thought about Sunny Lea too and how she got us all to play Kick the Can. We'd play outside until we had to go in and go to bed. Or sometimes we played Hide 'n Seek until it'd start to get dark. Lots of times I was still hiding. That's when it really got fun 'cause you didn't have to hide behind anything. It was dark and nobody could see you. On hot days in the summer it would be cool then and the cool would feel really neat on your skin. Soft. You could see into peoples' windows too and make up stories about what they were doing and what they were saying. I'd think about Mom and Brew at home. Like they forgot about me being out so late, 'cause Mom hadn't called me. And it was scary too. Thinking about going home down the hill in the dark alone. Then I'd go zooming into the tree that was our home base. I'd smack my hand on the rough bark and yell, "Ollie, Ollie Oxen free."

When I went to California, Mom gave me a bunch of penny post cards that she put our address on in Multnomah. She wrote it right under where THIS SIDE OF CARD IS FOR ADDRESS was printed in green ink. A penny stamp with President Jefferson's green face was already printed on there too. So sometimes, I would write one of those to Mom—*How are you? I am fine*—and take it to the corner where Scotty showed me there was a mail box.

One day coming back from the mail box after I mailed a penny post card to Mom, I had an idea. 'Cause it was cooler in the room I always wanted to get back there. But that day it seemed as hot inside as it was out. Outside it was different too. The blue sky that made everything so dry was gone and it was just icky gray sky. Lou Ella called it muggy. My jeans were wet through when I came in and so was my tee shirt. Scotty was playing with Larry and Dad and Lou Ella were out front, so I went slow to the middle of the room and got down on my hands and knees. I put my finger in the little hole in the gray brick linoleum and pulled. Up came the little trap door and right away it was cool on my face from the air that came up. There was the creek bubbling by under the house. You could see clear cold water going white over the bigger rocks down there. Hear it gurgle over the little ones. I pulled the door all the way over so it went flat upside down on the floor, then laid down and put my face down in the hole. My chin rested on the floor. Cool. Cool. My tummy felt cool and easy on the floor through my wet tee shirt. Cool watery air on my face. It smelled like fog, the smell of damp that gets in your nose and like rain on pine bark. Cool and dark around my face. It felt so good. I couldn't remember when I felt that cool feeling. It seemed like forever since I felt that cool feeling against my skin.

~

I must of went to sleep 'cause then I heard a crash from out front and I woke up. Dad and Lou Ella were screaming at each other.

Lou Ella screamed, "I didn't do it, you moron."

Dad's voice roared back like some animal, "Well, who then?"

Then Lou Ella all sing-songy, "I'll give you two guesses."

"God damn it. Why can't you keep an eye on him?"

There was another crash and something broke out front, "He's not my damn kid."

Right away, I knew who they were yelling about but I sure didn't know what I did. It must of been something awful. I never heard people scream at each other like that.

The creek hole door went down soft with a thunk. Closed, so nobody would know it was open. Outside was where they couldn't find me. But without going through the shop, I couldn't go outside. Their screams were sharp on my skin. Like thin sharp blades. Each time jabbing at me. Then quiet. Nothing. I could hardly breathe while I waited for one of them to scream again. My skin goose bumpy.

Scotty's room or Dad and Lou Ella's were "off limits." Nobody was supposed to go in there. No place to hide under that dumb old camp cot. My jaw hurt from biting down. The table where Scotty and I ate our cereal every day was the only place to go. Just sitting at the table for no reason, though, felt pretty stupid. My ears were burny hot and sweat was running down behind them. Every time one of them screamed my body wanted to jump out of the chair.

Then Dad came in. His face was all really red and his blond gray hair was down on his forehead. Wet from sweat. He saw me sitting at the table and his legs just stopped. Then he looked around the room like he couldn't figure out what was happening.

"What're you doing?" he said.

"Nothing," I said.

"Well, what're you just sitting there for?"

"I don't know," I said.

Then I thought, Well, it's too hot to do anything else, but I didn't say it.

Dad took a big breath and right away his suspenders went a lot longer, then shorter when he let his breath out. Then he stopped, no breath at all.

"Dave, come out front for a minute, will you?"

My legs felt like they went to sleep. Like there was no feeling in them at all. They could hardly move. The tight feeling was back in my chest. And a pounding in my ears. The stove and the sink, even the table were beating like a drum and a misty red floated around the room. Dizzy in my head made me feel like I might fall down but I didn't.

We went out through the Peony curtains and he walked real slow over by his work bench to the box thing that looked like a little tunnel.

"Dave," he said, "have you been playing with this?"

Drops of sweat were running down my face and down my chest under my shirt.

"I was driving my cars through it for a tunnel," I said.

"Well, Dave, most of the time I don't mind you playing with my things but you have to be careful."

His face wasn't red anymore and he reached out and messed up my hair.

Ugh, it was too hot for that.

"Do you know what this is for?" he said.

"No," I said. "I know it's not a tunnel. I was just pretending it was."

"I know," he said and his kind of pretty mouth made a little bit of a smile. "I use this for de-magnetizing. Metal parts of watches get magnetized by mistake sometimes and if they're magnetic they stick to each other and the watch won't work. I put the parts in this little tunnel and turn it on and it takes the magnetic out of them. But if this other switch over here gets touched," he pointed at the switch that I played with, "it does just the opposite and all the parts I put in get magnetized instead."

He put his hand on my shoulder then and looked in my eyes. His hand was heavy on my shoulder, almost like he was trying to push me into the floor. It didn't feel good like it did that first day when I wanted him to touch me. I learned since that day that he only touched me when he thought he had to. When he thought he had to teach me something or tell me not to do something. Like it was his duty. Not because he wanted to. It wasn't the nice warm touch that Uncle Herb had because he liked kids. Because he liked *me*.

Dad's eyes looked sad and gray and like he really didn't want to be there talking to me. Like he really wanted to be somewhere else. That's what it was. I knew then what was the same in his eyes as Aunt Pearl and Grandma Williams. They all looked all the time like they wanted to be somewhere else.

"So please don't move this switch. Okay?" He swatted me on the fanny then and said, "Now why don't you go outside and play?"

~

After that, I stayed outside most of the time. Even if it was too hot out, I didn't want to hear Dad and Lou Ella scream at each other. And I didn't want to do anything to make them scream about me.

Most of the time Scotty was over at Larry's but when he was around, Scotty and me, we went on hikes. But they were just long walks in the hot sun and dry grass where I got fox tails in my socks. I sweated the whole time and funny dots got in front of my eyes and the fox tails were scratchy on my ankles. Scotty said the heat would fry an egg. Then I started getting stomach aches every time we hiked very far. I didn't want to go home and lie down like Scotty told me to 'cause Dad and Lou Ella were there working. And besides, I really wanted to be with Scotty. So sometimes we would just go to the creek and sit on the dusty bank by the water. We sat by the creek and I would feel better.

I found an old hat of Dad's that he didn't want. When I went outside, I wore it because there was so much sun all the time, I started getting sun burned. My nose got really red and it hurt. Then it peeled and that made it hurt worse because so much skin came off. Since Dad didn't go outside much, he said I could have his hat. He said it was old anyway. The big brim kept the sun off my face. It came down over my ears but I didn't care. The dark brown felt was really soft. It was a swell hat and it made me feel grown up. Like a business man.

And it was my Dad's hat. He gave it to me.

Sometimes Scotty and me, we'd get a butterhorn. But not if we went on a hike because my stomach would be yucky.

~

After I had an apricot butterhorn one day, I had to go to the bathroom really bad but I didn't want to go back to the shop because of Dad and Lou Ella. I told Scotty I had to poop really bad.

"So why don't you just go in the bushes?" he said.

"Out here?" I said.

I never went to the bathroom outside before. "What if somebody sees?"

Scotty's eyebrows scrunched down over his eyes and he threw a rock down hard into the water.

"Oh, you're such a sissy sometimes. You get sick on our hikes and now you're scared to use the latrine."

"What's that?"

Scotty got up like he was going to leave he was so mad.

"It means to poop in the bushes, dummy. We do it in Scouts all the time."

I didn't want to be a sissy. Did he think that I get sick to my stomach on purpose or something?

"Well, I don't have any toilet paper."

Scotty took a big breath and his eyeballs went way up. Then he spread his arms out in the air like he was really tired of explaining things.

"Geez, you can use the napkins the bakery gave us."

So I took the two napkins and tried to find a place where the bushes were pretty big. I was glad the bakery lady made us take napkins this time.

Like always, new things can be scary but exciting too. There was a place in the bushes where maybe nobody could see me but there were bees buzzing around in my tummy anyway. I unbuckled my belt and undid my jeans and pulled them down. I started to take them off but then I'd have to take off my tennis shoes. So I left my jeans pushed down around my shoes.

Then there was a tingling feeling in my underpants. My Thing started getting hard. That was strange. I didn't really want it to do that. But little by little, it was bumping up against my shorts. Like I didn't have anything to say about it. I pushed my underpants down and my Thing just stood straight out in front of me. It felt good though. Kind of like tickling. There was something else that felt kind of good though to stand there like that. It was like something was free. Something that had to stay in a hot dim room all the time got to get outside. The hot air blowing through the dusty bushes really felt good on my fanny. The rest of me felt good too like it felt to touch the smooth red drapes in our front room at home. I looked down. It was bigger than that time with Billy by the Pussy Willows. I never saw my thing get so big. For some reason, that made me feel strong. Maybe like Larry felt when he showed off his muscles.

It was the first time that all that Nevada City heat didn't feel so bad. It wouldn't be so bad to live in this hot old city if I went around naked all the time. Then I looked over the bushes. The backs of the stores were right there behind the bushes. What if someone upstairs in one of those stores looked down here and saw this naked kid standing there in just an old brown hat and his Thing sticking out? So I squatted down real fast. I really had to poop but I never pooped with my Thing hard. It felt weird.

I finished and went back to where Scotty was sitting on the bank. He was watching those little bugs on the creek that looked like they were water skiing and throwing little pieces of gravel at them. He looked up and smiled a little bit at me. Just the corners of his mouth went up a little. Scotty was like the Williamses. He hardly ever smiled.

"You okay?" he said.

"Sure," I said.

I sat down on the bank again and Scotty looked back down at the creek.

"See, it wasn't so bad, was it?"

"Nope," I said, "but my Thing got hard."

Scotty quick looked around at me. Face all scrunched like he didn't hear me.

"What?" he said.

"I said my Thing got hard. Why did it do that?"

"How should I know?" he said. "Why ask me?"

"Does yours get hard when you use the latrine?"

His face got all red like it does and makes his hair look orange. He shook his head back and forth with his face still scrunched.

"I guess so. I don't know."

Then I saw that same look. Looking inside or away to some other place. Like he wasn't really there. That look that Grandma Williams had and Aunt Pearl and Dad. That look like they wanted to be somewhere else. Like he wanted to be anywhere else but here talking to his little brother about my Thing getting hard.

That made me mad.

Well, I knew what it felt like too to want to be somewhere else. Since I came to this hot stinkin' Nevada City, I knew for the first time in my life what it felt like. And right then I wanted to be anywhere else but there.

26

Forty Niners

The next day, Dad was arrested. Two big men in checkered shirts and overalls came into the shop and took him away.

Scotty and me, we were eating our cereal in the back room. There were some loud voices and laughing out front so we looked out through the peony curtains. We saw the one big ugly guy in an old straw hat and wooly black beard tie Dad's hands behind him and then the other one with the red beard and thin stringy red hair take Dad's arm and lead him out of the shop.

Lou Ella was the one who was laughing. Her curly black hair sticking out in crazy black clumps and her cackle laughing big like it was the funniest thing she ever saw.

Dad was not laughing.

"Where are they taking him?" Scotty said.

"To the stockade," Lou Ella said. She was gasping, like she didn't have any breath. Her face all red from laughing. "They built it last week up on Main Street. Oh don't worry, it's all part of the Forty Niners' Celebration. You know, to celebrate the Gold Rush."

She was wiping tears away from her big bug eyes with her fingers that had long bent dark red fingernails on them and still going, "uh huh, uh huh."

"But why did they take Dad?" I said. "Did he do something wrong?"

She kind of snorted through her nose then.

"Oh, he just wouldn't grow a beard for the celebration. It was just too beneath him. All the men have to grow a beard or go before the kangaroo court."

She yanked a Kleenex out of the box on the glass counter.

"Kangaroos?" I said. The picture in my head was really weird. A bunch of kangaroos in a jury box. Kind of like the picture of Alice playing croquet with a flamingo in the book Mom read to me.

"It's a kind of fake law court. Uh huh, uh huh. They'll probably just fine him and let him go."

She blew her nose in the Kleenex. All wet and messy. Yuck.

"But first he has to spend some time in the stockade—the jail up on Main Street."

"Can we go see him?" Scotty said.

She slow wiped her bug eyes with the messy Kleenex.

"Sure, I don't care. I might as well go too. We're not going to get much work done here today."

Scotty kind of jumped up and down so I did too.

~

The stockade was split logs with the bark still on them and fixed in a square like bars around a room. Inside they put sawed-in-half logs like stumps for the men to sit on.

It was before noon and even that early it was muggy. The sky over Main Street was gray clouds and the air was warm and sticky. My shirt, even my jeans, were sticking to me. My shirt collar was all wet and rolled up against my neck. The little hairs at the bottom of my hair cut were sopping wet and my stomach was yucky.

I didn't even go on a hike and my stomach was yucky, for cryin' out loud.

There were only two other men in the stockade with Dad. A crowd was around the outside though. A lot of men with bushy beards mostly. They were laughing and yelling things at the three men inside.

"Hey Pansy, couldn't grow a beard?"

"Look at that lily white chinny, chin, chin. Shaved pussy."

My neck got really hot then and my ears started to burn.

Dad was sitting on one of the stumps with his head in his hands. He didn't look mad like he did that day with the tunnel thing. Not red in the face. But his jaw was biting down hard and his shoulders hunched up. His eyes looking down at the street that was the floor of the stockade.

Lou Ella was laughing again like the crowd around us and pointing at Dad. I didn't know what was so funny. Dad looked really sad. I didn't want to laugh at him.

When he heard Lou Ella, Dad looked up and kind of smiled. He looked like a little kid who did something he wasn't supposed to. That's when Scotty started laughing too. Dad got up and came over to the log bars then and said, "Okay, okay, I think that's enough." He was still kind of smiling. His pretty mouth just turned up a little. What else could he do with everybody else laughing? But his eyes had that look, like he wanted to be somewhere else. My throat was burny. I didn't think he was ever happy being where he was.

A prayer was in my head right then. Not the prayer Mom taught me. The one that goes I pray the Lord to guide my ways, but one that said I pray to be happy right where I am and not to wish to be somewhere else like most of my Williams family did. I really didn't want to be like them. All the time unhappy. Gramma Williams sad about Uncle Harold getting killed. Aunt Pearl unhappy being married to Uncle Herb. Dad just unhappy about everything. I decided right then that I wanted to be more like Janie in her café. Happy right where I was.

~

Dad came back that afternoon. Scotty was over at Larry's and Lou Ella was out front in the shop. I was in the back laying down on my camp cot 'cause my stomach was still yucky. My prayer wasn't gonna be easy. It was hard to try and be happy when my stomach was all the time yucky and Nevada City was all the time so hot and sticky. But I had a plan that every time I felt unhappy, I would do something I liked.

I just finished writing one of the penny post cards Mom gave me. That made me feel better. So I laid down to look at the sky. That's when Dad came in the front of the shop. I could tell because they started yelling out in front. First I heard the little bell that was on a spring over the door ring like it always did when the door opened. Then I heard low talking and then BAM. Dad was yelling at Lou Ella about closing the shop that day and Lou Ella was screaming back.

I was up off the camp cot and started to go to the creek hole but that wouldn't make the yelling stop. I needed to work my plan. So I took two of my toy cars out of my suit case. One was my favorite old metal one from home that got all the paint washed off when I left it out in the rain and Pop came out to visit with his chocolate covered cherries. It made me sad but I tried not to think about how I wanted to be there instead of Nevada City. I quick went through the peony curtains. It would be hot outside but I didn't care.

As soon as they knew I was there, Dad and Lou Ella stopped yelling. They both went stiff like when you play statue. Lou Ella's mouth was still open but nothing came out of it. No sound at all. She looked really shocked. Like she forgot I was staying there. Then Dad turned around and saw me behind him walking through the shop to the front door and his fist came down hard on the counter. The bell on the door rang and I was out the front door.

I didn't know where to take my cars to play. Maybe behind the shop on the oily road in the alley or down behind the bakery by the creek. Then I saw Janie's Café sign across the street. I guess I knew all the time that's where I'd go. It would be cooler over there with her big fans on the ceiling. And Janie would be happy. She was always happy. I never went there except to eat though. But maybe it would be all right.

Janie looked up from where she was wiping off her big horse-shoe counter. Big smile. Solid gold tooth. Must be worth a lot.

"Hi Hun, "she said. "What can I get you?"

It wasn't time to eat so I just shook my head.

"Nothin,'" I said.

"So you just came to see me, huh? Well, that's mighty sweet." Then she winked at me. She put her cloth down and picked up her toothpick and put it in her mouth. Still holding onto it with two fingers.

"Sure is muggy out there, ain't it?"

"Yup," I said.

"Well, why don't you have a seat at one of the back tables. I'll get you a glass of water and you can play with your cars there on the table."

"Okay," I said and there was something nice and warm that opened up in my chest like when I went to see Mrs. Baldwin.

Nobody else was there, so when she brought the glass of water over to the back table, Janie sat down with me. She brought her cigarettes and ash tray in her other hand.

I liked to watch Janie. Everything she did was so careful. Like she was a scientist or something working out a problem with the space ship she invented and she had to get every movement just right.

The toothpick was still in her mouth but she took it out and set it on the table just so. After she pulled a chair out and sat down, she peeled the red strip off her cigarette pack and curled it around her finger. Then she put it in the ash tray all curled up. She slipped the cellophane off the top of the pack and pulled the silver foil off. Both of them got folded in neat little squares before she put them in the ash tray too. She gave the side of the pack a whack on her hand. A cigarette popped out and she stuck it in her mouth, snapped her lighter and lit it. A long trail of smoke blew out of the corner of her mouth away from us.

"Ah that's better," she said.

She looked at me for a minute. Gray blue eyes that looked like Mom. Looked at me like she was trying to see inside. Figure another science problem.

"Listen sweetie," she said. "Whenever it gets too much for you, you can come over here. Anytime. You hear me?"

I didn't know exactly what she meant. I mean, how would she know why I wanted to come? But I said, "Okay." I really liked Janie.

~

I made a garage out of the napkin holder and parked my cars in there. The glass sugar thing was the modern city tower where I worked. It was really fun playing cars at Janie's.

At dinner time, Scotty came over. He just sat down at the table and Janie came back over to take our order.

"Pretty rough over there today?" she said.

And Scotty, first he looked at me like he was gonna ask a question, then he looked down. "Oh, yeah," he said. "They're goin' at it strong." His eyes looking at the old paper of a straw he was twisting in his fingers.

Even if it wasn't so hot at Janie's, I didn't feel much like eating but I had my black walnut milkshake anyway. It didn't taste good like it did all the other times though and my head was aching by then too. I didn't even feel like slurping with the straw and making that noise at the end.

As soon as Scotty and me got back across the street to the shop, I knew I was gonna throw up. I ran into the bathroom at the back of the shop. There wasn't even time to lift up the seat and there was black walnut milkshake all over the toilet and the floor. I was on my knees looking down through the toilet seat like I did all the time looking in the creek hole except this wasn't nice. There were little flecks of black walnut floating in the water and chunks of white milky stuff and I kept heaving and heaving. Like all the black walnut milkshakes I had at Janie's since I came to Nevada City wanted to come shooting out of my mouth. The whole bathroom smelled a stinky sweet smell and sour milk.

My stomach pushed up from the bottom like it wanted to come out through my throat and couldn't. Then it would try again. Even when there was no more milkshake, my stomach was still trying to come out. Finally, it stopped.

Dad was there then. I didn't know where he came from but all of a sudden, he was there. I thought maybe it was a dream. But then he wiped my face with a cold wash cloth and picked me up. That made me feel better. His body warm against me. His big, smooth arms around my whole body. His clean smell, kind of like grass and rain. My dad was hugging me like I always wanted. But then I saw in his eyes. That look was still there. Like he wanted to be somewhere else. And there was that sharp foxtail feeling in my chest again.

He carried me past the Peony curtains and put me down on the camp cot. My teeth were clicking up and down and my skin was all over goose bumpy. I couldn't stop myself from shivering. So Dad, he put a blanket over me.

After all that hot, I couldn't believe I was cold.

"Dad," I said, "why am I so sick?"

Dad looked far away inside his eyes somewhere.

"Oh, I don't know, Dave. Probably because it hasn't rained. You're used to rain and it just hasn't rained here it's so hot.

That sounded really right. Dad was right. What I needed was some rain.

Finally I got warm and the pillow case felt cool on my cheek. It smelled clean like laundry soap.

I went to sleep that night praying. Not so much for Dad to love me but for rain.

~

In the morning, I opened my eyes and what I saw through the window in the ceiling was a miracle. It was raining. I guess sometimes prayers work. Rain was pouring down on the window in the ceiling. Great big blurry swirls of water and white sky. It roared and splashed on the other side of the window over my head. The room smelled fresh and cool like it did looking through the trap door at the creek under the floor.

Scotty came running into the big room from his bedroom in his swimming suit. Big smile. He hardly ever smiled.

"Come on, Davey. Get your bathing suit on. Let's go out and play in the rain. Dad says we can."

Then I couldn't find my swimming suit. I pulled out my suit case from under the camp cot. It was where I kept my clothes and stuff. I didn't have a dresser like at home. Every time though it was hard to pull out 'cause it was so heavy. Not as easy as when Dad slid it under there. I finally got the suit case out and looked through the whole stupid thing. Underwear, socks, my cars, Mom's post cards, tee shirts, jeans. No swimming suit.

I was stamping my feet and hitting my suit case with my fist and Scotty said, "I guess you're not sick anymore."

He was right. I didn't feel sick. Just kind of tired. And hot now—mad that I didn't have my swimming suit.

"Oh come on, Davey," Scotty said, "you can just wear your Jockey shorts."

"You think so? My underpants?"

"Sure," Scotty said in his Jack Armstrong voice. Chest out big. "Nobody'll care. Come on, let's go play in the rain."

He took off out the peony curtains to the shop.

Well, I already had my underpants on 'cause I slept in them. So I ran out front after him.

Outside the front door, it was like a curtain of water was coming down from the building. Standing there in my underpants, my Thing started getting hard like it did sometimes but I just stepped my bare feet into that curtain and let the water come down on top of my head and the feeling went away. Then my head went back and my eyes closed and the water poured over my face into my ears. It was really warm for rain water but it felt cool on my skin after all those hot days. My mouth went open and I let it pour into my mouth. It tasted clean. Cloud tears in my mouth—tasted like heaven. Like my prayers. I let it run into my throat and gargled loud. Washed out that hot summer. The black walnut milk-shakes. The sick from last night.

I stretched up my arms into the rain and let it pour through my fingers. Big heavy ropes of water. My hands grabbed handfuls of warm clean rain and smashed them against my skinny chest and I hollered. Then my fingers followed the slick wet down over my ribs and belly. Standing there in my underpants with the rain pouring over me was almost as good as going naked in the city like I thought about doing when I pooped in the bushes.

Scotty was out in the street stamping his feet in a puddle and making splashes. The rain was coming down so hard though, it filled in the hole again right away where the puddle was.

I ran out there and just jumped both my bare feet in the middle of the puddle and got Scotty good. It was really just a hole in the black-top. Water with little bits of gravel and dirt all the way up to his bare chest. Rain water coming down on top of him and dirty water coming up from the puddle.

Scotty's head went back in a big laugh and his face went all red. I never saw that before. Scotty laughing. He looked so different without his glasses, his face all red and laughing. Having fun. He was so happy it made me laugh too.

All at once, he jumped both feet in and splashed me. The water came all the way up to my face. Gritty stuff in my mouth. But it was so good not to be hot, I just started to yell. My head went back again and a big laugh came up from the band on my wet under-pants and shot out of my mouth. It made me think about how I was sick the night before. Throwing up. But this time it was nice. My stomach was happy not yucky like then.

Scotty reached out and grabbed my hands and we started dancing around in a circle in the mud puddle laughing and yelling. Rain pounding down on us. The puddle water started getting us muddy then like it was when Billy Rogers was dancing around muddy singing, "mud people, mud people."

I pulled my arms away from Scotty and started waving them in the air slow back and forth like Billy and singing, "mud people, mud people." Everything was going slow like it knew I wanted it to never end. Scotty laughed so hard then he fell down and just sat in the muddy water.

Pretty soon, the rain slowed down too and there was just a warm drizzle. I was really tired then. My stomach was better than last night but it was tired too. So I just sat down on the curb on the sidewalk beside Scotty in his puddle.

"Boy, that was fun," I said.

Scotty's face got red again though, but darker and he looked away from me. His hair all dark orangey and wet. He wasn't laughing this time.

"Not like Oregon though," he said real soft.

We just sat there then. Smelled the dry dusty smell of wet cement in the air and listened to the drips coming off the building plopping onto the sidewalk.

"Maybe I could borrow one of your penny post cards and write to Mom," he said.

"You think?"

27

Movin' On

Mom was standing in the doorway of our house holding the screen door open. Her red plastic glasses swooped up on the corners almost to the white scarf tied around her head to cover up her pin curls. She had on her white peasant blouse that ruffled around her arms up high and dipped down from her shoulders and a long skirt that came down from a wide elastic belt and ended just above her bobby socks like usual. Today she didn't look like a movie star. She just looked like she did most days around the house. But she looked like the best thing I ever saw.

It was two months in that awful Nevada City since I saw her and now there was only green Oregon grass between her and me at the skinny little Maple tree that Brew planted in the front yard. Over that grass, I ran like I never ran before. Not like Scotty and me did on the Moo Cow Hill. That was more like falling. And pretend. This running was like I was really flying. I didn't even feel my feet on the ground.

Then her arms were around me. My legs around her waist. That place in my chest finally didn't hurt anymore. It was so open it was like it was gonna bust out of me.

The screen door banged against us.

"Ouch," she said and I laughed.

Her face was red from holding me. Her voice squinched.

"Oh my word, my little boy has gotten heavy. And I swear you've grown at least two feet in those two months."

I was lost in those gray blue sky cloud eyes of hers. My arms around her neck and I buried my face there. Where that tiny brown mole was. In the clean smell of her soap and grown-up female smells.

"Ugh, Honey. You're just too heavy. I'm going to have to put you down."

A big wet kiss from Mom on my mouth I had to wipe off.

Then John came up with his old maple-tree-limp onto the little cement front porch with my suit case and I was home.

Real slow I looked around the house like I never lived there before. The front room with the fireplace and the smooth dark red drapes. The Robin's Egg Blue dinette set in the kitchen. The boogie man closet that used to scare me when I was a little kid. The glow-in-the-dark stars on the ceiling in Scotty's room and the lonely-girl-watching-the-bird picture on his wall. Most of all, I couldn't wait to see my room. Teddy sitting on my dresser, Gramma Williams' name quilt on my bed with the colored snowflake stars, my chair with the carved lion paws where you put your hands.

No more grey brick linoleum and camp-bed.

But there wasn't any Teddy, no colored snowflake quilt. The only thing the same was the chair all alone in the empty looking room. It looked like I really never lived in there. There was a fast-going-down elevator in my stomach and I grabbed the doorway.

I was there in the doorway looking when John—or Brew like everybody else called him—brought my suit case up the stairs and set it down in my room. He didn't slide it smooth under the bed, just set it down in my room. Nothing complicated. Simple. Always had a smile. A joke... for everybody else.

Everybody knew that about Brew. Called him by his nick name.

"Where's Teddy? Where's my stuff?" I said.

Outside through the windows I heard a truck stop in the road. Screechy brakes. Then a door slam. Lots of loud scraping. The ice man at the man's house across the street. It was Monday.

Brew stood in the middle of my room. A white tee shirt and some old cords. He looked his dark eyes at me. Smiled so his widow's peak moved up with his black eyebrows and said, " It's all in the closet. We'll get it out later." He meant in that spooky place in the attic.

But it didn't even look like my room. Why was all my stuff in the closet?

"I bought a case of Nehi pop from a guy who came by the shop. Got a good deal on it. Want one?"

For the first time, I saw that Brew had a dent in his cheek like Billy Rogers when he smiled at me.

"Sure," I said. Not really hearing. I hardly knew what he asked me. Teddy stuffed in the closet. Another part of me a long way away. in a hot dim room, a window on the ceiling, with a man in neat slacks with a crease, saddle shoes and who didn't want to be there.

Brew's eyes crinkled all around with little lines. Big smile. And he squeezed my shoulder.

That woke me up. It was almost like a hug. My head was tired though. Trying to figure out about Brew.

"Come on down to the kitchen," he said.

~

I sat down at the dinette set with my Nehi root beer. Let it fill up my mouth with the cold smooth taste. Tried not to think about step-dads changing their minds. Or black walnut milkshakes. But it was like that thing people say: *don't think about monkeys.*

~

After playing in the rain that day in Nevada City, Scotty and me, we finally went in and got dressed. It was so much fun we didn't want to go in but we got hungry. So we got dressed and went over to Janie's.

Janie was behind her horse-shoe counter like usual. Waiting on the bald guy with the strings of hair over the top. He was there almost every day like us. Janie waved at us and her gold tooth flashed when the big slow fan went in front of the light on the ceiling.

She came over with her pad and took the pencil out from behind her ear.

"You two are early today," she said.

Scotty nodded and then tossed his head to get his red hair out of his eyes. It was getting so long, it kept falling behind his new round glasses.

"Yeah we were playing in the rain. That big pot hole out there in the street."

Janie's brown eyes squinted up when she laughed.

"I saw you two. Looked like you were having a ball."

My face started to get hot. Janie saw me out there in my underpants. It made me so embarrassed, I wanted to hide under the counter. That's when I knew I couldn't go around naked like I day-dreamed about.

But Janie seemed really happy that Scotty and me had so much fun in the rain.

"So, Davey," she said, "want your black walnut milkshake?"

When she asked me that, Scotty says my face turned really green. I could feel my tummy kind of rolling.

So Scotty told her how I heaved all over the bathroom. How the house and shop smelled like spoiled milk. All that yucky stuff. I almost got sick again hearing him tell her all about it.

She said she was really sorry. That it was probably the heat.

That day I had a hamburger and a root beer. Root beers are good. I don't think I will ever want to have a black walnut ice cream milk shake again. Not ever again. Even that buzzing noise that the milk shake mixer makes, makes my stomach yucky.

~

When I finished my Nehi root beer sitting at the dinette set with Mom and Brew, I couldn't wait anymore to go see Billy Rogers. All the way home on the bus, I didn't think of hardly anything else. I needed to see my best friend. So I told them thanks for the Nehi and took off out the screen door. It was great to be back in Mudnomah.

I ran up the dusty road in front of Craig and Dale's house next door. Outside smelled smoky and the air looked kind of fuzzy like Fall makes it. Like Fall was already happening. I skipped down Spring Garden trying to miss the ruts of dried mud in the road. Past the blackberry patch that was turning red and brown now. All the berries dried up or gone.

All the time I was in California, I pictured Billy in his woods. Maybe sitting on his teeter totter waiting. No one on the other end. Maybe smoking a Camel. Maybe naked. Outside in his woods though. Trees all around. Feeling the cool air. Not trapped in a stuffy room filled with crappy old furniture and unhappy people all around him. Yelling at each other most of the time.

On the other side of the road from the blackberries, the Baldwin's house peeked through the red leaves on the bushes but I didn't want to wait anymore to see Billy. So in front of their house, I just cut into the field and headed for Billy's.

That field was always different. In the winter it was wet and muddy with only a few weeds. In the spring it was really green with skunk cabbage and lots of purple and white and yellow flowers. Then in the summer the grass grew and got taller than me, the same grass that turned yellow dry in the fall and crackled and rustled like it did now.

It whispered all around me that day I pushed through the high grass to Billy's house on the other side of the field. It was like if I listened real close, I could hear what all the grass was saying. I stopped to listen but then the grass stopped whispering like it didn't want me to hear.

I started to laugh thinking how silly I was and laughing too because I was gonna get to see Billy. That made me run again.

I came up onto the road and there was Billy's woods and house beside it. It all had been waiting right there for me for two months just like I knew it was. I jumped in the air and came down springy on my tennis shoes.

"Yes."

But. It looked different. The house. There were pine cones all over the porch. Billy's yard was always so beautiful. His dad and mom always took real good care of their yard. In front of their house now, the grass was almost knee high and full of dandelions. Some of them even had fuzzy heads. Like they were just about to let go of their little parachutes. I couldn't figure that out. Why would they let it all get so messy?

I started up the grassy driveway to the yard. Then I heard someone out in the road.

"Hey you, Kid."

I turned around. Frank. His golden eyes squinting. His top lip pulled up over his teeth. He looked like he might even growl any minute.

"Oh. Little Davey B. It's you. I wondered who was going up to Billy's old house."

There was that look again. Like he knew something I didn't, and there was no way he was gonna tell me. His one eyebrow up. That know-it-all smile. His legs spread and his hands in his pockets like he owned the street.

My stomach got tight. Then yucky. Black Walnut milkshakes.

"I was just going up to see Billy," I said. "Just got back from California." Like California might make me seem a little more important to Frank. Tried to use Scotty's Jack Armstrong voice and put my chest out like him.

But Frank only said, "Oh yeah. When'd you get back?" He didn't move. Just his mouth smiled a little more.

"This morning."

"Uh huh," he said and bent down and picked up a rock from the bottom of the driveway. Then he just quick spun around with his back to me and pitched the rock across the road into the field like it was a hardball.

"He ain't here," he said. Kind of grunted it out when he threw the rock.

I wasn't sure I heard him right.

"What?"

He whipped back around with his lip over his teeth again.

"I said he ain't here. Billy ain't here no more."

"Whata you mean? Where is he?"

"Damned if I know," he said with a big smile. Happy to see me not knowing what he was talking about. His eyes swimming like pancake syrup.

Two black birds flew out of the woods on the other side of the driveway cawing at each other like they were fighting. Dad and Lou Ella. Frank picked a long dry piece of grass and stuck it in his mouth. Just looking at me. Then he bent down real slow and picked up another piece of gravel and turned around to throw it. Just before he let it go, he said, "Moved away." Then tossed it like he was shooting a basket. "About a month and a half ago."

There wasn't any air in me all of a sudden. Like my chest forgot how to breathe. My hands were really cold and my chest couldn't breathe. It was like I was gonna faint..

"He didn't tell anybody where they were movin' to," he said. "Just picked up and left."

Billy gone. Just like my dad.

He took the dry grass out of his mouth and looked at it. Then said, "Guess you're gonna have to find yourself a new friend."

The last little bit of air in me came out with the "Yeah" I said.

Frank threw the grass away like it was disgusting.

"Little fruit," he said and walked away.

I wasn't sure what he meant. He said it like he was calling me a name but right then I didn't care. My body could hardly move. I got my legs to work, though, and went up the side of the driveway into the dry grass there and into the woods where the crows came out of. There were fir branches laying around everywhere in the paths. Little branches that fell down. I never saw that when Billy was there. He must of picked them up all the time.

All around the teeter totter were gray green and brown pussy willow leaves. Curled. And crunchy when you stepped on 'em.

I sat down facing the wrong way on the teeter totter with the handle between my legs. Couldn't think. It was like what was in my head was dead or gone away somewhere.

My elbows were up on the pipe handle and my face fell into my hands. They could feel my face but my fingers weren't telling my brain what it was. I closed my eyes and just went inside. My chest was in the vice on Brew's workbench and someone was turning the handle, closing it more and more. My shoulders were gonna crack if it got any tighter.

Then in my head, I saw my dad sitting on the stump in the stockade with his face in his hands and it made me think of my plan: Be happy where you are. Do something that makes you happy.

I took a big breath and looked around at Billy's woods. The pussy willow with most of its leaves gone, the fir trees, tall like giants. Listened to the whoosh that came from their high up branches. Smelled their sad, damp Fall smell.

Then up off the teeter totter, I went over to the big fir tree where Billy hid his camels. I got down on my knees and brushed the fir needles away. Took the moss out of the little V in the roots. There was the Camel pack. I took it out.

It was empty.

That's when that place in my chest broke. My whole body shook. Then it shook again, and then again, and my voice jumped out of me every time. My throat grabbed at my voice trying to stop it but the sound came out anyway. Dirt and needles were all around me and tears were making mud in the ground under the big old fir tree. My stomach started doing that same thing it did when I threw up. It started in the bottom and slammed up against my throat like it was trying to get out. I pulled my knees up and held onto my stomach and rolled in the fir needles but I couldn't stop crying.

~

When I got back home, I snuck in the screen door and went upstairs to the bathroom. There was this weird creature looking back at me from the mirror. Like a werewolf from the movies. He had dirt and tree stuff all in his hair and brown stripes of mud all around two blue eyes staring back. I almost laughed but I was too tired.

There was a comb in the medicine chest so I started to comb my hair but was getting crud all over the basin, so I combed it over the toilet and then flushed it.

Mom must of heard because she called up the stairway, "Davey? Is that you?"

I needed to wash my face. Shoot. I wish she didn't know I was here.

"Davey?

"Davey? Can you come down here for a minute?"

"Okay, Mom. Just a minute."

I real quick wet my wash cloth and wiped my face. I looked a little better in the mirror, so I went down stairs.

~

There was something strange about the Robin's Egg Blue dinette set right then. How it surrounded Mom sitting there. How it took up so much of the kitchen.

~

"Davey, would you sit down here for a minute? I have some bad news I have to tell you," Mom said.

There was a loud noise out in the garage. I looked out the kitchen window at our old lopsided garage. Looked like it was leaning more than it used to.

"It's okay," Mom said. "Brew is getting ready to paint the car out there. He has to make room."

Mom had combed her pin curls out and put her face on as she said about putting on her makeup. But her face was kind of pale and it made her lipstick look bright red. Maybe the lipstick made her face look white. The lipstick, her face and the table. Red, white and blue. All of it really strange. Like a dream. But really she did look pale and tired. Too tired to smile.

I was tired too.

"Good grief. Where have you been? Your face looks muddy."

My stomach got kind of tight again when she said that. Like when you think somebody's gonna sock you there. I didn't want to tell her about Billy. So I just said, "In the woods."

"Well, after we talk I want you to wash your face."

"Okay," I said.

I climbed up in a chair and pulled my leg up under me.

Mom waited for me to sit in the chair and then she looked at me like Janie did. Like she was trying to see inside me. But her eyes that were most of the time sky cloud blue now were just gray fog.

They made me think that maybe I did something I shouldn't of. Like without knowing it, I made her feel really bad or something.

"Davey," she said. Her voice scratchy sounding. "You know that your Gramma Jones—Mama—was really sick when you went away to California, don't you?"

"Yeah, I know," I said.

Mom's eyes were looking real hard at her hand that was on the top of the table sliding a piece of paper around.

"Well, sweetie, after you left, your gramma got really sick and needed someone to take care of her full time."

"Uh, huh," I said.

Mom's watery eyes looked at me then and I wondered how she could see me her eyes were so full.

"So..."

Her hand picked up the piece of paper—a post card—that was on the table and tapped the edge against the Formica top. Tap, tap, tap.

"So she came to live with us."

"Gramma did?" I said. "Here?"

"Yeah. We fixed the dining room up as a bedroom for her and she stayed here so I could take care of her."

Mom put the card down and her hand went under the Formica and into the pocket of her skirt. A Kleenex fluffed out and she wiped her eyes.

"She was really sick. In a lot of pain. And she didn't know who we were anymore. John and me. She thought we were some people holding her prisoner or something."

Her eyebrows pulled down and made deep winkles in her forehead and her eyes filled up again. She wiped them dry and blew her nose in the Kleenex.

"See, the cancer affected her mind. She just wasn't the same person anymore. It was so hard."

Mom reached in her pocket again and pulled out another Kleenex. Pressed it to her eyes and just held it there.

I sat there and waited. I never saw Mom so sad like that. My stomach felt yucky again and I was scared. Scared about what she was saying.

Then she started to talk again. The Kleenex still pressed against her eyes.

"One time she even ran out the front door. She was trying to escape from these strangers who were keeping her here. That just breaks my heart. I—"

Then Mom couldn't talk. She just sat there and I could hear the refrigerator come on. She took a big breath and started again.

"I ran out after her and tried to catch her. We ended up down in the dirt in the flower bed. I had to get Craig's daddy next door to help me get her back to bed."

It was like a nightmare in my head. My beautiful Gramma Jones in her floaty white night gown running out the door and Mom tackling her in the flower bed. Pulling her down in the dirt. For the second time that day, somehow I couldn't get any air to breathe.

Mom took the Kleenex away from her eyes and rolled it in her hand. Her eyes had red all in the white part. Her other hand reached out for my hand on the table. It was so cold it didn't feel like Mom.

My eyes looked down at the red sparkle—eight carat, French cut.

"Sweetheart, the reason I'm telling you this is I want you to know, because she was so sick, she wasn't the same person anymore. She wasn't your Gramma Belle. She wasn't my Mama. She was in so much pain and her mind was gone. So what happened was for the best."

My voice said, "What happened, Mom?" but I really didn't want her to tell me.

"Honey, she died. It was a blessing. She went to sleep and didn't wake up."

I could feel Mom's hand cold around mine. There was a gurgle from the refrigerator. The clock on the mantel over the fireplace ticked in the front room. Then there was Brew out in the garage pounding on something.

"I'm so sorry to have to give you all this bad news just when you get home but you need to know what's happening."

Her thumb was rubbing the top of my hand slow. Almost the same beat as the clock ticking in the front room. Tick-tick, tick-tick. Rub-rub, rub-rub.

~

Then Mom and me, we were at another table, a little table just big enough for two of us. A car horn honked on Broadway outside the window. Dishes clinked around us. There was soft candle light, kind of golden, and some violin music you could hardly hear. Gramma was standing beside the little table in a dress with wide shoulders. It was silver and it sparkled when she moved. Shimmery like a silver snake. Her hair was short and silver too with little waves that rippled down the sides. She turned the wide shoulders away from us to a lady that had a brown fox with gold eyes hanging over her shoulders snarling like Frank. The lady said, "Isabelle, how nice to see you." Then a man in a black suit and bow tie said to Gramma, "Madam, you're wanted on the telephone" and he danced away fast with the fox and the lady.

"Sorry, you two. A crisis every minute in this joint," Gramma said. "Have to go."

Gramma's gray blue eyes turned to me. Her eyes were bright stars and there was dirt in her hair and dead flowers hung by her ears.

"Davey, I love your singing. You are a real artist. You'll make your Grandma Belle proud."

Then Pop picked her up and carried her away through the restaurant. Her dress was white clouds and floated in a little trail after them.

~

Brew dropped something heavy out in the garage and Mom was saying, "It really was for the best, honey. Better than all that pain."

Mom needed for me to say it. I didn't want to. I loved my gramma so much. I liked how she liked me. I liked how she made me feel like I could do anything. How could I feel like that without her?

But I said it. "Yeah Mom, I guess it was."

The clock ticked in the front room. My leg was going to sleep sitting on it. Kitty jumped up on the kitchen window sill and scratched herself. Thump, thump, thump on the window.

"Honey, that's not all," Mom said. "Scotty sent this post card."

Mom let go of my hand and slid the post card over to me. It was the penny post card he got from me the day it rained.

"Dear Mom," it said. "Dad needs me right now. I don't think Lou Ella and him are going to stay together. So I won't be coming up to go to school this year. Scott."

I wadded the card up in my hand. Watched President Jefferson's green face crumple in my hand. Mashed it up tight as I could get it.

Part Three

Let's Pretend

28

Non Cents

Skipping down the sidewalk in front of Sunny Lea, my feet were like dancing in the air more than on the ground. I threw my notebook up in the air. Yelled, "Yea." It went spinning up over my head. Right then, on the last day of second grade, I was just about as happy as I was scared of something new on the first day.

School was over. We had the whole summer to play. Then the note book came back down. Couldn't see how to catch it 'cause I was right under it. This big thing spinning down at me. I ducked. It sharp hit my shoulder, whacked me in the side of the head and bounced on to the sidewalk.

Sunny Lea laughed.

"You're really silly," she said shaking her head. Her arms crossed over her note book she had in front of her.

I rubbed at the hurt in my shoulder. "Well, aren't you happy?"

"I guess. But I like school. I'm gonna miss it."

I picked up my notebook. Lucky my papers didn't fall out. The ring thing on the back was bent a little and one corner was smooshed from the cement sidewalk. With my fingers, I tried to smooth it back down like it was supposed to be. But the blue cloth was torn a little bit, kind of ragged, and gray cardboard was poking out where the corner was smooshed.

"Look what you did to your notebook," Sunny Lea said. Her mouth all puckered and her eyebrows pulled down to her blue eyes.

"Well, it looks better this way." I held it up for her to see. "More used."

But it really didn't. I always tried to keep my school stuff nice. But Sunny Lea, she thought school stuff was like the Bible or something. Anyway, I was happy school was out and didn't want to feel bad about my notebook. It was bad enough I couldn't catch the stupid thing.

It was spring, the sun was shining and school was out for the whole summer. We only had to go half a day that last day. And best of all, Robby and Joey were going to come from The Dalles to spend a lot of the summer with us.

Sunny Lea and me, we came to the middle of Multnomah right then. Past the mom and pop grocery store. Right across the street in front of us was the Rexall drug store where the soda fountain was. We crossed the street and I saw Allen and Beverly from my class go in the front door.

"I wish I had some money for an ice cream cone," I said.

It was a special day. One to celebrate.

"My mom and dad only let me have an ice cream cone on Saturdays," Sunny Lea said. "My dad and me come down here when he gets home from logging camp and he buys me whatever flavor I want."

Her lips were tight together and her head nodded up and down saying yes. She liked her dad a lot.

"That's pretty nice of him," I said. "It must be nice to have a dad that does that."

I had a picture in my head then of Brew and me walking to Multnomah to buy ice cream. Him holding my hand. Talking to each other. My throat got burny then 'cause that would never happen.

I looked in the men's store window next door. Like I was looking at a shirt in there.

"I have to come and get my own ice cream. But I don't have to wait 'til Saturdays," I said. "Just when Mom says I can."

~

When I got home, Kitty scooted out of the kitchen and out the back door when I came in. A nice big sandwich was on the table for me with lettuce and tomato in it like I like and a pan of soup on the stove. Mom was sitting in the sunshine at the robin's egg blue dinette set reading a book.

"Hey, honey, you have a good morning?" Her eyes still reading. Still thinking about the book.

She took the library due-date-card-thing out of the paper pocket in the back of the book. Stuck it in her place and put the book on the table. Patted it. Her swooped up glasses all slid down on her nose.

"Last day," I said. "Now I have all summer."

Mom pushed her glasses up to look at me.

"You seem pretty happy."

She was right. There was still a buzzy feeling in me. Made me want to jump up and down.

She got up and turned the knob on the stove.

"I can't wait for Robby and Joey to come," I said.

Mom's head went back and she laughed. Big laugh. Not little heh, hehs. Big ha, has. Brew calls it her hearty laugh.

"You always look forward to Robby coming down and two days after he gets here, the two of you are fighting like cats and dogs."

She poured the tomato soup into a bowl. Put it on the table between the sandwich and a spoon.

"Oh Mom. We were just little kids then. We're older now."

Her one eyebrow went up like she does and she looked at me out of the side of her eyes.

"Hmmm," she said. "We'll see. Now eat your lunch before it gets cold."

I was still thinking about the Rexall drugstore though and since it was the last day of school and all, I said, "After lunch, can I have a dime for an ice cream cone?"

She looked at me with her eyebrows all scooched together.

"You want to walk all the way back to Multnomah for an ice cream cone?"

"Yeah it's really a special day."

Her shoulders went up and down then and she said, "Well, I guess. If you want to."

~

I stuck the dime in my pocket and held my arms out at the top of the moo-cow hill. Let myself fall frontward until I had to run. The wind blowing my hair up. Cool by my ears. Felt a cape on my shoulders like Superman. Or maybe a knight or gladiator with a sword too. That's something I would do this summer. Find me a cape.

My legs stretched out over the holes of dried out mud puddles and mounds of old mud. Past Sunny Lea's cow eating grass. Everything quiet flying by me. Queen Ann's lace and wild sweet pea. Ran half way up the other side until I had to walk. It was so much fun to run on moo cow hill. The big hill down did most the work.

Up at the top of the hill I stuck my hands in my pockets. Felt the dime there. Took it out. It was new and shiny. One with the woman who had wings on the side of her head. That would be neat. Have wings on your head. Never thought of that before. Sometimes I could fly in my dreams at night but I had wings on my shoulders like angels or sometimes just my arms worked for wings. One time I had this really neat little square platform that flew. Just a little bigger than my feet. It had a flag pole in the front corner by my right hand to hang onto with a flag flying from it. A triangle flag like on a boat. I was flying in front with all my friends flying behind me on little platforms that had flags too. Sunny Lea and her friend Donna. Craig and Dale. Gary and his little brother, Jack. Like they were my soldiers and I was the leader. That was a neat dream.

I tossed the dime in the air. When it came down, I tried to catch it but it fell on the dirt road. Tried again. Same thing. My face got all hot and I stamped my foot. Made me mad I couldn't catch.

Maybe I could learn though. If I tried enough times when nobody could see me.

I tossed the dime in the air again and reached my hand out to catch it. It hit me in the forehead. Felt the edge and then it plinked in the gravel. So I bent down and picked it up out of the road again.

Somehow, I just couldn't tell where it would fall.

I tried again. It hit my nose. Could of hit me in the eye. But it didn't matter. Think I had my eyes shut.

Then I had an idea. If I moved back just a little, I could catch it with my mouth.

Bingo. Tasted metal on my tongue.

Got it. That was neat.

I tried it again. Bingo again.

Once more. I started to laugh. This was so neat. I caught it with my mouth. It clicked on my teeth. Slippery round dime.

Then nothing. It was gone.

Laughing was a mistake.

My tongue looked around my mouth. Nothing. The dime went right down my throat.

Oh my God. I could feel it going down.

It was then it hit me. Now I couldn't have my ice cream cone.

Poop!

It was such a good day at first. Now, I had a dime inside me. And I had to go home and tell Mom. My eyes were getting burny and wet.

How dumb. I couldn't catch anything. Swallowed my stupid dime just trying to learn how.

~

Back home, Mom said, "You swallowed your dime? My God, Davey. Why did you have it in your mouth? I thought you were old enough to know better."

Her face was red and her glasses were slipped down. You could tell she was mad.

But I never told anybody about me not being able to catch. And catching with my mouth was pretty dumb. So I didn't tell her why it was in my mouth.

She let out a big breath.

"Well, just stay here. Don't go anywhere. I'm going to call Doctor Brunkow."

I sat down at the robin's egg blue dinette set. It was all quiet after Mom went in the front room to call the doctor. On the table, Mom's book was smooth under my hand. The King's General. Daphne du Something. The refrigerator gurgled. I could hear the clock on the fire place mantel ticking. Pretty soon, I heard Mom's voice on the phone. Kind of high sounding. Singy. Like she was trying not to be upset.

She came back in the kitchen then and said, "His nurse said you should eat a piece of bread. She said it will probably stick to the dime and guide it through."

"Guide it through?" I said.

Big breath out. "So it will come out in your B.M."

My face got hot. I never thought about that. It wasn't gone then.

"You'll have to do your big duties in a pan or something until I find it," she said.

"Find it?"

"Yes. Of course. I'm going to have to look in your poop until we find it."

Oh boy.

Even my ears were burny then.

~

In my bedroom, about a week later, I could hear voices coming from down stairs. I ran down the hall by the stairway and looked through the window out front. Robby and Joey's aunt and uncle's car was out in front.

They were here.

I ran down the stairs two at a time and into the front room. Robby and Joey were on the davenport all dressed up. Brew's sister, Eva, their aunt was talking to Mom and their uncle Fred was sitting on the chair by the phone. They all stopped talking when I ran into the room.

Then the uncle said, "Hi Davey. How're things?"

At first, I didn't know what to say. Then I said the "thing" that was most important. "I swallowed a dime on the way to the drugstore and then last week I went and bought an ice cream cone with it."

Mom looked over at me. Her face all red.

"Davey, I don't think they want to hear about that."

"But," he asked, "how'er-"

"Mercy, what on earth?" Eva said. Her eyebrows way up and holding her breath.

Mom looked mad. Her eyebrows scrunched down. "Why don't all you kids go outside and play?"

Robby and Joey jumped off the davenport. Yelled, "Okay" and headed out the front door.

I ran out after them.

Heard Mom say, "His first anatomy lesson."

Then everybody laughed.

29

Paint Pants

Every Saturday Robbie and me, we got a dime to go to the movies in Multnomah.

As long as I promised Mom to keep the dime out of my mouth. Sometimes if I had a nickel left over from my twenty five cents allowance, I could get popcorn or a box of Black Crows or Good 'n Plenty. Licorice is my favorite.

On the first Saturday Robby and me went to the movies that summer, we came home around the back way. Past the Baldwin's and up the hill to our house. The last Black Crow wouldn't come out of the box. I couldn't get it out in the movies 'cause it's kind of dark in there and I couldn't see. Really, everything gets gray or black and shimmery like it's moving when the movie's on. It makes it really spooky if you look anywhere but at the movie. My finger could feel the kind of sticky gum drop though, so I tried to get it unstuck not looking. But my finger was just too short. So I was walking along with Robby after the movie, holding the box up to my eye looking at the Black Crow stuck in the middle. 'Cause my finger couldn't get it out from the top or the bottom.

Walking along the bumpy dirt road with my eye in the Black Crow box that was jerking up and down on my face, I almost didn't see Arthur Baldwin with his arms full of wood.

Robby had his eye on that wood though.

There was a real piney smell in the warm air. Like in the woods on a hot day. But more. It was coming from the Baldwin's big pile of wood somebody delivered.

"That's pretty nice wood you got there, Mr. Baldwin. Almost good enough to build something with."

That was the way Robby did. If he had an idea, he never said it right out.

Always started somewhere else so you wouldn't know what he was thinking. If he wanted some of Arthur's wood, he wouldn't just ask.

"Sure is a job, this wood," Arthur said.

I hardly never saw Arthur without a suit on. Always with a vest, a white shirt and tie. Getting ready for a student. Today he had on an old hat and a kind of yellowy white shirt. Cuffs rolled up on his shirt and pants too. He put the wood he was carrying in his garage and took a big hanky out of his pocket. Wiped his forehead. Then his neck. His face pretty red.

"You say you want to build something from my wood?"

Robby's face got all pink. His brown eyes looked up at the house away from Arthur. Like he got caught doing something he shouldn't of.

"I just said it looks good enough to build something."

Maybe Arthur was getting a little deaf. Or maybe he could tell Robby really did want some of his wood. Hard to tell.

"You want to build something, you boys are welcome to take some," he said.

Robby didn't say anything. His head just quick turned to me. His brown eyes looked at me hard like maybe it was my idea. I just looked back at Robby. Shrugged my shoulders. Robby started it. It was his idea. Whatever that was. Then I felt bad. He was my brother. Step-brother.

"Could be fun," I said.

Robby stuck the point of his collar in his mouth. Chewed. Looked kind of mad.

Something was prickly on the back of my neck and my eyes had to look away. He was still that little kid that used to break other kid's toys. Step on their toy cars. Smash their dolls.

Then he squinted up his brown eyes at Arthur.

"We don't got any money."

"Money?" Arthur said. Then laughed a little bit. Kind of ducked his head. Made his face tight. But I could see he laughed. Been around him a lot.

"Oh, you don't have to pay me," he said.

He took his hat off. Wiped the inside with his hanky.

"Tell you what, though. You take what pieces you want and then come back on Monday morning and help me put some of this in. I'm bushed. Not going to do any more now."

"Hey, okay," we both said.

That sounded like fun. We were just about run out of ideas of what to do, Robby and me. Stacking wood sounded pretty fun.

The wood must of come from a saw mill. Brew's dad, Grampa Charlie, used to work in a saw mill. Brew told me one time, when they cut up a tree, there's some of that tree won't make lumber. The outside still has some bark on it or round edges like a tree. That was this wood.

Looking through the pile of wood, Robby and me found five pieces for each of us. Mine felt really neat on my hand. Smooth and soft and they had a nice smell. All five pieces about as big as a seat on a chair or a little table top. All of them about the same size. Square and nice and smooth. We told Arthur we'd be back on Monday morning to help and headed up the hill to our house.

I punched Robby easy in the arm. Tried to let him know what he was thinking was all right with me. That he didn't have to keep stuff secret. Like we could be friends.

"Pretty good idea of yours we build something," I said.

He pulled away. Looked around at me like he was shocked. His eyes too wide. Jaw way down. Still pretending. Like I might believe he never had some plan in his head. Then his face got red like he was mad.

"Not my idea. That old man can't hear very well, can he? Crazy old coot."

"He's pretty smart," I said. "And he can hear better'n you think."

Arthur was my friend. It wasn't right for Robby to call him names. He was just mad at Arthur 'cause he couldn't fool him. At me too. But Robby's always like that. Always got something going in his head he doesn't want you to know. Wants to keep it secret. Thinks he can fool you. But he's not very good at pretending. His eyes always look over to the side or somewhere else or when he does look right at you, he's not really there behind his eyes.

Right then he had something going on in his head again. Chewing on his collar.

"Hope Dad'll let us use some tools," he said.

Ever since when I got into Brew's wood tools and chiseled the basement floor, Mom and Brew tell me an awful lot not to touch things that don't belong to me. So I told Robby I didn't want to say anything about tools to Brew.

When we got home, Brew was out in the garage working on the car and Robby said he would ask him for the tools. So we headed for the garage. Outside the door, Robby stuck out his arm in front of me like a cross-walk monitor at school.

"You wait out here," he said. "Let me talk to him."

Like I said, always got something going on in his head.

I walked around to the side. Waited in the back yard by the side of the garage. Put my ear up to it so I could hear. Brew must of been under the car though 'cause he was talking real loud. Even without putting my ear there I could hear him.

"What is it, Son?" Brew said.

He always called Robby, Son. He called me Davey. Not Son. But I guess that was right. He'd have to call me, Step-son. That woulda sounded pretty dumb.

"How you doin', Step-son?"

Robby said, "Well, Dad, I got some wood from that old Mr. Baldwin. From his wood pile? And I was thinking I might like to build something. But I'll need some tools."

When Robby talked to Brew, he pretty much left me out of it, so it'd be just him and his Dad, I guess.

I squatted down beside the garage. Picked up a stick there. All the skin was peeled off. Smooth, white wood with some little nobly bumps on it. Poked in the dirt with it. I was all by myself. My throat all burny.

"Yeah?" Brew said inside the garage.

I could almost see Robby chewing on his collar.

"So I was wondering if I could use some hammers and nails."

A worm popped out of the dirt in front of me. Stretched out on the ground. Wiggling. Kitty rubbed up against my fanny. Then along my leg. Sniffed at the worm.

I wished Robby could be more like Kitty. Friendly. Instead of more like Mrs. Allen's dog. Always behind that fence. Always mean.

When I first saw that dog on the way home from school, I went up to her fence and talked real nice to him. He just backed up and showed his teeth growling at me. Mrs. Allen told me I might as well give up, he just wasn't friendly. I kept trying though. Everyday I passed her house, I tried to talk to that dog but he got meaner and meaner. Barking and snarling. I was afraid he might jump over the fence and get me. Finally, I started going home a different way.

But I really didn't want to give up on Robby.

Then I heard Brew say, "Sure, Son. Don't see why not, since you asked. As long as you take care of my tools and put 'em back when you're finished. Don't want you kids in my tools 'less you ask. Okay?"

I was pretty sure Brew would say yes to Robby. Brew would of just told me no.

Brew made grunting noises like he was getting out from under the car. I didn't like being outside the garage alone so I threw the stick down and went in the garage too.

Brews face was all over black grease smudges and his tee shirt too where he wiped his hands. He had on his dirty cords and just the top part out of an old hat so's not to get grease in his hair.

"Where's your wood?"

"Basement." Robby said.

Brew smiled big at Robby. Then he spread his hands open, all over black, and looked down at them. Like he didn't see me there. Picked up a rag off his work bench and twisted his fingers in it one at a time trying to get that black grease off.

"See how nice Robby asked for the tools?" he said to me not looking up. A tight smile on his mouth and a little snort through his nose.

A smile was on Robby's face too and he tapped his foot on the dirt floor. I looked at my shoes. Kitty meowed. Curled herself around my legs.

Then Brew said, "Let's go see what you got."

Robby and me showed Brew our neat stack of the ten little table tops or chair seats on the basement floor and how we figured we could put the pieces together to make two chairs. One piece for a seat, one for a back and two or three underneath to hold it up like legs.

Little Joey came jumping down the basement stairs like thunder right then. Both feet jumped down two wood steps at a time and he ended up running at us with his red hair standing straight up, his blue green eyes shining like head lights in the dim basement. He plowed into Robby but Robby just pushed him off with his hand. Kept talking like this happened all the time. Like Joey was just a pest.

Joey stood up straight then. Looked at the little stack of wood on the floor. His hands on his hips trying to stick his chest out like he was a big construction worker figuring out a project. Only stuck his stomach out though. His teeth biting his bottom lip trying not to laugh. Like he could see how funny he looked.

In a second though, his face changed like you could see him thinking.

"I wanna build something too," he said.

Robby looked down at him, his mouth all pulled together.

"We only got this wood here. Not enough."

Joey only came up to Robby's belt. His fist hit him in the hip.

"I wanna."

Brew looked at us all, that deep line between his eyes like he wasn't very comfortable. His dark eyes back and forth at us like the daddy Robin flying around the baby bird that fell out of the nest. Not knowing what to do. Like somebody should do something.

So I said, "Maybe we don't need all our pieces."

"Yeah," Joey said and grabbed two pieces off the stack.

"Hey," Robby said and started to go after Joey.

"Wait a minute Robby," Brew said. "You only want two pieces, Joey?"

Joey grinned. His two front teeth gone.

"Yup," he said and tucked the two pieces of wood under his arms looking happy.

"Well then," Brew said. Big breath out. "You guys could put just two pieces underneath instead of three."

Robby didn't look too happy. His head went down and he scuffed his tennis shoes on the cement floor.

"Oh, okay." he said.

Brew gave us two hammers and some nails and showed us how to put the wood in his vice to hold it while we nailed the other piece to it.

Joey decided to just nail his two pieces together on one edge like an "L."

"I got a chair too," he said. He put it down on the cement floor and sat on one piece and leaned up against the other piece nailed on the back letting a big breath out like he just sat down after a hard day at work. Then pretended he was smoking a cigar. Holding it in his two fingers. Putting it up to his mouth. Smoke blowing out of a little round oh in his lips. Joey was always being a clown. Trying to make us laugh. Trying harder not to laugh at himself.

They always worked, those goofy little jokes of his. Joey never had any trouble getting attention. Brew couldn't pretend he wasn't there. Like he did me sometimes. Brew was laughing.

"Don't you want me to find you some wood around here for some chair legs?"

Joey was still leaning back. Enjoying his cigar. His eyes closed like he was going to take a nap.

"Don't need no chair legs. My legs are pretty short anyway. I can stretch 'em out like my friend, Majetti."

Brew's eyebrows went up to his widow's peak. A surprised look like he just swallowed a dime.

"Who?"

"My friend, Mr. Majetti," he said and blew out a big cloud of smoke.

Brew looked over at Robby and me working on our chairs at his work bench. His eyebrows still up, arms spread open.

Both of us put our shoulders up and shook our heads.

We had a neighbor, across the street down to the moo-cow hill a little, named Mr. Majetti. Nobody ever saw him. Except maybe Sunny Lea. She said he was always complaining about pigs 'cause Petunia's pig pen was right on the other side of his back fence. Joey couldn't of seen him. Nobody did.

"How do you know Mr. Majetti?" Brew said. His dark eyebrows down, worried looking. Like he did when Robby or Joey got hurt or something.

Joey didn't open his eyes. Just stubbed his cigar out on the cement floor. "He's my friend."

Brew looked over at us. His eyebrows still way up. His shoulders and arms went up too. Like he had no idea what Joey was talking about. But he was going to let it go.

"You might want to paint those chairs when you get them finished," he said. "I got some old paint you can use."

He gave us a can of paint and some brushes. Super neat paint. It got us really excited when we opened it up. Silver. We were gonna have silver chairs. The can said Aluminum. Robby couldn't say that though. He could only say alunimum. Robby did that a lot. Got his letters mixed up. So we called it silver.

Pretty soon Mom came down to see what we were doing.

"You can't paint the chairs with those clothes on," she said. "You'll get paint all over yourselves."

"Aw, Mom," I said.

She always did that. Well, maybe not always. But when I got really excited about something, she would make it hard to be excited.

She thought for a minute. Her eyes kind of went inside. Then she said, "Well, I'll get you something to cover up your clothes then." And she went back upstairs.

When we sat on our chairs, they kind of moved from one side to the other like they might fall over. So Brew put some little braces beside our leg pieces to make them stand still.

Mom came back down with three dresses over her arm. Kind of soft, drapey old house dresses. One with spots and the other two with little flowers.

"Okay you guys, here are some old dresses of mine you can wear over your clothes so you won't ruin them,' she said and pulled one of the dresses open in front of her.

Robby and me looked at each other. Robby's eyes big like mine.

"Dresses?"

Mom nodded and smiled her lips tight at us. Put the fist of her empty arm on her hip like there wasn't going to be any argument.

"You'll be like French artists. Painters there wear smocks over their clothes."

Joey got up off his "chair" on the floor and put his fists on his hips. His jaw went tight and he said, "I ain't wearin' no dress."

Brew turned around and looked at Joey standing there with his little three year old legs set apart and his belly stuck out like he does. Brew kind of snorted trying not to laugh. Like we all were.

"Don't worry, Sport, I've got some old pants you can wear."

Joey smiled and bobbed his head. Punched his little fist in the air.

"All right. Paaint Paants." His lips puckered and exploding on the "P"s. "You guys gotta wear paint dresses. But I'm gonna wear ma Paaint Paants."

~

Joey was like that—even at three years old—always fascinated by little things, new things, words like Majetti and Paint Pants.

30

Chair Pictures

The chairs looked funny. Not funny, Ha, Ha. Just silver. Silver wood. It was Monday morning and the paint was dry. We could sit on them but they were just plain. Plain and silver. They needed something.

Robby and me planned to go to Multnomah and find something to put on them after we helped Arthur Baldwin.

Arthur already was started stacking up the wood against the wall in his garage when we got there. So we got right in helping him. We told him about the chairs and he laughed. Shaking his head back and forth. Like he couldn't imagine his wood painted silver. Said he was real glad he could help out with the wood. Then he said, decals. Maybe we could find some decals to put on them. We didn't know what decals were though. So he told us pictures. Some pictures to stick onto the wood. You could buy them at the Variety Store. My favorite store in Multnomah. That sounded pretty nice. I started seeing pictures in my head that maybe we could buy. Maybe horses. Or mountains. Even some pictures of flowers would be nice.

Arthur's garage was like ours. Separate. Not part of our house like in the new houses. But his was real clean and neat. And he didn't have a car. Our garage had dirt for a floor and leaned a little bit sideways. Up against the backside of Craig's garage next door. So it wouldn't fall over. You could only see that from the backyard. But from there it looked like the garage in that thing people said, "There was a crooked man who lived in a crooked house." And it was full of car.

Arthur's was very neat though. His lawn mower against the wall. Clean and shiny. Like brand new. And all his garden tools, a shovel, a hoe, pitchfork and rake, all on the wall like never used. But he had a big garden in back of his house I could see from Scotty's old bedroom upstairs in our house. Or that time I was on the roof. Lots of times I could smell the grass he was cutting, even hear the little whirs his lawnmower made when he pushed it while Mrs. Baldwin and me looked at magazine pictures in their front room. So his lawnmower wasn't new. Neither were his other tools. He was just neat.

Robby and me watched how he stacked the wood like he was building a nice wall. Then we did it too. But after a little while my part started to lean like our garage. Almost fell over. So Arthur showed me it was because I stacked all my pieces right on top of each other. That was like Scotty. Teaching me. He said they wouldn't do that if I stacked one in the middle of the two underneath. Like a brick wall, he said. I never thought about that before, but it worked. That was neat.

Robby looked at me sideways though. His eyes rolling around, and his head shaking. Like he thought Arthur was crazy. But Arthur's garage felt nice to me. Nice inside. That good feeling you get when things are clean and new. It was nice to be in his garage. Everything so neat. It was comfortable and homey like a house. Not like our old crooked garage with the dirt floor and things so dirty you didn't want to touch anything.

Arthur didn't have that much wood so helping him was pretty easy. Took us about an hour. Not so easy for an old man though. When we finished with the wood, Arthur handed Robby a broom.

"Only got two brooms," he said. "So I'll use one. Just sweep up and we'll be finished."

Robby looked at me. Eyebrows and shoulders way up. A big breath out when Arthur started to sweep. I was kind of jittery just standing there not doing anything.

So I said, "Mr. Baldwin, let me sweep."

Big smile from him.

"Well, all right then," his deep voice said with almost a laugh in it. You could tell he liked me asking.

Eyes rolling around from Robby.

Arthur handed me the broom and touched the back of my head and neck with his big hand. Kind of a pat. Made my stomach feel kind of warmish and good inside.

Arthur was sure a nice man. Robby just didn't know.

We swept all the little pieces of wood and bark out of the garage. It looked so good then, I kept going and swept off his driveway too. Just a little patch of cement.

"You boys worked so hard," Arthur said when we finished, "I want to give you something for your trouble."

His hand went into his pocket and he pulled out a hand full of change.

"But you already gave us wood," I said.

"Oh yes. But now you need some decals. Perhaps you can use this to decorate your chairs."

It was his deep principal voice. Arthur always seemed to know what was best for kids. But he didn't talk to you like you were a little kid. His hand reached out to Robby.

"You seem to be the organizer here. You can divide it with your brother."

Robby was chewing on his collar like he does, so it was hard to hear him say thanks. But he did. And I thanked Arthur too.

We went down the road, back the way we came from the movies on Saturday.

Robby was busy counting the money Arthur put in his hand.

So I said, "How much d'he give us?"

His eyes were down over his hand full of change and he just shook his head. His lips counting the money.

I walked along beside him. Watching. My shoulder next to his. Trying to see the money Robby had in his hand. Tried to guess how much. My feet kept stepping down into old dried up mud puddles though banging my top teeth down on my bottom teeth. Almost bit my tongue.

Finally we got to some pavement where it was smooth.

Robby looked up and said, "Here's your half."

He was only six months older than me and we were the same size but he always acted like he thought he was bigger and older than me.

He dumped some change in my hand. His eyes looking away from mine.

I counted a whole dollar. A quarter, two dimes, nine nickels and ten pennies. Put them in my pocket. That was a lot more than a whole month's allowance. Made me giggly inside. They felt smooth and the nickels heavy sliding through my fingers in there.

Then we were on a dirt road that should have been a road but hardly anybody used it anymore. Just dried up mud and raggedy weeds. It went onto a path that went through a kind of swampy place before you got to the old railroad tracks that go under the viaduct. On the other side of the old railroad tracks is the back of Multnomah—the town.

"So he gave us two dollars?"

Robby didn't look at me.

"Yeah, I guess," he said and shrugged his shoulders.

Robby just walking beside me. Chewing his collar. Not looking at me, like there was something going on in his head again he wanted to keep secret.

Maybe his secret was Arthur gave us more. Maybe Robby didn't know how to count money or something and that was his secret.

I was tired of him always keeping secrets so my voice came out a little bit mad.

"What do you mean, you guess?"

"Well, it ain't mim- mim- miminun wage, you know." His face all spotty pink.

"What?" I said. I couldn't figure out what he said. What he said or what the word was.

"What're you griping about? You got yer half, didn't ya?" he said loud and turned his body to me. But not his eyes. They looked over my head.

I was busy watching Robby's eyes and tripped on a root growing in the path. My voice wanted to holler at him then but I didn't let it.

"I just want to know how much Arthur gave us."

We were in the swampy part now. Little scrubby bushes kind of sick looking growing in the mud.

He stood still in the path looking mean at me. "Oh, Arthur, Arthur. Yer stupid friend, Arthur. What difference it make how much we got?" he yelled. Red coming up his neck to his ears. He was really there then behind his eyes looking at me.

I got mad then. 'Cause I knew he was lying to me. I really didn't like it that he thought I was stupid. I grabbed at his hand that had the money tight in a fist.

"Let me see," I said.

He jerked away from me and stepped in the swampy mud beside the path. His foot slid and he almost went down on his knee. A sound then was like it was trapped in his throat broke through and came out like a scream, then a howl like a dog. His arm snapped up and a shower of dimes and nickels and quarters flew from his hand in a spray across the swamp going everywhere. His face turned to me all twisted and red. His teeth snarled back like Mrs. Allen's dog spitting at me.

"You," he screamed. "You want everything. You got my dad. What else ya want?"

~

The words came at me like they hit me in the face. I couldn't see anything then. Only white. He was there in front of me but I couldn't see him. Only white. My face and hands, and my stomach too, felt like I just went outside in the snow. They were so cold. Like I was holding ice sickles.

Then the white...slow went away. Like fog in the sunshine. And I saw him then. Running back up the road the way we came. Gone.

There were no sounds around me. I couldn't hear anything. Everything still. Sick little bushes growing out of the slimy mud. It smelled strong. Yucky. A little like garbage. Little like poop. The old railroad tracks at the end of the path. The blank dirty backs of the buildings in Multnomah on the other side of the rusty tracks.

Nothing was in my head. No sound. Then.

The Variety Store. Decals.

The cold was going away too. Like the white.

Little birds ticking, clicking in the bushes.

I felt better, the Variety Store in my head.

~

The railroad tracks came at me slow up the path. All the little birds flew up at once. The sound like flipping pages real fast in a book. My shoes went up over the rusty rail, walked in the gravel and gum wrappers between the ties. There was a smell of tar. Then the other rail. I went up the short little hill into Multnomah. Then down the street to the Variety Store.

The Variety Store is my favorite store in Multnomah. When you walk in, a little bell rings over the door like Dad's shop in Nevada City and the people that work there smile at you. Then there's the smell. It's a lot of smells all mixed up. I used to think it was the cards, 'cause when I bought valentine cards for everyone in my class, they smelled that way. But the store always smells that way. Not just Valentine's day. It's cards and tools and wax on the floors and cellophane wrapping, plastic and rubber mats and candy all mixed up together. The tables up in front where you come in are covered with all kinds of things. I can always find a birthday present there for Mom. Last time, I bought her a real nice glass ashtray. You can get things for your kitchen and your bathroom and for your bedroom. Even things for your car. But I didn't know what decals were or where they would be. If they were for your bedroom or your kitchen or what. And it's easy to get lost there. Especially in the back where they have aisles with high shelves not just tables like in front. It's almost like the fun house at the Oaks Park. But more fun.

So I made my face smile. Tried to look like a big person even if the counter came up as high as me and asked the lady at the cash register, "You got any decals?"

I felt kind of stupid. But there were so many different things there. Maybe everybody has to ask.

She was a chubby lady with gray hair. Not a movie star kind of lady. More like my friend Gary's Mormon mom but this lady had rosy cheeks not a pale washed out face and when she looked down over the counter at me, she had a nice smile. Her eyes went inside for a minute. Like she might find the decals in there.

Then she said, "Babies," and smiled down at me again. Her cheeks real round on her face. "There in Babies. Aisle ten."

I must of looked lost because she came out from behind her cash register and held her hand out. It made me feel kind of silly to take her hand but that was what she wanted me to do so I did.

"Here they are," she said. "Just pick what you want and bring them up to me, sweetheart. Okay?"

Her glasses were kind of steamy behind when she smiled down at me then. Maybe just dirty.

I said okay and she went away.

These weren't what I had in my head. There was a pink giraffe with purple spots on his neck. A blue teddy bear with his arms stuck straight out to the sides. He had a goofy smile that made me laugh. A yellow dog that didn't look so babyish would be all right for Robby. But these were not the pictures I had in my head when Arthur told us decals. Some horses running in a field or Mount Hood all white with snow and Lost Lake, blue underneath it or maybe even Crater Lake was what I saw in my head.

Then I saw a fuzzy smiling orange lion. It was still like for a baby but a silver chair with a lion on the part where your back goes would be pretty neat for Robby. He could put the dog on the seat. The teddy bear and the giraffe would be okay for me. They were twenty five cents apiece so that was what I had. One dollar.

I took them to the rosy cheek lady.

"Don't you have any other kind?" I said.

She looked real sad at me. Droopy eyebrows. Cheeks.

"No, I'm sorry, Sweetie. That's it."

"Okay," I said.

I gave her the money and she slid them into a little flat paper sack.

"Come again," she said and her cheeks went up again.

"Yeah," I said.

~

When I was on the path walking through the swampy part again, I heard Robby's voice hollering in my head. Like what he said was trapped in that slimy place between the sick bushes.

"You got my dad. What else ya want?"

Robby just didn't know.

Then that old voice always inside my head, sometimes in my dreams. Me standing in front of my new dad for a good night kiss. He jumps up instead. Widow's peak really black. His black eyes looking down from way up there. Arm out straight. His big hand like he's pushing me away. His big voice pushing me away too. Saying, "Men shake hands."

I stood still on the path in that same place where it was quiet before. Those voices bouncing loud in my head. My throat and my eyes all burny. Chest tight. The sick little bushes all blurry though my eyes. Voices and pictures making me dizzy.

Robby yelling, "You got my dad."

My head spinning, *His dad. My dad. My brother, Scotty. Billy.*

I could feel some crying in me. It made me mad.

I didn't do any of this.

I stamped my foot. My tennis shoe hit that stinky mud and slid. My knee went all the way down. Down in the stink. My face got hot and I screamed, "It's not like chiseling the basement floor, for cripe sake."

Then I screamed up at those bushes and the white sky even louder, "It isn't my fault."

It made my throat hurt like I swallowed a rock. But somewhere else way inside me hurt more. More than when I fell on the cement wall. Almost put my eye out. Somewhere inside me it really hurt. I couldn't tell where.

My feet tried to stand up. Slip, slide. Stinky mud. I grabbed at one of the little bushes with my hand that didn't have the paper sack in it. Got up.

I was gulping air. All over hot. Taste of salt and snot in my mouth.

Then I had to get out of there. Away from that place. If I got away from there, I'd be okay. My legs started to run. Tripped over that dumb root again. Almost dropped the sack. But I kept running.

I wanted to get home and show Robby the decals.

31

Henry Aldrich

Robby liked the decals. Our chairs looked finished with the blue teddy bear and pink and purple giraffe on mine. The lion and dog on his. Mom helped little Joey with a color paper cut-out of a baseball cap to glue on the back of his "chair."

Robby and me, we never talked about the money he threw in the swamp mud or what he yelled at me. But Robby smiled more. Was more friendly. His eyes looked at me more.

We both loved to listen to Henry Aldrich on the radio. Couldn't wait to hear his mom call him at the beginning of the program every week. "Henryeeee. Henry Aldrich." Like Mom called me out on our back porch when I was outside playing.

One day when Robby and me were playing, we decided to play Henry Aldrich. We were out on the platform over the septic tank. We made it Henry's front room. I was Henry and Robby was his sister, Betty. I thought her name was Mary but Robby said it was Betty. I said that was Archie's sister in the comic book but Robby said Betty was Henry's sister. So he was Betty.

We made up a story that Betty had a boyfriend that Henry didn't like. Pretty soon the story got so silly, we both were rolling around on the boards laughing.

"Hey," Robby said, "this is really fun. We should get some other kids so we could have the whole family."

Robby always did like pretending.

So the next day, we got Craig from next door, Gary from up the hill and my friend Sunny Lea and told them what we were doing. They all thought it sounded like fun. Of course, Sunny Lea wanted to be Betty but Robby wouldn't let her. Said that was him. So Sunny Lea decided to be Betty's best friend, Sally.

The platform over the septic tank was almost like a stage with a door to the tool shed under our back porch where we could come on the stage and go out.

We all talked about the story. What it would be. How it would turn out. So it would be like the radio program. Then we started. That was the first time. We started a lot. We had to keep stopping 'cause everybody had different ideas. And Robby had a lot of trouble remembering what to say or what the story was about. But then we all decided Robby should just sweep a lot and not say anything. He was good at sweeping.

See, Betty had a boyfriend Henry didn't like. She was mad that Henry didn't like her boyfriend so she didn't want to talk to him. She was just mad and sweeping the floor. Wouldn't talk to anybody. Henry's best friend tries to talk Henry into liking the boyfriend. Even plans funny things with the boyfriend. But nothing works. Then Sally, Betty's best friend comes over to talk to Henry about it. Henry really likes Sally. So it all works out.

Robby put on his "paint dress" to be Betty. The baggy dress with his tennis shoes. When we looked at him most of us forgot what we were supposed to say.

We were laughing so much, Mom came out to see what was going on. We told her it was Henry Aldrich and she stood in the grass that needed mowing and watched. Her Aunt Jemima scarf tied around her pin curls. Her swooped-up glasses. Arms folded over her peasant blouse. Grass up over her saddle shoes. Pretty soon she was laughing too. Then she went and got Brew and little Joey who was helping Brew in the garage.

So then we had an audience. Brew in his half-a-hat standing in the grass behind Mom. His hand on her shoulder. Little Joey's red hair. Freckles grinning. Arms crossed like Mom.

When we were done with our story, Mom said, still kind of laughing, "You guys should invite some neighbors to watch your play."

We all just looked at her like she was nuts. I felt my mouth go open and Sunny Lea put her hands over her mouth and twisted around so Mom wouldn't see her laugh.

Gary was chewing on a Tootsie Roll and had a hard time making his mouth go up and down. But he said, "Would anyone wanna watch us?"

"Well, why in the world not," Mom said laughing. Making her mouth go up and down too. "Your play is funny."

I wanna be in the play," Joey said and ran up on the "stage" to the shed door.

We all looked at each other. Everybody had their mouth wide open. Eyebrows up. Didn't know what to do. None of us wanted a three year old in our play. Robby was used to dealing with his little brother though.

You could hear his air go in. Then his mouth yelled, "Don't go in there. The Boogie Man lives in there."

Joey stopped right in front of the door. Snapped around. His freckled face looking at us all. His red hair bright in the sun. Sharp little blue green eyes wide open. He quick jumped off the platform and grabbed a stick off the ground. Held it over his head and ran back at the door yelling, "All right Boogie Man. Here I come."

We all started laughing so hard he turned around and looked at us. His freckledy face red. His eyes all wild. Then he bent over laughing himself.

~

The next week all five of us went around the neighborhood and invited people to our play, Henry Aldrich.

We told Joey we didn't have time to put him in our play now. But he could be in the next one. So he said okay.

After we went through our play two more times to practice it, it didn't seem very funny anymore and we all started to wonder why we invited people to watch. But on the afternoon we were going to do it, all the chairs we got from our house and the Herman's next door and the two old lady sisters who lived on the other side of us were full.

Robby was complaining that his hand hurt from a blister he had from sweeping and Craig said he couldn't remember what he was supposed to say. But I just went up to our back porch and opened some of the windows so people could hear me. Then I made my voice high-sounding and hollered, "Henryeee. Henry Aldrich," and the play was started.

Everything was going pretty good. We were almost at the end. At the place where Sally comes over and talks to Henry about the boyfriend. Robby was sweeping and Sunny Lea, Betty's friend, and me were talking. The words Sunny Lea was saying were supposed to be Betty's but Robby couldn't remember them so we made them Sunny Lea's words. It wasn't a funny part but people were laughing in the audience. We kept talking but we all wondered what was funny. Then people started laughing real hard. Like holding their stomachs laughing. Sunny Lea and me, we stopped talking and people were still laughing. I looked around the platform and didn't see anything funny. Just Robby sweeping.

Then Robby looked up behind me and Sunny Lea. His face went tight. Like he was trying not to laugh. He stopped sweeping a minute then looked down at the platform and started to sweep again. Head down.

I turned quick around and there in the window of the porch above us was a flat freckledy face up against the window. Joey. Just then he backed away from the glass and did his favorite face. His tongue out, curled in the middle, so it looked like a whistle he was blowing. His eyes were crossed above his freckles and his hands up beside his face spread open and his fingers wiggling. The people were almost falling on the grass laughing.

Joey was in the play after all.

32

Mister Majetti

Brew's Oldsmobile came zooming down Spring Garden into the driveway pulling a big swirl of tan dust behind it one Saturday afternoon that summer. Robby and Joey and me were playing cars in our dirt hill beside the road in front of the house. The car door quick opened in the dust swirl that caught up with the car and Brew jumped out in his dirty white cords and tee shirt from his half-a-day at the shop.

"Hey you kids," he said, "come on in the house for a minute. I've got good news."

Then he quick went in the house.

It was hot out and Robby and me didn't feel like hurrying up over the dirt hill through the yard into the house. But Joey's little dirt covered butt and red hair was through the screen door and it slammed shut before Robby and me even got up over the dirt hill.

When we got inside, Joey was dancing around in a circle doing a kind of tap dance, singing, "We're goin' to the beach. We're goin' to the beach."

Brew rented a house down at Rockaway for a whole week for us. So Mom and me, and Robby and Joey were going to the beach for a whole week. It was like when Mom or Brew or somebody says, "Were going to the movies" and I didn't know about it before that. Just tells you. Then you go. That kind of surprise is really fun.

We had to go to the beach right away 'cause Brew had to come back Sunday night to go to work on Monday. He was going to come back down on the next Saturday and drive us all home on Sunday. A whole week at the beach.

~

The Romsperts' house at Rockaway was big. It had three floors. And it was right on the beach. Just some tall beachy grass in front. The top floor was all ours. Right out the big front windows was the Pacific ocean. All rolling and churning blue and white in the morning sunshine.

Us kids, we woke up early and all of us ran out into the front room to wake up Mom and Brew. They were sleeping on a pull-out davenport bed.

Mom started to sit up in bed and then she grabbed the blankets around her bosoms. Where I came in the front room, I could see down in the bed. Inside the covers. She was naked.

I stopped running and stared. My head was kind of dizzy. Like when you sit on a swing and spin around. All the way down her back and side by her bosom, my eyes could see her naked fanny. It was really pretty but I never saw her naked before. I didn't know she ever slept without her clothes on. I mean, a night gown or something.

She was laughing at us being so fired up. Joey was standing at the big windows looking at the ocean with his mouth open. Just looking. All he said was, "Wow."

But I could tell Mom was kind of embarrassed too. We never saw her without her clothes on. Brew was sitting up and Mom was kind of leaning on his chest that was naked too. Her face real pink, holding the covers tight to her.

She said something low and quiet and Brew, he said a lot louder, "Whyn't you kids go out to the beach and let us get dressed? Then we'll have breakfast." Like we better do that.

So we all ran back out of the front room and down the stairs. I could hear Mom and Brew making under the cover giggles together. Like they were kids or something. It was a kind of sad itch inside me, Brew and Mom naked together. The itch like sometimes you get in your teeth. The sad part inside me was my real dad, Earl, fixing watches in that muggy Nevada City heat with a want-to-be somewhere else in his eyes.

Right out the door, we were on the side of the house away from the ocean and we heard a train whistle. The tracks went right by that side of the house in front of us beside the road and we could see it coming down the tracks. A big ol' giant engine blowing steam out the top and sideways along the tracks on both sides and screaming its head off. Whoooee. Whoooee.

Slow going through town, it was pounding the ground. A pounding that came through my feet. Everything was shaking. Every time the wheels went around my whole body jiggled and my teeth rattled in my mouth.

Then it was going past us. There was a man sitting in the little window of the engine leaning his arm on the window bottom. A cap with tiny gray and white stripes, something like a baseball cap, on his head and a short white beard on his chin. He saw us standing there and he waved. A jolly wave, like Santa Clause. Red cheeks. Big smile.

Robby and me waved back kind of like you wave goodbye but little Joey, he was waving and jumping up and down yelling, "Hi Majetti. Hi Majetti," in the roar of the train going past. The ground just a steady rumble now. Like thunder that kept on going. We were still waving when the long train with all the logs and the box cars that creaked and groaned ended and the caboose went by.

It was all of a sudden still and quiet...

"That was my friend, Mister Majetti," Joey said when he looked up at me, squinting from the sun in his eyes.

Joey ran back up the stairs of the house to tell Mom and Brew about Majetti. Robby and me were really hungry so we went up after him.

In the kitchen Mom was making scrambled eggs. She had her clothes on. I was glad of that. Her jeans with the big rolled up cuffs, a dark blue sweater with a red and white checker-board collar coming out around the neck. The only time she wore jeans was to the woods or the beach.

All these dented pots and pans were around her in the kitchen and all different kinds of dishes. None of them looked alike. The stove was white with red trim but it was all banged up and chipped. Funny old linoleum on the floor with wind mills on it.

There was something nice about everything in the house though. I mean, those things made it nice to be there. Like when you sit in an old chair that lots of people already sat in. The front room was like that too. Just wood floors. Kind of gritty with sand. Old furniture you didn't have to be careful about.

"Funny dishes," I said to Mom cooking the eggs at the stove.

"Well, it's the beach, honey" she said and took the iron frying pan off the burner with an old pot holder. She pushed her swooped up glasses up on her nose and looked around at the shelves and drawers of kitchen stuff. "Sure a lot of them though. There's more stuff in this kitchen than I've ever had at home. Don't even know what some of these tools are for."

There were lots of scrambled eggs then. Smooth and creamy. They never tasted that good at home. And cinnamon toast, my favorite, with just the right amount of cinnamon and sugar on top the melted butter and crispy toast. A cup of cocoa too that was hot and sweet with a marshmallow. The beach was a good place to be.

Joey jumped up after breakfast and went in the front room. We were all sitting around the table and Brew was talking about what we could do that day.

"Anybody want to drive down to Depoe Bay and watch the fishing boats come in?" he said.

Robby and me wanted to just play on the beach but Mom explained we could play on the beach all week long but this was the only day Brew would have with us. The only day we would have a car all week. There went my chest getting tight. We hardly never got to see Brew. He was always working. Even if he didn't notice me much, it was more fun to have him there.

Just then there was a loud noise in the front room that was something like a trumpet or somebody trying to sound like a trumpet. Little Joey came through the kitchen door with a red fuzzy bedspread over the top of his head and dragging behind him on the windmill floor. His face peeking out under Brew's white Civil Defense officer's cap that he found somewhere and was wearing on top of the bedspread. He looked like one of those French Legion guys in Africa we studied about in school but shrunk to only three feet tall. He marched around the kitchen in a circle with his stomach out big, playing an invisible drum that he made sound with his mouth—putta putt putt putt, putta putt putt putt. And then blew his trumpet again—ta tah—and stopped, looking at us all.

He said in a funny deep voice, "I'm Majetti." His freckled face all red from pushing his chin down to make it growly. "Glad ta meecha."

We were all laughing so hard I choked on a piece of cinnamon toast and Robby started hitting me in the back to make me cough. Too hard. I had to hit him back to make him stop so I could breathe. 'Course, we got bawled out for fighting.

Anyway, Joey was such a funny little kid. I was sorry we didn't let him really be in our Henry Aldrich play. He was better at pretending than any of us. Even with his imaginary friend, Majetti. But not just funny, Ha, Ha. He was funny in different ways. In different ways you didn't expect.

Whenever Mom handed him his clean clothes she washed and hung out to dry and then folded up for him, his eyes would get this look like he went somewhere else and he would put his little freckle nose on the stack of clothes in his arms and breathe in their smell. Like it was the best smelling flower he ever smelled. Then he would close his eyes and just stand like in a dream. Lost somewhere for a minute.

Nobody could make him do anything he didn't want to do though. Like we told him he couldn't be in the play and he said okay. Then got in it anyway. And if Robby ever tried to make him do something he didn't want to do, he had to be ready for a fight.

"All boy," everybody said.

But then one time that summer he saw a lady in our neighborhood feeding her baby with a bottle. The next day he was carrying this naked little doll around that my cousin, Katy left at our house once. Not like you'd think, by one arm, all boy, swinging it. He got a towel and wrapped it up and carried it everywhere with him, with his arm bent under it like the lady in our neighborhood. Like it was his "baby." Sometimes he would just sit and talk to it. Make sweet little sounds to make his "baby" feel good. Like he was kind of lost in a dream.

After about a week he asked Mom if she would get him a little bottle so he could feed his "baby." That's what he called it. His baby. So Mom did. She made him promise to only use water in the little doll's bottle she got him at the Variety Store though.

Brew rented the house at Rockaway from the Romsperts but us kids never met them. We just always called the house the Romsperts'. Robby and me agreed they were probably old people like Mr. and Mrs. Baldwin and they never came down to the beach anymore.

Every day after breakfast that week the three of us would go across the rail road tracks together. Then across the highway and into town a little bit to the penny arcade. I always tried to take a hold of Joey's hand so he wouldn't go running out in the highway without looking. But he wouldn't let me. He'd jerk his hand away. Then I was worried he might really get hit trying to get away from me. Like usual he wouldn't do anything he didn't want to.

Mom and Brew had a penny jar where they kept most of the pennies that were left over in their pockets and purses. They brought that jar with them to the beach and Mom let each of us have ten cents to spend at the penny arcade.

Robby and me didn't really have a favorite thing to do at the penny arcade like Joey. Except maybe Robby liked the crane a little bit more than the others. It was a crane in a glass box full of toys. Mostly like stuffed animals. Teddy bears and dogs. Some other toys too that you tried to pick up with the crane. But I got tired of that one real fast 'cause I could never get hold of anything with the crane. It was worse than trying to get hold of little Joey's hand to cross the highway and it felt like I was throwing my pennies in swamp mud.

The thing I did like best was the laughing lady. She was a lady, not a real lady, but a funny looking kind of painted statue lady with an old hat and veil. Like the ladies' hats Robby and me used to laugh at on the bus. A raggedy old fox was wrapped around her neck and she had on a kind of house dress. White gloves on her hands and old lady shoes on her feet.

When you laid a penny in the little cut out metal place in the handle and pushed the end of the handle in, she started to laugh. Kind of a low laugh and slow. Like way off thunder before the rain comes. Then her laugh got bigger and higher and all cackley like Witch Wintergreen on the Cinnamon Bear and she started to rock back and forth. The laugh kept getting bigger until she was bending over frontwards laughing loud then tipping all the way backwards. Her head back like Mom and Gramma Jones did in their big, loud HA HA laugh. It always happened exactly the same. And with me too. When she got to bending over laughing, it always made me laugh too. It bubbled around in my stomach and spilled a little bit out my mouth. Then it would get louder and louder. My eyes all wet and me just standing there laughing and laughing. At nothing. Or maybe at her. It was better than the crane. I always got something for my penny.

Joey did have a real favorite though. Most the time he spent all his pennies on it. It was the foot tickler. It looked kind of like those things in the drug store where you stand up on a place for your feet to go, then put money in and it gives you a piece of paper with how much you weigh on it. But this one didn't give you a piece of paper. It gave your feet a little shock. It had an electric shock thing where you put your feet. Just a little bit. Made your feet tickle. He liked it so much he stood there the whole time grinning his freckles just feeling it. Eyes closed lost in a dream again. Spending all his pennies getting his feet tickled.

After lunch, Mom and us went out on the beach and played. Me and Robby found two pieces of old rusty metal on the beach on Wednesday. They were kind of square like. Perfect for cutting wet sand into little square buildings for sand cities down by the ocean.

One time we all went to the Natatorium to play in the water. It was a really huge indoor swimming pool with heated ocean water. Mom thought she'd be smart and just put her hair up in pin curls under her bathing cap and comb it out when it was dry. She did. And it really looked funny. Like a brown haystack. Straight, sticking out all over her head. She said it was the salt water. She was kinda mad but we thought it was funny.

On the next Saturday, Brew was there and we all went out to the beach. Mom and Brew put a blanket down so they could lay in the sun and Robby and me took our metal pieces down to the water so we could build a city. Pretty soon, Brew and Joey came down to help us. Brew took one of our buckets and made a round building a little bit outside our city. It was really different. Then he made three more in a square and built a wall from each one. He said it was a castle. He got little sticks and seaweed and made flags out of them and put them on top of his round buildings. Little rocks and shells made roads then that he made go around his castle and through our city. Joey's building had lots of little sticks he found on top for a roof.

His blue green eyes snapped up at me when I told him that was a good idea. "Majetti lives here," he said.

Brew's lips puffed out and a laugh like starting a motor cycle came out.

His eye winked at Robby and me then and he said, "Whyn't you guys build a moat around your city? Protect it."

We didn't know what a moat was but he showed us that if we dug a deep ditch around our city, when the ocean came it would help keep it out. When we finished, Brew stood back looking and told Robby what a good job he did, like always. But it didn't stop the water and pretty soon our city was just little hills of sand and the waves pulled all the flags and roads out into the ocean.

We went back to the blanket where Mom was and Brew said he was cold.

"Who wants to go get my shirt at Romsperts' for me?"

Joey, like he was a jack-in-the box, shot up getting sand all over Mom and hollered, "I will," and took off to the house.

Brew was half sitting down on the blanket. His legs went out and he fell the rest of the way. His face all red brown from the sun was laughing again and he yelled, "The plaid one in the kitchen, Sport!"

For those last two days there was something everybody called the Japanese current and the ocean was warm. Not really, really cold like most time in Oregon. So Robby and me went out to play in the ocean. Right away we started jumping waves like we did. We went out past the crawly water that just snuck up the sand. Out to the waves that came up to our knees. Sometimes higher. A wave would come and we jumped over it to the smooth water behind it before it hit us. Sometimes Robby and me held hands so if we fell there was something to hold on to. So the waves were coming and we were jumping them.

Then, all at once, Robby and me jumped a big one. Robby came down and I felt him pull. He yelled, his hand jerked and his other arm was flying around in the air trying to keep standing up and he went down. He kept stumbling, trying to get back up but he like slipped on something, got hit hard by a wave and went back down again. By the third time his hand pulling me, I was going down with him. We were back up the beach in just a little bit of water though. That's when I saw the fish. He kept slipping on a fish.

He finally got standing up on the wet sand just above the fish that wasn't swimming. Just floating back and forth in the little crawly waves. A silvery wide flat fish turning rainbow colors in the water washing over him. The wave started coming back pulling the fish into the deeper water where I was. So I ran at it and made waves in the water with my hands. That pushed the floating fish back to Robby but it came at him so fast it was under his foot again just as the water washed away from it and he stepped on it. Something like ten tiny fish about an inch and a half came out of it from somewhere onto the sand. All little wide flat fish silvery with rainbow colors moving over them.

"Is it dead?" Robby said. The top of his head in front of me looking down.

"I guess," I said, looking down at it too. "I wonder if those are the babies."

Right then we heard someone singing. A plaid shirt was flying in the wind down to the beach. Brew's shirt came all the way down to little Joey's feet and came whipping out behind him like a cape. The long sleeves were flags flapping over his arm-wings he was holding out and he was running zig zags down the beach singing some song he was making up. He came zig zagging right up to us and stopped. The shirt drooped and little Joey's head tipped down too. Just stared down at the fish and all the silver rainbow babies that were slid out onto the wet sand.

"Wow," he said.

"Hey Sport, can I have my shirt?" It was Brew coming up to us. All in a group looking down at the sand. "What's going on?" He stopped and looked down too. "Well, look at that. You got a fish."

"Yeah, I got it," Robby said.

I looked up at Brew squeezing Robby's shoulder with his big hand.

"You think those are the babies?"

"Could be. They look just like the big one. Probably Perch." Brew got the bucket and picked the Perch up by the tail and flopped it in the bucket. "Maybe dinner," he said.

The fish didn't look so nice then kind of bent in the bucket with wet sand stuck to it.

Little Joey scooped up the babies in his hands and we started up the beach to Romsperts'.

"You're quite the fisherman," Brew said. His eyes smiled at Robby and his arm went around his shoulders.

I walked behind them. Looked down at their footprints in the sand.

~

Mom cut the fish open in the sink but we found a big brown spot inside and Brew said he didn't think it would be good to eat.

Joey laid the baby fish real neat in his sun glasses case and for the rest of the day and all day Sunday he carried it around with him. Like something precious. In the hard little case with a flip top, they looked like the sardines Pop liked to eat. But whole. With their heads still on. And kind of pretty. Every once in a while Joey would open the case and they would wiggle. The top ones were probably stuck a little bit to the cover of his glasses case so the little fish looked like they jumped when he opened it. But he would stand looking at them. Like he looked at his "baby." Dreamy. Waiting for them to move again.

On Sunday night when we were getting ready to leave, Joey asked Brew if he could keep his fish.

"No way, Sport," he said. Brews black brown eyes looking hard into Joey's little blue green ones. But smiling.

After the long drive back home with us pretty quiet in the back seat, tired from a whole week playing at the beach, Brew asked us to help unpack the trunk of the Oldsmobile. So we all got out when we got to Multnomah and went and stood by the back of the car until Brew opened the trunk. The trunk lid came open and a really awful stink came out of the trunk.

"Oh ish," Robby said.

"Yucky poo," I said. The smell was awful.

Joey just stood there and grinned like he had a secret.

Brew said, "What the...?" he reached in a box and pulled out Joey's sunglasses case and held it in front of Joey. His eyebrows up and his forehead wrinkled up into his widow's peak.

Joey tried to push his chest out like he did. 'Course it was only his stomach. Put his thumbs into the chest part of his tee shirt like he was holding out suspenders. Grinned his freckles and said, "For my friend, Majetti."

33

Family Jewels

Then the summer was over and Robby and Joey were gone. I was alone again. No brothers.

There were five or six more days before school started though and I was bored. Most of my friends were gone away still. I just came back down from Gary's house. He wasn't home and Sunny Lea wasn't either. Mom said she wanted to go down to Multnomah to take her library book back so she wouldn't have to pay a fine. So I told her I was going to see Mrs. Baldwin. Looking at magazines was better than not having anybody to play with.

So I went out the front door before Mom to go down to the Baldwins'. The grass in the front yard was almost all dried up. The little maple tree in the front yard that Brew planted when he took out the really big one that got split in two by lightning looked thirsty. The leaves just big limp dark green pieces of saggy skin were hanging down from the little branches. Soft and kind of folded. Not spread open and perky like they were last spring. It looked like, if the two poles Brew pounded in on both sides and wired it to weren't holding it up, it might just bend over in the middle and touch the ground.

The sun was hot. The air was still and dry. The road, before I got to the black top, deep with dust. I crossed the little bit of new black-top on Spring Garden that went up the hill then started down to the Baldwins'. The blackberry bushes on the way down the dirt road where the Collie dog bit me in the eye were all red and brown and there were grass hoppers popping in and out of the edge of the road. Click-thump. And a little puff of dust. Click-thump.

The Baldwins weren't home either.

I turned around and went back up the dirt road to our house.

The shades were down and the house was cool and dark and empty after being outside. Quiet. Nobody home. Even Kitty wasn't there. It was like I was the only one on this planet.

I wandered around in the house pretending I didn't live there. Looking at things like I never saw them before. There was a voice in my head saying things like, "I wonder who lives here," and "I wonder what this is for." It was a game I liked to play for myself when I felt really alone and somehow I didn't belong there. Like I came from a different planet and didn't know what these things were that humans had. Like I didn't know what a kitchen was or a bathroom or what a stove or a toilet was for.

They didn't need to go to the bathroom where the different planet guy came from. He thought the toilet was for washing your feet. They didn't wear shoes.

Lots of times my "other planet guy" would come when I was getting dressed in the morning. So there were two of us there—in me. I had to explain to him what pants were and what they were for. A shirt and underpants too. Even how to tie shoes. While I was getting dressed, I talked to him. I slow put one leg at a time in the pants to show him how we got dressed and explained how clothes kept us humans warm.

Slow walking through the rooms. Touching things and wondering. I walked into the extra bedroom we use for a dining room. But then the bed was still in there that Gramma Jones used when she was sick. Mom's walk-in closet too. Still slow walking, showing planet man Gramma's bed. Telling him how she had cancer. Then we were at Mom's closet. I wasn't supposed to go in there. But my person from the other planet didn't know that. He went in. Just turned the knob and opened the door wide and went in where Mom always got dressed.

On one side, all her clothes hanging. The other side, on the wide shelf under the window was the box of treasures. Her jewelry box.

The box was beautiful polished wood. Brown and tan and blond wood fitted in a design, a rose, on top. Green felt around the edges, so the lid opened and closed real quiet. Soft. Like a vault in a bank. Or like the shoe sound walking on a carpet in a jewelry store. Muffled.

Something else my different planet guy didn't know was Brew who lived here was in the jewelry business. Every birthday or Christmas or Mother's Day or anniversary he bought Mom something. Brew always said, "I'm saving three hundred percent mark-up." Even when Mom sometimes would like "costume jewelry" better, she got "the real stuff."

My planet person lifted the lid. There before him were the jewels. A pirate's chest filled with treasure. Hanging on hooks from the lid and heaped in piles inside. Rubies and topaz and gray blue sapphires with stars in the middle. Pearls and tiny diamonds, twinkling. Gold and silver pins, rings and chains. Necklaces and bracelets. And a long, long rope of clear blue stones Mom has had since she was a little girl. From her grandmother. Left over from the flapper time. When they wore necklaces all the way down their front, Mom told me.

Like in a dream, my other planet guy lifted the heavy box off the shelf and carried it out of the closet and put it on Gramma's bed. He knelt down beside the bed and put his hand slow in the box. Lifted a sparkling red stoned bracelet from the box. Garnets. Watched it glitter in the dim lit afternoon room. Felt the heavy gold and stones pulling at his fingers. Then he laid it as carefully on the bed as Father Fletcher in our old Church handled the Host.

Again his fingers are in the box. Lifting the long rope of pale blue stones. Watching them spill their water color through his hands. Watching it curl around his hand and wrist like a clear blue snake and he remembers...

Early in the morning on the other planet. My planet guy's sleeping in grass blades of cut emerald under a pale sky. Little stars over him in gray blue sapphire. He's awake. A sound. Through the sparkling grass like water in a creek, sliding, it's a clear blue snake. Fangs out. Spitting poison. He's up. No-shoes-feet running fast in the grass.

Slipping past the green felt on the lid, planet guy's other hand finds a purple stone and lifts it on its chain like a rising purple sun over the edge of the jewelry box. Like one of the suns on his planet, its rays turn blue, then red, then green in the yellow light coming through the window shades. Swaying like a pendulum on a clock. Hypnotizing my planet guy.

The sun is up. He's safe now in the gold jagged branches of his home among the giant cherries. The snake's head smashed and bleeding blue beneath the tree. His purple sun gleaming on the round ruby cherries.

The purple sun still hanging from his hand, his eyes catch the flash of the big yellow topaz with tiny pearls all around it in the bottom of the box. Its angles flashing gold from the afternoon sun coming through the shade. Through shadows of branches from the cherry tree in the back yard.

A topaz planet surrounded by tiny moons. Light years away.

Through his trance is the sound of the front door opening.

Mom is home from the library.

And it's all different in my head then. A voice, "Don't touch things that don't belong to you," and being thrown across a room. Landing against a wall. Falling on a bed with Brew's face all red mad in the doorway. Changing his mind.

Oh, my God. They'll probably both change their mind if they catch me playing with Mom's stuff.

No time to put them all back in her closet. I grab up all the jewelry on the bed in my two fists. Chains and bracelets. Ear-rings and pins. And run out in the hallway, past the bathroom, through the kitchen. Trip on Kitty who's there now and wants to curl around my legs. Then out the back door. I'm running in the dust, then the black top and up the hill. Running. Running. *Can't get caught. Can't get caught.* Outside Gary's gate to his back yard, I'm looking down at my hands full of Mom's jewelry.

I'm so stupid. I should of just put it back in the box. Now what am I gonna do?

It's so hot. Can't think.

Gary's back gate is open. He's not home. Nobody is. I go in his back yard. Standing on the broken up little side walk to his back door. Where I stood a year ago when we had our earthquake and when I was looking down at it shaking, it felt like that side walk came up at me and hit me in the face. Now I'm standing here and can't think 'cause my hands are full of Mom's jewelry.

The old dried up garden is down by Gary's back fence. There's a mole hole going down into the dried up dirt. Hard old clay and some rocks. It's almost like the cement of his broken up side walk it's so hard. A round hole some mole dug in it a long time ago going down straight. I don't know what to do. That crying feeling's in me again. I kneel down and put some of Mom's jewels in the hole.

There aren't any sounds here. Not even grass hoppers.

"What'er ya doin'?" a voice says beside me.

It's Craig from next door. He kneels down beside me.

"I saw you run by my house. Yer Mom's looking for you."

His face close to mine. He's littler'n me. Looking up at me. In my eyes. Trying to see inside. His cowlick there. Like a big wet cow tongue licked his hair. My eyes say to laugh but in my head says to cry. I just try to swallow.

"Are those yer Mom's?" he says and puts his light little bird feather fingers on my hand that still has gold chains and ear-rings, the purple sun, in it.

"Yeah," I say. It comes out my mouth like ripping a piece of paper. All jagged sounding.

"Maybe you better take 'em back home," he says.

"Yeah," I say again and all my air goes out with it.

Craig helps me get the stuff out. His hands fit better in the mole hole. A bracelet. Some pearls. Ear rings with dirt on them. Can't see any more in there. But it doesn't feel like all of it. Doesn't weigh the same in my hands. Feels lighter.

Mom is on the front porch. Her hands reach out and I put all the jewelry in her hands. She looks sad. Her eyes red. The centers more gray than blue. No glasses. She swallows and the little mole in the V of her throat bounces.

Craig opens the screen door for her and she turns around. Goes into the house.

That night at dinner nobody talked. The warm air in the kitchen didn't move. It was like the roar of the train going by down at Rockaway, the quiet of the air in my ears. We just all looked at the food we were eating. Forks moving in the food. Then up to our mouths. In the food again. Sometimes Brew like sneaked a look at me. He cleared his throat then. It was loud in the quiet. The fog horn at the beach.

I went upstairs after that. Fell asleep listening to Fibber McGee. Even before he opened his closet. The part everybody waited for 'cause every week everything always fell out. Even though his wife Molly tried to stop him.

In the morning, I sat down at the robin's egg blue dinette set and Mom put my oatmeal in front of me.

"Why, Davey?" she said. Looking at me worried like. Her eyebrows pulled down below the top of her glasses. Then a big breath out 'cause I didn't answer. She put the bottle of milk on the table beside my bowl. "I still can't find my garnet bracelet or the topaz."

After breakfast, I went outside. Walked in front of Craig's house. Pretty soon, going up the hill, I could feel him walking behind me.

"Where you goin'?" he said.

"Gary's," I said. Not looking.

I went in Gary's back yard through the gate.

Craig was helping me dig in the mole hole when Gary came out. He stood looking down at Craig and me digging in the mole hole. Sucking on a tootsie pop. Chocolate. Brown stuff around his mouth.

"Why'd you take that stuff of yer Mom's?" he said.

In my head, there wasn't a good answer so I didn't say anything. My shoulders just shrugged.

Craig and me, we didn't find anything. *They were here, weren't they? Or did I drop them?* My throat was all burny. Like crying. But I didn't.

That night I was in bed. On top my colored snowflake quilt. Hot. Couldn't go to sleep. I was still trying to get an answer in my head. Answers kept going around and around.

I just didn't want anybody to find out. I didn't want to get caught.

Then my other planet guy came talking through the sleepy fuzz in my head. "Maybe you were just mad. 'Cause everybody keeps going away. Maybe you just wanted to keep something nice that wouldn't go away. Maybe—"

"Yeah, maybe," I said back quick to make him stop. I was tired of thinking about it.

The moon squares came in the window. Landed on the bedroom floor.

I closed my eyes. Still couldn't go to sleep.

34

Bad Dreams

Still couldn't go to sleep. Or it was hard to. I heard awful voices when I tried to.

Mom and Brew went visiting a lot. They went over to Pop's after dinner sometimes. My Aunt Ethelyn lived with Pop still. And my cousins, Katy and Margo. Mom and Brew visited other friends too. Mary and Fred and their son, Stan that lived by where we used to live before Multnomah. Bud and Myrtle, old friends of Brew's.

When we went to people's houses to visit, I was supposed to go to sleep at my bed time. Usually on top of the people's bed. That's when I heard voices.

They're gonna leave you here. You touch things that don't belong to you. Steal their jewelry and do other bad stuff. Run around naked in the woods. Maybe Brew changed his mind. Maybe he doesn't wanna be your step-dad any more. Maybe Mom doesn't wanna be your Mom. They let Scotty go. Your mom let your dad go. Now they're gonna let you go.

I tried to get the voices to stop. I yelled at them. Those voices. Sometimes I just cried. Then Mom would come in the people's bedroom and ask me what was the matter. I didn't tell her about the voices. I just said I couldn't sleep. She'd get me a glass of water and put her hand on my hot forehead. Push my hair back. I could feel her ring. Cool. Eight carrot, French cut. She waited til I drank the water. Told me to go to sleep now.

Then she would leave.

The voices came back.

Sometimes I did go to sleep and the voices came into the dream. Really bad dreams with more than voices. A steam roller rolled over me or I got stuck in a sewer pipe trying to get away from the voices telling me how bad I was. I tried to wake up then and even when Mom came into their bedroom from me hollering, I couldn't wake up.

The pretty day dreams I used to have of knights and ladies when I was little changed to nightmares and voices that didn't let go once they got hold of me.

One day, just Mom and me went to visit Mary and Fred. Stan was my age and I played with him outside all morning. Then Mom said I should take a nap after lunch. I really didn't want to 'cause I didn't want Stan to know about my bad dreams but Mom said I had to at least try. So I laid down on their bed. I was really tired from running around in their yard with Stan all morning, so I went to sleep right away. I didn't hear any voices.

Flying over some trees. Not like I did with my friends in the neighborhood behind me, my soldiers, but alone with big wings on my back. They were see-through wings that turned all rainbow colors like they did sometimes in dreams when the rain hit them. Like oil-on-water colors. It was raining. Not hard. Soft rain with big drops. Just one or two. Down underneath me, through the telephone wires, I could see Billy. He was running naked in the grass—really pretty and I kept yelling trying to get him to look up. But he wouldn't. I kept calling him but he kept on running and I couldn't see where he was running to. I swooped down close. And then I saw.

My dad, Earl, was dancing along in the tall grass with Scotty. They were twirling and jumping, lifting their legs up high out of the grass. I never saw Earl or Scotty act like that. Earl was in a tuxedo and Scotty in his Scout shirt and they looked so happy. Happy to be going somewhere. Away.

Gramma Jones in her silvery dress was dancing with them too then and Uncle Herb in his cowboy boots and hat. They were all having a wonderful time, laughing and singing and swinging around in a dance together. And Billy was still trying to catch up with them. Running and falling naked in the grass and rolling over then running and laughing again. Then he caught up with them. They were all running to a green, green place in the grass down between the green trees. I kept calling and calling but nobody heard me.

Nobody looked up above the trees to see me. Nobody.

When I looked down at my body flying, there was only half of me. Like looking into the bathroom mirror and the steam covers part of you. Or like the blackboard at school when part of it's erased. No wonder they couldn't hear me. I was being erased.

~

Then Mom was waking me up. I was walking around in Mary and Fred's dining room. She said she was trying to wake me up for ten minutes and I was walking around jabbering and hollering in my sleep. She said none of it made any sense.

Mom called the doctor after that to ask him about what was going on and she told me that he said, "Oh, is he having those? Most times those kind of dreams only last a couple of years after having ether. Not as long as this. It's been a lot longer than that since he had his tonsils out."

Her eyebrows were all creases between them and her lips puckered up. Her eyes were even more cloudy than they always were and she said, "I'm sorry, Sweetie, he said you just have to out-grow them."

They just got worse though.

One time on a warm afternoon at home in the middle of a nap where I was sleepwalking, Mom got me to stop walking but I couldn't wake up even though I could hear her and talk to her. There was like an invisible wall. I could see where she was but I couldn't get through it, out of where I was.

It made my brain hurt.

She got me to sit down on the davenport and asked me to tell her what was happening.

My throat was burning and my eyes hurt. I tried shaking my head to get rid of the dream but I couldn't wake up. I stamped my feet and hit my legs with my fists 'cuz it was like when your foot goes to sleep. Then I tried hitting my head. Still I couldn't wake myself up. It was like my brain went to sleep, or one of the little wheels in my head, like the ones in watches that Earl worked on, got magnetized and stuck together with another one and I couldn't shake it loose.

Mom sat close to me on the davenport. Her swooped up glasses looking into my eyes, waiting.

"I know that it isn't right," I said. "It can't be right, but it's what's in my head. You are the floor," I said, "and I'm up above you, hanging upside down on a Christmas ribbon. I've only got one leg left and my hands and arms are disappearing too."

Mom's mouth went open, like she was going to say something but then it just stayed there. Her eyes got watery and her swooped up glasses all foggy.

Me? I just cried. It was worse than getting stuck in a sewer pipe or getting rolled over by a steam roller.

Mom took off her glasses and put her arm around me, pulled me real close to her.

PART FOUR

Being Me

35

Being Me

{March 1949}

The water looked really clear and clean coming through the hole and over the little slanted chrome thing in the water fountain. The chrome thing bigger this close to my face. The shiny nicks and scratches in it magnified under the bubbling water. If I turned the handle quick, the water would bounce up and tickle my nose. I was bending over the water fountain in the hall outside Sunny Lea's class room watching the water bubble up, feeling it tickle my nose, and singing, *"I'm gonna buy a paper doll that I can call my own, a doll that other fellows cannot steal and then the flirty, flirty guys with their flirty, flirty eyes will have to flirt with dollies that are real."*

Sunny Lea's teacher was keeping her late at school. So I was waiting for Sunny Lea to walk home with me. Hardly anybody wanted to walk home with me lately.

The white tub that the three chrome water fountains were in made my voice sound really neat. Kind of echo-y like a record. Almost like the Mills Bothers that sang it all the time on the radio. *"I'm gonna buy a paper doll that I can—"*

"Davey I didn't know you could sing," said a voice behind me.

I jumped and so did the water 'cause my hand was still on the handle. The water hit me right smack in the face.

It was my fourth grade teacher, Miss Wilson.

Me looking stupid. Water all over my face.

"I'm sorry," she said, "I didn't mean to startle you. I just didn't know you had such a nice voice."

I could feel my face heating up even all wet.

She pulled a cream colored hanky out of her pocket, all folded up neat and handed it to me.

Miss Wilson was a tall lady. Tall and skinny. She had kind of light brownish blond hair that was almost the same color as her skin. No make-up. She always wore wool skirts and jackets that were the same color as her hair and cream colored blouses. She looked like a glass of milk walking around school. But she was nice.

"You know," she said in her soft little voice, "it would really be wonderful if you'd sing for us in class sometime."

I didn't know what to say. The hanky on my face smelled like vanilla. Across the hall, in the playground outside the two doors with chicken wire in the glass, a kid was dribbling his basketball on the cement. *Tapa tapa tap. Tapa tapa tap.* When she said that, my body got really bouncy like that basketball. All it wanted to do was just run across the hall and push on that bar that opened the door and get far away from her as I could. Sing for our class? How could I do that? They'd think I was just trying to show off or something. What was she thinking? I couldn't sing for kids my own age, especially ones that knew me. Not right now.

"Well, I don't know." I said and handed the hanky back to her.

A little frown came into her pale forehead.

"Don't you have something you'd like to sing? It could be anything. I know we'd all enjoy it."

Geez, she was like so many other big people. Not a clue how kids think about things. Whatever I sang, in front of her they'd pretend to like it. After school it'd be different.

And besides, I didn't want to spoil it. Singing was a great way to not think about bad things that happened to you. I didn't want singing to *make* bad things happen to me.

"Yeah. Well, maybe," I said.

Her little frown turned upside down.

"You think about it," she said.

Then she kind of waved the hanky at me and her little cream colored heels clicked away down the tile squares in the hall.

So there I am standing with part of one of my mom's old nylon stockings stretched over my shaved head. The thigh part. It was there in the mirror for almost eight months now. My white, white head with the dark brown bristles. My little silly round head. Not the big bald genie-from-a-bottle kind of head. Just a silly little head and crusty pink ringworm circles through the bristles. Big ears sticking out. And Mom's nylon to top it off. It looks really stupid. And it was how I learned how mean kids can be. Putting up with that was worse than the sleep walking bad dreams that kept happening for a long time whenever I forgot and took a nap on a warm day with the windows closed.

~

It all started last August even before fourth grade when Craig next door found a couple of kittens in the bushes up by Gary's house. We all thought they were real cute. His mom let him keep them 'cause she thought they were real cute too. The next day Craig had the kittens outside with him and he let all the neighbor kids pet them. Me and Gary and Gary's brother, Jack, Sunny Lea and her friend Donna. Robby wasn't there that summer. He was up in The Dalles with my other step-brother little Joey.

A couple of days after we played with the kittens, we all had ring worm. But I was the only one who got it on my head. I don't know why. I didn't put the kittens on my head, for cripe sake. Anyway, then my head had to be shaved and Mom tried all kinds of things to get rid of it. Every mom in the neighborhood told her something else. Vinegar, cigar ashes, vinegar and ashes, really yucky car grease, finger nail polish. A doctor finally told Mom that some athlete's foot medicine would work but it would take time. Time. It's March now and I still have to wear a dumb nylon stocking over it or some other stocking-cap that Mom finds at the variety store she thinks looks better and go down to the City Hall in Portland every week so they can look at my head under a purple light they call a black light. People in white coats scrape my head with wooden sticks and say "hmmm" a lot. But it doesn't seem to do anything to get rid of the ring worm.

When fourth grade started, I found out that kids at school were really not my friends. Of course, Gary and Craig and Sunny Lea didn't think I was weird but everybody else did. Except for Clayton, the boy at school who drooled and Ina who was the skinniest, ugliest girl I ever saw. But both of them started being my friends after I got ring worm.

When other kids started treating me like I had cooties or that my mom must of dropped me on my head when I was a baby, I started to know how Clayton and Ina felt. They were both kind of strange sometimes but they were nice to me. That's more than I can say for most other kids in school. When I walked home with Clayton or played with Ina on the school grounds, the other kids really started being mean.

There were lots of different ways I could walk home from school. One of the ways went right by where Clayton lived so when he asked me if I would walk home with him one day I said, "Sure."

Clayton was bigger than me. He was kind of puffy all over too. Like if you stuck him with a pin in his arm, he'd pop. His head was always down, looking at the ground, so you couldn't see his eyes most of the time but they were dark. Almost black. When you could see his eyes, it was like you could see in them forever. The sky at night without any stars. There was almost always a smile on his mouth. The corners of his mouth turned up like he had a secret inside. That was when he wasn't chewing. He chewed a lot but it wasn't like when Robby chewed on the yucky leather strap of his aviator helmet or when Pop chewed on his yucky cigar stub. Clayton just chewed. I don't know what he was chewing. And sometimes he drooled. His arms and legs didn't work very well either. He kind of limped and stumbled when he moved anywhere. But he was nice to me. He didn't treat me like a weirdo just because I had ring worm.

When we got to the middle of Multnomah after school that day, we cut down a street by the hardware store that went behind all the buildings on Capitol Highway, the main street in town. Me talking a lot and big ol' Clayton stumbling along beside me. The street went up to the old railroad tracks that ran under the viaduct and then, on the other side, turned into a dirt road through that kind of swampy part where Robby threw the money Arthur Baldwin gave us. The tracks weren't used for a railroad any more. They were covered with those weeds and some stuff like gum wrappers and old cigarette packs. But over them was a quick way to Clayton's house.

Just when we got to the railroad tracks, these three big kids were coming along the tracks about half a block away. One of them yelled, "Hey, Clayton, you moron re-tard."

Clayton looked up from looking at the ground, like he did. His head turned first at them and then at me. Like he was ashamed they called him that in front of me. Or maybe he thought I'd protect him. Maybe he even thought I was really just like them. I couldn't tell. But his black eyes were big and round. Like he just saw a monster or something. His mouth went open and he started to howl. Like a wild animal that couldn't get away. I didn't see it coming 'cause I was looking at Clayton being scared but a rock hit him in the neck and he screamed. Then he took off running. Arms and legs going every which way.

I looked over at the three guys and they were all picking up rocks. Nobody else could see what they were doing 'cause they were hidden by the cement legs of the viaduct. That was kind of creepy. Something like a cold trickle went down my back. My heart started banging on my ribs 'cause I was scared of what they might do to me. But when I thought about how they scared Clayton like that, I got so mad I started to shake. They probably thought I was just scared. But I couldn't believe they'd want to hurt a dumb kid like Clayton. He was like somebody's big dumb old dog, for cryin' out loud.

I yelled at 'em, "Hey, what's the matter with you guys?"

One of them yelled back, "You too, nylon pin-head freak" and threw a rock that hit me in the leg but not very hard.

One of the other guys yelled, "Yeah. What's under that nylon? Somebody's butt or your head?"

Then they all laughed.

Sticks and stones can break my bones but names will never hurt me was something Mom taught me. But like I said big people just don't seem to know how kids think about things.

I took off after Clayton who made it through the swampy part beside the tracks and was on the road up beside his house.

The road was hardly a road. In the winter it was mud but most of the rest of the year it was covered with grass. Today, just two dirt tracks in the grass and fall leaves. Cars didn't use this part much and there was a vacant field across the road from the side of his little house that was on a corner. A real road in front. The field was full of knocked down dry grass all gold in the afternoon sun.

When I caught up to him, he was crying and slobbering and out of breath. He stumbled into the side of his yard behind the little house. The little house looked like Clayton. The roof came way out over the sides of the house like it was looking down at the ground. You couldn't see the eyes.

His older brother was sitting there in a lopsided wooden chair made from tree branches. His blind eyes were ringed around with dark skin and he was rocking back and forth with his head back, just the opposite from Clayton, staring up at the slanting light coming through the yard.

He was making high moaning and wailing sounds. Pounding his tight little fists on his legs that seemed almost as small as the sticks the chair was made of. It was the first time I saw him but something told me they were the only sounds he could make and that he couldn't walk either. I knew someone probably had to carry him outside and put him in that chair.

For me, it was like I was running real fast and I fell in a hole. Like when I hit the bottom it knocked all my air out of me and my teeth came down hard and bit my tongue. But really, I just stopped and stared.

First, I was ashamed. All I had was a shaved head. Then my eyes got all hot and watery. Even with his Jack Armstrong stuff, Scotty was a better brother than Clayton's brother.

"They do that all the time," Clayton said. He was breathing really hard and was trying to grab a hold of a little tree that was growing there so he wouldn't fall down. His black eyes looked up at me and I couldn't see where they ended inside. "Why don't they leave me alone? I can't help-being me."

Then I was all over me hot getting mad again.

Nobody can.

And that time it really started pissing me off people call you names on top of it.

~

So, like I said, I'm standing there with part of Mom's old nylon stocking stretched over my shaved head waiting for Sunny Lea. Sunny Lea was put half a year ahead in school but she has to have some help from her teacher after class 'cause of stuff she missed.

I like walking home with her 'cause we're friends and besides walking to her house, we keep on Capitol Highway and walk over the viaduct instead of under it where those bullies hang out.

In the middle of the viaduct this day like always, we stop and lean on the cement railing. There are arches right underneath the railing that I used to look through when I was little. The railing is wide. Rough cement that has glittery flecks in it. You put your toes on the ledge below the arches, a little above the sidewalk. Then you hang on to the railing and look over. The railing is always a good place to stop and talk. Sometimes, we don't talk. Just look out all the way along the old deserted railroad. Like a really straight river running through the thick green trees on both sides of it. Or sometimes you just look down 'cause you seem so high up. But then I always get a yucky feeling that I never told Sunny Lea about. Like going down fast in an elevator.

"Miss Wilson wants me to sing for class," I say and drop a little pebble down on the rusty tracks. No big kids down there today. Then I have to put my feet down on the sidewalk 'cause of that yucky feeling.

Sunny Lea turns her blue eyes to me. Both arms folded on top the railing. Her brown bangs that are always so neat are blowing every which way in the air. Doesn't say anything until her eyes make me really look at her.

"That's good," she says. "Isn't it?"

"Aw, I don't know." I climb back up with my toes on the ledge under the arches and look down at the railing between my arms. "You know how the kids in my class are."

"Oh," she says soft. Then, "Yeah. Well, you shouldn't let that bother you. You sing pretty good."

I start to tell her she doesn't know how it is with all her hair and me without any standing up singing in class. But she never said my singing was good before.

"Really? You really think so?"

"Yup, I do. Cross my heart." She closes her eyes and nods her head 'cause she can't cross her heart like we do, hanging on to the railing.

"Well, I was thinking I could bring my Brer Rabbit thing and do that instead." The specks flash like tiny treasures in the cement railing. "That way, I could do all the animals' voices and be under the table up front instead of showing my shaved head to everybody."

I was lost inside the sparkles in the railing thinking how singing can make people happy but how it wouldn't make me very happy standing up there in front of everybody but when Sunny Lea didn't say anything, I looked over at her. She was looking out at the tracks that were long gold bars stretching out to Portland in the afternoon sun.

"Well, I guess," she said. "But I still think it would be better if you sang for your class." She got down off the ledge and smoothed her bangs down. Then she pulled the hood of her jacket up over her thick brown hair. Her eyes squinted into the sun and she started walking the rest of the way across the viaduct.

36

Brer Rabbit

Pop, my Granpa Jones, had a funny way of thinking about things. I mean, he seemed to think strange things were funny. Like giving people weird nick names. He didn't laugh out loud but you could tell he thought they were funny. Around his eyes would crinkle up and the crinkles made little sparks in his brown eyes. Like deep inside them, he was laughing. When I was little that used to make me kind of mad 'cause I didn't know what was funny. Like when he called me "Old Fraternity sister."

But I always wanted to think it was funny too 'cause he enjoyed those things so much. It was the same way he ate. He always enjoyed food so much he made you hungry just watching him eat.

One Sunday, Mom and Brew asked Pop if he'd like to go for a drive up the Columbia River on the scenic highway. He loved to get out of the city and he said he'd like to bring my cousins, Margo and Katy with him. Since Gramma Jones died, Pop took care of them a lot 'cause they lived in his house.

So on a warm sunny afternoon, we drove up to the Vista House. It was a beautiful building with eight sides and made of glass. Up high there on the cliffs at a bend in the Columbia River called Crown Point you could see way up the Columbia Gorge and down too. Even across the river to Washington. We never stopped at the Vista House on our way to see Robby and little Joey in The Dalles. We just drove by it. So I never thought about it before that day that you could see all the way to Washington from Oregon.

After we looked at the view, Pop asked all of us kids if we wanted an ice cream cone. Well, of course, we all wanted ice cream. Big people must just forget how it is to be a kid. So we went over to the ice cream shop on the other side of the parking lot. When we walked in the door of the shop, Pop looked down at us kids and said, "Well, what complexion would you like?" His eyes crinkled all around and there were sparks in the brown part, and I laughed. For some reason, calling ice cream by its skin color was funny. I finally got one of Pop's jokes.

Pop loved to tell stories too. I knew they were supposed to be funny but they didn't make me laugh. Pop's eyes showed how much he enjoyed them though and I wanted sparks in my eyes too, feel what it felt like to laugh inside.

His favorites were stories from down south where he came from. He loved to tell me stories about Brer Rabbit or read me stories by Mark Twain. I thought maybe I didn't understand them because they were about the south. Anyway, that's where Pop said Mark Twain was from.

One Saturday morning Let's Pretend, one of my favorite radio programs, was on and the announcer said if you sent two dollars and a box top from Cream of Wheat, they'd send you a kit with the play of "Brer Rabbit and the Briar Patch" with a stage you put together and cut-out characters.

Right away, two dollars I saved from my allowance was in the mail for that kit. I got ten cents every week. I was sure that kit was the answer. Finally I could find out what was funny about Brer Rabbit and enjoy it as much as Pop did.

Sunny Lea and me, we read the story together back when the Brer Rabbit thing came in the mail. But we really still didn't know what it was all about after we read it. That must of been the reason she said I should sing for the class instead of bringing Brer Rabbit. But to stand up in front of class with my mom's stocking on my head was not something I wanted to do. Besides, Miss Wilson would know what the story was all about. So I was going to do it in class to make Miss Wilson happy.

~

I unfolded the cardboard stage that came with the kit and set it up on the big table up in front of the class while all the kids were out to recess. It was pretty small now that it was in the class room. At home it seemed so much bigger. From the back of the room, you could see the red drapes painted around the opening but you could hardly see the tar baby sitting on the stage. But I put all the little animals that talked during the story on the stage and I got under the table. Under there, nobody could see my stocking cap.

All I could hear under there was my heart banging in my ears. It sounded like those big copper drums somebody played in our school orchestra. BaBoom. BaBoom. BaBoom. It smelled kind of funny under there too. Kind of like old food. My head bumped the bottom of the table and, when I reached up in the dark, my hand felt yucky old wads of gum and crusty stuff on the bottom of the table. I wiped my hand on my pants and scrunched down so my head wouldn't bump into that stuff. Then there was another sound. Chalk scraped on the blackboard. I forgot Miss Wilson was still in the class room. She was all milk colored that day like always and just disappeared next to the walls. Maybe that's why she dressed that way. Like a cape that makes you invisible. Pretty neat.

But really, I was thinking so much about Brer Rabbit, I forgot she was there. It was such a dumb story. But Miss Wilson read us dumb stories all the time, so I hoped the class wouldn't notice.

"Are you all set?" Miss Wilson's little voice said.

"Yup," I said from under the table. For the first time, though, like the Williamses, I really wished I was somewhere else. Out playing in the school yard. Chasing the girls like we always did. Anything else so I wouldn't have to be under this table with this dumb story to read that didn't make any sense.

"Well, break a leg," she said.

That was a funny thing to say. It kind of scared me. But there was nothing under there to slip on or anything. Just somebody's old Baby Ruth candy bar wrapper. Right then the bell rang though, like a real loud alarm clock. My heart started to beat in my ears so hard, I swear, it made my head jerk. Even if there wasn't anything scary under there with me, I just wanted to sneak out from under the table. Maybe go to the boys room and hide. Maybe I could tell Miss Wilson I was sick. What a dumb idea to read this story.

But then the door banged open and the room was filled with kids making noise.

"All right, Children. Hurry and take your seats," said Miss Wilson's voice from out there in the class room. "We have a special surprise for you this afternoon."

All the feet, right away, went and got under the desks. Shoes and socks all in rows between the rails that the desks were on.

It was quiet then. Some kids whispered, "What's the surprise?" and "What's that thing on the table?"

My mouth was so dry, it was sticky and already my knees were hurting from kneeling on the floor. Like they used to when I went with Mom to Catholic church. Maybe this is why Miss Wilson thought I might break my leg.

The story was on the dusty floor in front of me but the first sentence was so blurry, I couldn't even read it. It looked more like a snake crawling across the page than words. I took a big breath and picked up the pages that Mom stapled together for me. There was more light coming under the table up close to my eyes and I read to myself, *One day Brer Fox thought of how Brer Rabbit had been cutting up his capers...*

Stupid story.

Then Miss Wilson told everybody that I was going to do a kind of play for them called "Brer Rabbit and the Briar Patch."

Some boy, I think it was Allen Summers, said loud, "Where's Davey?"

"Well he's what we call 'Back Stage.' He's going to narrate the story for us."

Some kids whispered then, "He's under the table." I saw Julie's upside down pony tail and Allen's face hanging down. And there were giggles.

So then Miss Wilson told me it was time to start.

I was so thirsty, my voice kind of stuck at first when I said, "Brer Rabbit and the Briar Patch." Then a girl laughed when I got to "cutting up his capers." At least they thought it was funny so I kept reading. But, you know, I still couldn't figure out what the story was about. Maybe I should of asked Mom when I was practicing reading it with her. But I didn't. I bet Scotty would of told me. Anyway, I just kept reading each word. The next word and then the next. It would be over if I just kept reading each next word. But I still couldn't make any sense out of it.

Then out in the class room there were some whispers and somebody dropped a book on the floor. Giggles. Then somebody's desk squeaked. There was a cough. Then somebody said something. Don't know what. Some more giggles. And Miss Wilson said loud, "Class." So I started reading faster. Words and more words. I flipped to the next page and then the next and right then the words that I read really didn't make sense. It wasn't even a sentence. I looked down and saw I turned two pages at once.

I just kept reading though. It really didn't make any difference since the story didn't make any sense anyway. Just keep reading the words, I said to myself. Then there weren't any more words. I was at the end and it was over.

Miss Wilson was clapping her hands. Whack, whack, whack. Then some of the kids clapped.

I thought maybe I could just stay under the table but Miss Wilson said loud, still clapping her hands, "Davey come out and take a bow."

I came out slow. Stood up too soon and banged my head—stocking cap—on the edge of the table. Giggles. There were all the kids clapping. Making dumb faces. Some were crossing their eyes. Some sticking their tongues out. Some just looking like they couldn't figure out what I just did. Like it was totally stupid. And, there was Sunny Lea standing in the back of the room, the only one smiling. She was there, clapping and it wasn't even her class.

My neck was getting hot. It would have been really stupid to get back under the table so I just went and sat down at my desk instead.

The Brer Rabbit play was the last thing in class that day so Miss Wilson told us she'd see us all tomorrow. Everybody was in the way when I fast tried to get out of the class room. I bumped into kids and almost fell over the desk by the door. But Sunny Lea got out fast and was out in the hall right behind me.

"Davey," she said. "Wait up." Then she was beside me. Blue eyes looking up at me. "What's the matter?"

"Oh, okay. You were right. I should of sang a song," I said. "That thing was dumb. But I just wanted to get it over so Miss Wilson would stop asking me."

"It wasn't dumb," Sunny Lea said shaking her head. Her bangs so neat like always on her forehead.

"But the kids..."

"Oh come on. They're just stupid fourth graders. It was pretty good."

"You're kidding. That was the dumbest thing I ever did." My arms were really heavy. Dead meat. And my throat was kind of burny.

"No really. I finally understood the story. When you see all the characters on the little stage, it's easier to get what the story's all about. Except that part at the end where you left out what happened to the tar baby." Her blue eyes looked kind of like they were laughing then.

They made me almost laugh. too.

"Yeah, I turned too many pages."

"I still think you should sing for your class sometime. But you did good with Brer Rabbit though. Maybe we could do something like that with the rest of the kids in the neighborhood this summer."

"Really? You want to?"

"Yeah. I think it'd be fun."

My throat wasn't burny any more.

"You going home now?" I said.

"Yup," she said.

My knees didn't hurt any more either and we almost started to skip down the hall to the doors with the bar you push to get out of the school.

Right then Miss Wilson's little cream colored heels clicked up beside us.

"Davey, that was wonderful."

Like I said, not a clue how kids feel.

"But I still want you to sing for us." She pushed on the bar and the door opened. "Oh, in all the excitement, you forgot your little stage on the front table. Don't forget it tomorrow."

37

Back Seat

Me and Sunny Lea, we didn't say anything to each other until we got to our spot on the viaduct.

It was one of those windy days in March almost to my birthday. But it wasn't cold and it wasn't raining either like it is most of the time in Oregon. Just cloudy and windy. So we stepped our feet up on the ridge under the little arches and hugged on to the wide railing.

Wind was blowing Sunny Lea's straight brown hair and messing up her bangs. She got back down on the sidewalk and pulled her jacket hood up over her hair so just the bangs showed. Then she got back up and held onto the cement railing. She looked down the railroad tracks like she was trying to see all the way to Portland.

I looked over at her but she wasn't looking at me so I looked down the tracks too.

"Do you really want to do a play or something this summer?" I said and looked back at her.

She just kept looking ahead.

"Sure," she said. Then she turned her blue eyes to me but still looked like she was looking way past me. It was kind of creepy. Like she didn't see me.

But then she did and she said, "I was trying to picture how it'd work this summer. It could be a lotta fun. But you know, Gary's the only other kid our age in the neighborhood. Is Robby gonna be here or is he still sneaking out of the movies?"

The wind that blew down the railroad tracks at us on the viaduct was all of a sudden cold. It made me shiver.

What Sunny Lea meant was the reason Robby, my step-brother didn't come to stay with us last summer. See, almost every month Mom and Brew and me used to go up to The Dalles to visit Robby and little Joey. He was only four last year. But now it was just about a year ago that Mom and Brew and me all got in the Oldsmobile and went up the Columbia Gorge to visit them in The Dalles.

I always liked going up there. The twisty road, the one that used to make me car sick when I was little unless I went to sleep on the back shelf, went through the fir trees high up on the side of the mountains beside the Columbia river and it was always neat in there. Always cool and mossy even in the summer. Mom and Brew let me sit in the front seat with them when I got older. Sitting close together like that made it like we were more of a family. It was good to be snuggled close like that. Like in a big hug. We talked almost all the way. Brew was always working when we were at home except when we were eating dinner. At home, Mom and me, we sat and talked sometimes but it wasn't the same as when we drove up to The Dalles. All together like that was more like I finally had a dad.

And when we got there, we always did something fun. Took the ferry across the Columbia with the car and back again or went on a picnic or went to the Historical Museum. Mom and Brew always called it the Hysterical Museum 'cause that's what little Joey called it at first. The best part of the Historical Museum was the carriage house. They kept about twenty buggies and carriages there in a kind of old dusty barn and they let us play in all of them. My favorite was a beautiful carriage that must of belonged to someone who was rich. It was all leather seats and red velvet walls with buttons and it had straps with gold tassels to hold on to when a horse was pulling it over bumpy roads. Of course, the leather on the seats was all cracked and the velvet was pretty dirty but I loved to sit there and run my hands over the soft velvet and hold onto the tassel, pretend I was somebody important on a trip a long time ago.

There weren't any clouds in the sky that day last year and the sun was out making everything bright and warm. The big blue spruce tree next door in the Herman's front yard so blue and the laurel hedge across 37th Street in front of our house greener than I ever saw it. So Mom made a picnic lunch and packed it in our picnic basket with the red and white checkered table cloth Brew got from a restaurant one time but wouldn't ever tell me how. When I asked him this time about it again, Mom didn't let him answer, she just said we would find a nice place along the river in The Dalles to have a picnic.

I sat in the front seat with Mom and Brew. Mom smelled fresh like spring. Her sweet flower smell perfume. She had on her navy slacks that had the neat short jacket that matched them and the belt where it ended at her waist. Brew told some jokes. Then Mom did.

"I learned a new song from Gary and some other kids at school," I said. "Wanna learn it?"

Mom said, "Okay. Let's try it."

"I'll sing the first words, and then you just copy me," I said.

So I started singing *Found a Peanut*. When I sang, "It was rotten," Mom said, "Ooo, yuck." But we sang the song all the way through and then we sang it all again, louder.

We talked and laughed and sang songs. I got Brew to sing the song about the message in the beer bottle and we all laughed after that. The sun was bright over the cliffs of the scenic highway on the river. A bright, smooth strip of glass down in the Gorge. It was going to be a good day.

The Oldsmobile chugged up the hill to Robby and Joey's house like it was tired from the trip. The house where Robby and Joey lived with Olive, their mom and their step-dad Ralph was a little flat house on the side of a hill stuck between two others just like it. There were no trees or anything there. Just a kind of grassy yard on the side of a dried up hill in the sun. Even the dandelions in the front yard looked tired and half dead from trying so hard to live there.

We pulled up in front and Brew parked the car. I got out and got into the back seat, like always, so Robby and Joey and me could be together in the back seat. Brew went up the straight cement walk in the middle of the yard to the front door and rang the doorbell.

While we sat and waited in the car, Mom told me what she packed in the picnic basket. Cheese and lunch meat sandwiches. Potato chips. Some Jello. Chocolate cake.

"I even brought some of Gramma Brugger's dill pickles," she said. "I know how much you like them."

Then Mom looked out her window to the little house. Her eyebrows wrinkled down like she does. Brew was still standing at the front door. Nobody else was there.

"I'm getting hungry talking about the food. I wonder what's taking so long."

The car was kind of stuffy. Mom opened the wing window in front on her side.

"That's funny. It looks like maybe nobody's home."

Then the door of the little house opened and Olive was standing there talking to Brew. She held the door open just enough for her. Like she was keeping someone out or someone in. Like maybe they had a dog they didn't want to get out.

Her thin neck and kind of long nose. She wasn't smiling.

Then Brew's hand went up like he was saying something important. His palm up. Then his shoulders like he was asking a question.

Olive's face got ugly like she yelled something at him. Her teeth big and her face red. Then she slammed the door.

Brew just stood there looking at the door.

There was a yucky feeling in my stomach. The car was too hot with the windows rolled up but I couldn't move my hand to roll down the window.

Then Brew turned around really slow and walked down that straight cement walk to the car.

When Brew opened his door of the car, it still didn't let any air in. He got in and closed the door slow and just sat there behind the steering wheel.

Mom looked over at him, "Honey?"

There was no sound in the car. No sound anywhere. There were not even sounds outside the car.

Then Brew's arms were up on the steering wheel and his head fell onto his arms.

"Honey?" Mom said. "What is it? What's wrong?"

Brew's head came up. His widow's peak way down and really black in his white face. His eyes red.

"She won't let me see them. She said never again."

"Oh, Honey," Mom said. Her face white too.

Then his wail fills the car and Brew's arms go around Mom squeezing her tight.

His head goes on her shoulder and his face is all scrunched up. Big tears are coming out of his eyes and his mouth all slobbery. "Oh God, oh God."

I never saw a man cry before.

That can't be Brew crying.

My throat is burny.

There's a stain in the mohair on the top of the front seat I never saw before. Right near Mom's shoulder. I wonder if Brew's slobber is going to get on it and make it darker.

~

I'm sitting in the middle of the back seat but nobody knows I'm there. A foot away from Mom and Brew but I'm there all alone. What is in the front seat—those two people and their story—is not anything I'm part of. That man in front of me is a father after all, but not my father and that woman is his wife. My mom isn't there anymore. It's like I'm watching a movie of people I don't know.

Me sitting in the front seat with them like a family, our laughing, feeling close was all pretend—me sitting in a velvet carriage pretending I'm somebody important.

And in that hot car, I'm cold. Really cold.

~

A couple of weeks later Robby called Brew on the telephone. Brew told Mom that Robby said anytime we want to come up he can pretend to go to the movies and we can meet him there but he said he can't bring Joey 'cause he's too little.

"That bitch," Brew said. "How could she put kids through something like this?"

He always used words like that. I wasn't ever going to start using those words.

So anyway, since that time a year ago, that's how we see Robby.

I pulled the collar of my winter coat I was still wearing even though it was March closer around my neck and ran my hand over the sparkles in the cement of the railing on the viaduct. It was always rougher than it looked. The sun came through the clouds but it was still windy.

"Yeah," I said to Sunny Lea. "we still meet him outside of the movies. So he probably won't be here this summer."

"Well," she says, "maybe some of the little kids'll want to do the play with us."

38

Run-Away

The kitchen was all steamy when I got home. The big blue canner with the white specks in it was on the stove bubbling loud. The heavy air was sharp with cinnamon and apples. Mom was canning apple sauce from apples we got from Gramma Brugger's farm out in Aloha.

Mom's swooped up glasses were all steamed up so she didn't see me come in the back door. Her hair was tied up in a bandana like our Aunt Jemima cookie jar and she was singing a pretty song I never heard her sing before about a swan floating down a stream.

"That's pretty," I said. "I never heard you sing that before."

"Davey?" She took off her glasses and squinted up her eyes at me. "I didn't hear you come in. These jars are so noisy." Some of her big skirt was in her hand and she was wiping her glasses.

"How'd your Brer Rabbit show go?"

"Okay, I guess. But Miss Wilson still wants me to sing." My face was getting all over wet from the steam, so I yanked off a piece of paper towel and wiped my face.

"Well, I think you should. You have a nice voice."

That again. I was kind of tired of hearing that.

"Yeah, that's what Sunny Lea says too."

"She's right you know."

"Well, maybe, Mom. But I just don't want to stand up there with a dumb old nylon on my head." Big people. Really, they just don't get some things.

"Oh, honey, I know that must be hard."

Her face all sad looking, she came over by the back door and put her hand on my cheek. Her hand was hot and my cheek was wet. It was kind of yucky.

"Look, if you find something you want to sing, I'll crochet a cap for you so you won't have to wear the nylon stocking. How would that be? Would you like that?" Her face trying to look happy now.

I put my arms around her and hugged my cheek into her stomach. She really was a great mom.

It was just when Brew was around that she didn't seem that way. She never looked at me that special way then. She looked at him that way. Like when he was around, she was His Wife. When he wasn't, she was My Mom. And ever since last summer in the car when we were in The Dalles, I gave up wanting Brew to be my dad. He didn't ever act like he wanted to be, anyway.

"Can I choose the color?" I said.

She put her elbows on my shoulders and kind of rocked us from side to side.

"Sure. Why not?"

"Maybe I could wear it all the time if I liked it."

I looked up at her and she stopped us rocking.

"I don't see why you couldn't. The health department might want you to wear a nylon stocking underneath but if you'd rather wear a cap over it, I don't think that would hurt."

The air in the kitchen didn't seem so heavy then and the apples smelled really sweet. My arms were still around her waist and her arms were around my neck. Elbows kind of lazy like on my shoulders. It was good to stand talking like that with her special look on me.

"That was a pretty song you were singing when I came in. I never heard that before."

"Really? It's part of a song you know."

"It is?" It didn't sound like any song I knew.

"It's the middle part of *Home on the Range*. I guess it's not sung very often. You know the part that goes 'Oh, give me a home where the buffalo roam, where the deer and the antelope play, where seldom is heard a discouraging word and the skies are not cloudy all day.'"

Then we sang together "'Home, home on the range where the deer and the antelope play.'" We sang through the chorus pretty good. Mom singing harmony like she could do. She said we were both tenors 'cause of her smoking. But I wasn't really a tenor yet and she didn't smoke that much. But our voices sounded a lot alike. Kind of straight-no-vibrato-boy sound. People always thought I was her when I answered the phone. When we sang together, it was so tight together. Like parts in one of Dad's watches, made to fit together perfect.

Then she changed the tune going up higher and sweeter and sang that new part by herself. Her misty blue eyes all dreamy, "'Oh, give me a land where the bright diamond sand flows leisurely down the stream, where the graceful white swan goes gliding along like a maid in a heavenly dream.'"

It was so beautiful—the tune and the words—there was a picture in my head of Aunt Pearl's farm early in the morning out in the pasture with the horses. It was kind of a sad picture but parts of it were nice.

~

I went back for a whole month to stay with Aunt Pearl last summer. That was the third summer I was there but it wasn't the same as the two times before. Some of last summer was good 'cause after the first year I was there, I could ride the horses, but the bad thing was that third summer Uncle Herb was gone. I really looked forward to being with my Uncle Herb. He was the only relative I had that really liked kids. Sure, Pop did, but Pop, he just liked people. All people. Oh, and there was my Uncle Lloyd, Brew's older brother. He was pretty nice to me. Mom said he practically raised Brew. He owned an agate shop down town in Portland. And, of course, there was Mom. But she wasn't a relative. She was Mom. Uncle Herb though, he liked kids. You could feel it through his hands. Warm and gentle. Pop, he joked and called me Old Fraternity Sister. But he never got close enough so I could feel anything through his hands.

It was after breakfast in the kitchen one morning last summer, after Mom and Brew and me went up to The Dalles and found out Robby and little Joey couldn't come down for the summer. I guess Mom knew I was kind of lonesome not having them to play with. She called me mopey. Then she asked me if I wanted to go out to Aunt Pearl's dairy farm that third summer for a month.

Right away, I said yes because I wanted to spend some time with Uncle Herb. That first year I was there he taught me how to put the milking machines on the cows and how to get feed out of the silo for them. We even cleaned their poop out the stalls together. He treated me like big people or something.

The second summer I got to drive the tractor. Well, not really. But he let me sit in his lap and steer it. He showed me how to ride too. He even taught me to saddle up the horses and he said he'd start showing me how they break the wild ones the next year.

After that time in The Dalles last summer, I really missed Uncle Herb. He always noticed me. That all over big smile. And he showed me how to do stuff even when it took a lotta time. Like the time he taught me how to tie the cinch under Chubby's saddle. Took forever. Me, I was pretty dumb about knots and stuff. Not like Scotty who was the big Boy Scout.

When I was around Brew, he never even knew I was there. I'd watch him sometimes at his watch crystal shop, especially when he'd put a watch crystal in the little furnace to make it curve. Looking sideways at the little piece of glass when he was putting it in there with the long tweezer thing, his almost black eyes would see me and his eyebrows go up, surprised I was there.

In the kitchen that morning Mom called me mopey and asked if I wanted to go out to Aunt Pearl's again, I told her how much fun it was working on the dairy farm with Uncle Herb and how he told me he'd show me this year how they break the horses they bring down from the mountains.

"You know, Mom, I think the reason it's so much fun to be with him is because he really likes kids," I said.

In Mom's cloud sky blue eyes there was a kind of funny look like she was looking far away.

"He's not there."

I didn't know what she meant at first. Then I got a prickly feeling on my skin 'cause I was afraid maybe I did know.

"Well, where is he?" I said.

"I'm not really sure. He just went away."

That fast-going-down-in-an-elevator feeling was in my stomach again.

"Went away?" I said.

"Davey this is really hard to explain."

Her eyebrows came down and a line was deep between her eyes. It was like she wasn't gonna tell me but I just stood there in front of her in the kitchen. Like I wasn't gonna move until she did tell me. The refrigerator gurgled once like it does. The sound of a plane flying somewhere over the house came in the back door.

"Why don't we sit down and I'll try to explain this to you," she said.

At the robin's egg blue dinette set, Mom made a sound like there was something in her throat.

"This might be kind of hard for you to understand, Davey. You're right about Herb. He really likes kids. He'd make a wonderful father. He's one of the sweetest, most gentle men I've ever known. I think his love for kids is the reason he's not with your Aunt Pearl anymore."

Mom's eyes looked down at her hands on the table. Her ruby ring—eight carrot, French cut—was twisted around her finger almost underneath. She turned it back up right with her other hand.

"You see, Aunt Pearl's doctor told her not to try to have babies now because it might kill her to have anymore."

In my mind I saw Aunt Pearl's face crying. Squeezing my hand and crying in church that day when the man was standing up giving his testimony. How he used to be a drunk and beat his wife 'cause she couldn't give him any babies.

The little mole on Mom's throat was moving up and down and she was saying, "Davey, you remember when I told you how people use those rubbers to keep from having babies?"

"Yeah," I said. "I remember."

She looked down at her ring again real hard.

"Well, Aunt Pearl's church wouldn't let your Uncle Herb use those so that's why she wouldn't sleep in the same bed with him."

The wonderful big bed I got to sleep in when I was at the dairy farm. It was part of what was so great about staying there. I guess that was Aunt Pearl's and Uncle Herb's bed.

"Her church didn't believe in adopting babies either. But Herb really wants to have children. He really deserves to have them, Davey."

Mom's misty blue eyes looked right at me then.

Hard to look back, my eyes all watery. My throat burny.

"So anyway, he finally left the farm so he could be with someone, marry someone he could have children with."

Mom's hands went together like she was praying and the tips of her fingers touched her pretty mouth.

"Do you understand, Davey? I don't want you to think badly of him. He really is a wonderful man."

I didn't think bad of Uncle Herb and I wanted for him to have kids. But just then it was like I didn't have any insides in me.

~

Like Mom said I was mopey in Mudnomah back then. Nobody to play with. My friends gone to summer places. Robby and Joey not there. I wanted to ride horses. So I went last summer to Aunt Pearl's for the third time.

At the dairy farm Uncle Herb being gone made everybody sad. Aunt Pearl was sad. My cousin Velma was sad. Even the horses seemed sad. Their heads drooping down to the grass.

Velma was really different too. Not just sad. She used to be so happy. But now she was mad all the time too. She was mad at Aunt Pearl's church and she was mad at Aunt Pearl for being mean to her dad, Uncle Herb.

"It's that damned, narrow minded church that broke up our family," she said. "And Mom let 'em do it."

She never played her steel guitar any more either. Even when I asked her to.

"Don't feel like it," she said and stamped her cowboy boots out the door. She went out to the pasture. I saw her standing beside Star, her horse, her head on his back, crying. Then she hugged him around the neck, pulled herself up and threw her leg up on him bareback. And she was gone. That's all she did any more was ride off on Star. She'd go off sometimes half a day.

One time I asked her if I could ride Star. He was a beautiful black horse with a white star in the middle of his forehead. His head never drooped like those other horses and his eyes were always bright and really wide open. Like you couldn't fool him, no matter how you tried. Aunt Pearl said he had spirit. Velma's blue eyes shot at me like cold blue icicles when I asked that.

"Nobody rides Star but me. He's my horse. He won't let anybody ride him but me."

My whole body got cold then and hot too at the same time.

I liked riding Chubby. He was a good old horse. But he was an old horse. Kind of slow and fat. He'd plod along the side of the road and I wanted him to gallop. Sometimes he'd gallop for a minute if I used the heel of my boot hard in his flank like Aunt Pearl taught me. Then I'd pretend I was the Lone Ranger on my good friend Silver. But Chubby didn't like to run. You could tell 'cause right away he'd go all poopy again. And I wanted him to run because he wanted to, not because I kicked him. I wanted him to have spirit.

Star was a young horse and like Aunt Pearl said, he had spirit. He was so beautiful to watch. Even when he was just grazing in the pasture I could watch him for hours. His smooth muscles moving under his black silky coat. Quiet right then, but those muscles could explode and he'd be running in a minute. There was something still wild about him.

And I really wanted to ride him.

So I made a plan.

One morning I woke up really early. It was still almost dark out. I didn't want to take the time to saddle Star up because Aunt Pearl and

Velma or some of the farm hands would be up soon. So I quiet opened his stall and went in and stood in front of him, kind of like Scotty's Jack Armstrong—my chest out, swinging my arms a little bit, so he backed out. I soft patted his neck, high up as I could reach, and just walked him out of the barn. In the pasture, I climbed up on the rail fence beside him, took ahold of his mane to keep him steady and threw my leg over him like I saw Velma do. I guess since he didn't know what I was doing, Star, he jumped a little and snorted when I landed on him. But then he went calm again.

The grass there was cool and damp and Star yanked up a mouth full and started to munch. Light was coming up into the gray sky and glowed on the top of the hills around the pasture. A mourning dove was hooting every few minutes and there was the sour kind of sharp smell of buttercups in the grass that Star walked on mixed with his warm horse smell. A cool kind of damp breeze blew over the hills and down into the pasture. I was so glad to be at Aunt Pearl's again high up on this strong beautiful horse. His coarse mane twisted in my fingers. His muscles moving slow under my legs. To be taller than I ever was before. Like I fast grew to be a giant. Alice after she ate the cake that said 'eat me' on it. The buttercups then, tiny yellow specks down there. It was like a wonderful dream. But real. I didn't have to pretend any more like with Chubby.

Star didn't seem to mind me up on him at all. He was fine.

I took him once around the fence listening to him snort now and then like he was talking to me. Then out through the gate and onto the gravel road 'cause that's what he was telling me to do. He was calm as we started away from the farm. I leaned down and talked to him nice and he twitched his ears and snorted like he liked me talking to him.

When we got up beside the pavement, I let him run a little. He was still fine. So I thought we better go back before everybody got up.

We turned around toward the farm and Star was all a sudden different. His skin shivered under me like a little wave. His head snapped up and a high sound squealed up loud out of his mouth. It was like he was asleep and when he saw the farm and barns, he woke up and took off down the gravel road. His front hooves hit the gravel like exploding and I almost flew off his back. But my hands held on to his mane and his rear came up hard under my fanny. Then he was galloping. It was like flying. Not pretend flying like on the Moo-cow Hill, but really flying. Damp morning air blew by my ears and every part of my body jerked and pulled over his powerful legs under me. His body pounding my butt, rocking me in his rhythm.

A crazy buzzing came up from between my legs and into my chest. Then it came out my mouth and I couldn't stop it. I yelled, "Yahoo." Then again louder, "Yahoo, Star." Nothing was ever this exciting. Laughing was coming out of me and I yelled, "Yeah, go Star."

Aunt Pearl and Velma standing on the porch were statues. Statues standing next to each other staring at me and Star coming up to the house lickity split. Their arms limp. Mouths hanging open. Dumb cow looks on their faces.

I pulled on his mane and tried to slow him down but it was like I wasn't even there. He was snorting loud and lather came up on his coat. His smell really strong. He was going way too fast. Gravel crackled and banged against the porch flying up behind us as he tore down the road by the house.

I yelled at him, "Whoa, whoa. But he just kept tearing down the road. No matter what I did, Star kept going. He didn't even slow down when Velma started screaming, "Star, Star. Whoa, Star." He was going for the barn.

That exciting buzz turned scary in me

Velma threw something down hard on the porch. I think it was his bridal. She cussed and Aunt Pearl hollered at her but Velma jumped off the porch and started running for the barn.

All I could see then from where I was on Star was the top of the barn door coming for my head and my head split open by it. A big red splat all over the top of the barn.

I didn't think I could duck low enough to get under. But there was this pipe running all along just under the top of the door. Almost there, I reached out and it was in my hands. Star tore under it and the pipe stayed in my hands. It was really cold or hot I couldn't tell, but it pulled me off his back. Star's hooves were clomping on the cement floor in the barn, slowing down and I tried to let go of the pipe. But my hands didn't want to let go. They were stuck. Then this awful pain shot up my arms and I fell off the pipe onto the ground.

My hands were burning something awful. I sat up and looked down at what used to be my hands. Weird looking. Gray white skin. Just pieces. Skin was gone off of both of my hands and while I was looking blood started to ooze out. Little red rubies from under the raggedy edges of the gray white pieces. Like the ruby in Mom's ring. Then flashing sparks in my eyes. Black walnut milkshake yuck in my stomach.

"Oh my Lord, Davey. Are you all right?" Aunt Pearl said kneeling next to me on the ground.

"I guess so," I said. "But my hands-"

She reached out and grabbed my hands. Trying to see. Squeezed them in hers, she was so worried.

I hollered, "Ow." More black walnut milkshake yuck in my stomach.

"Oh, I'm sorry, Davey." Her face all scrunched. "You were hanging onto the freezing pipe. It runs to the cooling house to cool the milk." The wart by her bottom lip that made Aunt Pearl, Aunt Pearl quivered and she let out a big breath. "I don't know if it would have been worse to just hit your head."

"Serves him right," Velma said, standing over me with her cold blue eyes. "I told him Star was my horse."

Her eyes didn't make me feel cold this time or hot either. I was sorry I made her mad but she was mad all the time anyway and I really didn't want to ride her horse any more. I had enough of Star, the demon horse. And besides, my hands hurt way too much to feel anything else.

~

After that I was happy to ride my "half a horse," Chubby. And I loved being on Aunt Pearl's farm even though I missed Uncle Herb a lot. I kind of thought of it as my home on the range. So there in that steamy kitchen full of apple and cinnamon smells, Mom and me, we sang that song over and over—maybe a bazillion times—while I helped her lift the apple sauce jars out of the big blue canner with the white specks and set the jars out on the back porch to cool off. By the bazillionth time I knew the part about the swan gliding along really good. It was then Mom stopped singing and I was singing it all by myself.

"I think you should sing it for your class." Mom said.

I looked quick at her and she started to laugh. She's pretty smart, my Mom.

Her head went back and her mouth dropped open and she laughed. What Brew called her hearty laugh.

So I laughed too and said, "Sure why not?" I liked singing about my home on the range.

39

Ring A-Ding

The cap Mom crocheted for me was royal blue.

I got to choose it.

It made my white skin and freckles show up a lot but Mom said it was great with my blue eyes. So, okay. It was better than some dumb old nylon stocking.

The day that Miss Wilson wanted me to sing for class was a Monday. In her little milky voice, she said, "It'll be good to start the week off with a bang."

But Monday was the morning I had to go to the health department at the City Hall to have my ring worm checked. So, Miss Wilson said to sing on Monday afternoon.

~

Mom was downstairs getting breakfast and singing April Showers 'cause it was April and the rain from last night stopped that morning and the sun was out. I put my new cap on in front of the mirror in my bathroom upstairs and sang April Showers along with her long distance. That no-vibrato-boy sound. I let it echo me. Then I echoed her. No harmony 'cause I couldn't do that.

I was happy. No more nylon stocking. Well, almost. Since I had to go down to the City Hall, it was underneath my new royal blue cap.

After breakfast, Mom and me, we walked up Spring Garden Street to the bus. Me in my new royal blue cap. Mom in her gray going-down-town suit with a new white scarf with red poke-a-dots and red hat that had a veil just over her curly bangs. She had on new spring white shoes too.

She looked up at the sky. Her eyebrows pulled down.

"I hope it's not too wet for these shoes," she said. "Hate to get them all spotted."

Mom always looked stylish.

I was proud she looked so good.

She stuck her umbrella under her arm and we started up the black-top on Spring Garden that everybody in the neighborhood paid twenty dollars for. We were promised no more Mudnomah. Only problem was the black-top stopped just before the Herman's house next door and didn't go in front of our house.

The big nurse in the white coat at the City Hall led us into the room where the black light was. The white coat made her look like a white buffalo or something...

Poor woman.

They shouldn't make a big fat woman wear a white coat.

Her big cheeks went up in a smile, "I see you have a new cap. It's pretty. Your mother make that for you?" She winked at Mom.

"Yup," I said. I hated coming here and really didn't want to be friends with the people who poked wooden sticks around in my ring worm. Yuck.

I sat down in the high swively chair and the big nurse lady turned off the lights. There was that creepy look of everything in the black light again. Everything looked kind of like it does in a nightmare. Mom's face right beside me dull gray looking above her glowing white scarf with black dots and her teeth glowing white too. The nurse a huge burst of white electric light.

She took off both my caps and then there was the tickley tooth-pick scraping through the bristles on my shaved head. And there was the, "Hmmm," like always from the big nurse. Then another one. And another. A lot more than usual.

Then she said out loud, "Well, okay."

The lights snapped on bright. I squeezed my eyes. She looked at Mom with her round cheeks up in a big smile and said, "Gone."

Mom's eyebrows went up in two little arches like on the viaduct except even smaller. Her misty sky blue eyes just fixed on the big nurse lady.

"What?" she said.

"It's good news, Mrs. Brugger. The ring worm's gone. You made this cute blue cap just in time. He won't need it much longer. He can let his hair grow out again. The ring worm is gone."

I couldn't believe it. No more Desinex for athlete's foot on my head. No more shaved head and no more stocking cap. My eyes were full of tears and they started running down my face. I was crying, for cryin' out loud. And in my head was what Mom told me when I sang for Gramma Jones that Christmas before she died. "Sometimes people cry when they're really happy."

I was really happy.

40

Sing A-Ling

The lunch lady was starting to take the metal pans away in the Cafeteria by the time I got back to school. Mom said I could eat in the cafeteria. She didn't make my lunch 'cause of going to City Hall and the health department.

Macaroni and cheese like almost every day in the cafeteria.

That place always smells like macaroni and cheese. That left-over-old-food-dirty-laundry smell. Even when it's the auditorium and there isn't any food there, it smells like macaroni and cheese. The school calls it the cafetorium. The shows we give there always smell like macaroni and cheese. The choir, even the school orchestra smell like macaroni and cheese.

I didn't care though. I didn't care if I had dog food for lunch, I was so happy my ring worm was gone. So the lunch lady put a big pile of mushy orange and brown macaroni she scraped up from the bottom of the pan with a roll and a little carton of milk on my tray and I ate it in the empty cafetorium. Kids hollering outside on the playground. The lunch lady banging trays and dirty dishes and silverware. Then the big clicking clock on the wall said it was time for me to go sing for my class.

I had on my royal blue cap. I didn't have ringworm anymore. And I didn't care if the kids liked my singing or not. Skipping was absolutely the best way to get to class that day. My arms flapping and my feet making a ta-dum, ta-dum, ta-dum all the way down the brown tile hall from the cafetorium, past the boys room and art class, to my fourth grade room.

Miss Wilson was waiting for me. She was sitting at the piano that was always in the corner in front of class under the bulletin board with our colored art paper art-work on it. *Home on the Range* music was sitting on the piano. The brown wood piano really made her show up. She didn't disappear into the wall like most times.

"Well, Davey, the bell is just about to ring. I guess we'll just have to wing it."

Her little voice was so soft, or maybe I just couldn't figure out what she said. So I didn't say anything. Tried not to be stupid.

"I meant, I guess we don't have time to rehearse," she said. "We'll have to wing it."

"Oh, yeah," I said. "That's okay."

There was this itchy bubbling inside of me, like I wanted to laugh or something. No more ring worm. So I quick just sat down at my desk.

"I think you'll do fine," she said. She stood up then and disappeared against the wall.

The bell rang. The door flew open. Kids yelling and pushing all around me. My body was all jumpy like I wanted to run around pushing everybody and yell, "It's gone. No more ringworm."

~

I didn't even hear what Miss Wilson was saying. I was so far away being happy. But then I heard her say my name.

"...Davey, who is going to sing for us today."

Some kids clapped slow then. Like we clap for those dumb school movies about how they make sawdust or how they deliver mail in Costa Rica. Where ever that is. Some of them just giggled or hissed through where their front teeth were supposed to be… And I heard Allen groan. Like, "Not again. Wasn't Brer Rabbit enough?" But I just didn't care.

Miss Wilson looked at me. Then she did that com'ere thing with her finger. So I got out of my seat and started up front. Royal blue cap and no ringworm still making itchy bubbles through me.

Miss Wilson sat down at the piano and then turned around again. Big smile in her creamy face.

"Most of you know some of this song but Davey's going to sing a part we've never heard before."

Then she winked and nodded her head real big to me—big for Miss Wilson who always did everything small—and started to play the piano.

~

Something happened to Miss Wilson then. She really changed. My Aunt Ethelyn with the funny thumb could play the piano but not like this. When Miss Wilson started to play, it was like you could hear a whole orchestra. Big chords came rolling out of that piano like they were really cellos and trombones and those big copper drums. Her little hands came down on the keys so strong she could of lifted the whole piano with one of them.

She was like Clark Kent. Look it's a bird. It's a plane. It's Miss Wilson. I never heard anyone play the piano like that.

Then she slowed way down and looked at me. I was listening so hard, I forgot I was supposed to sing. But she nodded again real big at me and I remembered. So I started to sing. It was great. It was more than great. It was like a whole orchestra got together to make my singing better. And I heard Mom sing too. Singing harmony with me. That no-vibrato-boy sound.

It was like a lot of people wanted to help me sound good.

The crazy buzzing that I felt riding Star at Aunt Pearl's came up again from between my legs and filled up my chest. This was really exciting. Like riding bare back. I just let that buzzing come up and out of my mouth. This was really making music. The picture of Aunt Pearl's farm in the morning, no more ringworm and Miss Wilson's orchestra filled up the class room. I was running around pushing everybody and yelling, "No more ringworm." But really I was just standing there singing. Singing about my royal blue cap and no more ringworm. Singing for me. Not for Gramma or to make bad things go away. Just standing there singing 'cause I was happy.

I got to the last time of the chorus. Mom singing with me and Miss Wilson's orchestra both in my head. And Miss Wilson turned to the class and hollered, "Let's everybody sing." Then the whole class started to sing. Like they wanted to help too. *"Home, home on the range where the deer and the antelope play."* I could hear ugly Ina's high soprano voice. Really pretty. And Allen just kind of yelling. *"Where seldom is heard a discouraging word."* All our voices together. *"And the skies are not cloudy all day."*

Everybody was yelling and clapping then and banging their feet on the floor. Ina was laughing and jumping up and down. Allen let out a loud whistle. That hurt-your-ears kind of whistle between your fingers I could never do and wished I could. And all the kids came up front pushing and bumping around me and patted me on the back and stuff. After all those months of not wanting to get near my ringworm.

Allen said, "Great, man." He looked like Scotty doing Jack Armstrong. Chest out, arms swinging.

In my head, all the kids lifted me up and put me on Allen and Eddy's shoulders and marched me around the whole room and down the hall. Cheering. But really, they didn't.

Clayton was there looking down at the floor in all that noise and shoving, saying something. I heard, "Good," so I told him, "Thanks." My throat was burny then. So my hand squeezed his shoulder and he looked up and smiled.

~

I don't know what happened the rest of that afternoon. I can't remember anything. Except Sunny Lea was in the hall outside the room after class. And she asked how my singing went.

"It was great," I said.

Her blue eyes looking at me closed then and she said, "Told you so."

41

Bare Back

I already knew that singing was a great way to not think about bad things that happened to you. But that day I sang for class, I learned that singing when you're happy, can be like riding bare back on a wild horse brought down from the mountains. It can be the most exciting thing that ever happened to you.

42

Hocus Pocus

You'd think that whoever makes the good stuff happen would of thought that they gave me enough for a while. But I guess that's not the way it works.

Mom says life is hills and valleys. Some days it's hills. Some days valleys. I guess, some days when you're on a hill and you think you've got to the top, you haven't. Same as the valleys.

It was raining really hard after school that Monday and I slopped home with Sunny Lea and Gary through the mud puddles and clumpy wet weeds. High as your knees in places along the way from all the spring rain. Down the big hill on 39th Street and up the other side. Along Sunny Lea's field filled with zillions of daffodil leaves and stems wet and blowing in the wind. Not blooming yet.

It was good to get up to the new black-top on Spring Garden Street. My jeans soaked almost to my knees and cold. The wet bottoms slapping heavy on my legs. I just wanted to get home and take them off. So I said, "See ya later," to Sunny Lea and Gary and ran down the black-top to our house. Half way home from school the rain stopped but those jeans were yucky wet on my legs and I wanted to put dry ones on.

Mom wasn't home from work yet. So after I changed my jeans, I went into the bathroom and took off my royal blue cap that she made for me. The hood on my jacket kept it dry in the rain but it was hot on my head 'cause I still had that crummy old nylon stocking under it. I took it off. And all of a sudden a prickly tingle went through me and I was happy all over again. It was the last time I was going to take that nylon stocking cap off. The last time I had to wear that stupid thing.

In the mirror my head was just kind of pink and normal under my bristly short hair. No more ring worm. When I put the royal blue cap back on, it looked real good. My friend, Mrs. Baldwin would love the color too. Like I did. She really liked colors.

I put my jacket back on and went out the front door to show her my new cap and tell her about my singing. I didn't need the hood because the rain was over and the sun was out on the edges of gray clouds in the sky.

Everything was wet and dripping though. April Showers. The laurel hedge across the street was shiny wet and the weeping willow tree, at the top of the hill down to the Baldwin's, was really weeping. Rain tears dripping down from the droopy branches.

I started down the hill in the muddy ruts where the black-top on Spring Garden ended. Watched my feet so I wouldn't step in any big globs of mud. Singing to myself that pretty tune, *where the graceful white swan goes gliding along like a maid in a heavenly dream.* Half way down, I looked up and across the field to Billy's old house.

~

There, across the field, in the road in front of Billy's house, was a curly blond headed boy looking across the field to where I was standing. My feet stopped walking and a shiver went all the way from the top of my head to my feet standing in the muddy road.

There was a huge giant's hand grabbing tight around my chest, squashing air out of me. I couldn't move and my voice was being squeezed too.

Then the boy saw me and he waved. A slow motion, big wave. Like you wave to the engineer, the conductor, the whole train speeding by you on the tracks.

The giant let go then. I didn't do that funny com'ere thing, no you com'ere, that Billy and me always did. I just screamed, "Billy," and jumped down into the wet muddy field and started running to the other side.

Tall wet weeds and grass slapped me in the face and tugged at my jacket and the gooey mud made sucking sounds pulling at my shoes like it was all trying to keep me from getting to the other side. Like in one of those nightmares where you're trying to get somewhere and you can't get there.

In my head I heard Billy singing, "Mud people, mud people."

It didn't matter how wet or muddy I got. I just had to get to the other side. I pushed through the soggy weeds whipping at my eyes making tears so I could hardly see. But that nightmare mud, it didn't want me to get there. It pulled at my shoes until it pulled one of my shoes all the way off. Before I could stop, my foot with the sock on it went right in the cold gooey mud. My sock plowed into the yucky mud and cold slime oozed through it and around my foot inside the sock. One of Brew's cuss words almost came out but I just yelled, "Stupid mud." And was down on my knee trying to get my shoe back on over my muddy sock.

Those wet jeans on my skin coming home from school weren't anything next to this.

I look up then, like he might not still be there, but he's standing there watching me. Waiting. I scream, "Billy," again and get back up running. The weeds and mud still pulling at me. My shoe trying to come off again. My sock squishy in the shoe.

I'm climbing up on to his road when he says, "How did you know my name?"

The muscles in my legs just don't want to work. I trip on some rocks on the bank. And there's something like the ocean in my ears. But when I hear what he says, I look up at him again.

Wrong face. Wrong body. Wrong smile.

~

It wasn't Billy.

The giant grabbed me again and I almost fell down but I got up to the road and just stood there like an idiot trying to get my breath.

"How'd you know my name's Billy?" he said again.

It was like that giant took his fist and pounded me on top the head into the pavement. My ribs were crushed. My head ached. My legs crumpled and I was only two fingers high. My voice came out like I was just that small.

"M-my friend, Billy, he-he lived in that house," and I pointed my tiny finger up at Billy's old house.

The new Billy's eyebrows scrunched down under that curly blond hair that was just like the other Billy's and his blue eyes laughed the same way. Crinkles around them like I said something funny.

"We just moved in there yesterday."

It was over two years since I saw Billy. But this kid wasn't him. He was too short.

I looked down at my muddy shoes. My clean dry jeans all over wet and muddy. Scotty's voice from somewhere, "Stupid."

Out of the top of my eyes I could see the new Billy look down at his clean shoes and he real soft said, "Were you good friends?"

"The best," I said, and looked up at him. But he was still looking down at his shoes.

His face got all over red, especially his neat little ears that didn't stick out like mine did.

"I don't have any friends here. Yet." He watched the toe of one of his shoes push into the wet gravel by the road. "You wanna come up to the back yard and talk?" He looked up at me then.

This new Billy, his eyes weren't always laughing—like he knew something I didn't. This Billy was kind of shy. And maybe it was like I was older than he was. Maybe not.

But even when I was all over wet and muddy and cold, something warm started in my chest and went through my whole body. Made my body relax then. The giant was gone.

"There's a porch on the garden shed we can sit on."

"I know," I said.

So we went up through all the weeds where the driveway used to be to the garden shed up in back. It was a little bit cold and wet but the sun was really out from the clouds now. Kind of underneath them. Like just before it goes down. It was shining right on that little porch. On the steps where we sat and talked.

He told me his name was Billy Walters and he was really nervous coming from another school and everything. But I told him most of the kids were okay. It would just take time to get to know them. He was in the same grade as me so I told him I'd get him to know everybody.

"Is the teeter totter still out in the woods?" I said. "I mean, your woods?"

"Sure," he said. His eyes did look like they were laughing then. Like maybe we were too old for that. "Do you want to teeter totter?"

My face got red then and I laughed. "Yeah. You want to? I really like that ol' thing. Billy and me, uh, the other Billy, we used to spend a lotta time there."

"Okay," he said.

So we walked down where the path used to be into the woods. The path was almost gone now. All grown over with grass and weeds. But it was almost summer, school was almost out and we could make it a real path again.

43

Dream Things

Like I said, you'd think that whoever makes the good stuff happen should of thought they gave me enough for a while. But the good stuff didn't just end when I met Billy Walters. At least I kept telling myself it was good stuff.

My favorite radio program, Gene Autry was on. I was doing my art homework upstairs in my bedroom and listening to my old wood radio with the carved wood flowers on it.

I was really excited about the homework 'cause it was the first time since I showed Gramma Jones my picture when I was little that I ever drew anything that looked like what it was supposed to be except for mountains. I don't know how it happened.

There was some paper on my kind of drawing board desk thing I used for school. Really, it was an old sick-table Mom and Brew got for Gramma Jones when she was at our house with cancer. It would fit over the covers on the bed to eat off of or you could tilt it so it would make a drawing board. I had it tilted and was sitting on the edge of my bed.

So, I had some paper on it. Just blank paper. I didn't know what to draw. I was bored 'cause nothing was happening, so I started playing around with stuff.

There was this left over candle in my bedroom from Christmas. It was sitting there for months. There was even some dust around the wick. I lit it and it crackled and sparked burning the dust. Then the flame jumped up and it kind of hypnotized me. After a little bit, I picked up this old magnifying glass and fiddled around with it by the blank paper. I don't know how it happened but it made this neat design on the paper from the candle shining through it. Like an hour glass shape made of light. If I moved the magnifying glass just a little, it changed the design. One way made it taller. The other way shorter. The design was most of the time fluttering. But then it just stopped and held still. An hour glass made of white light floating steady on the blank paper. That made me look back at the candle.

The candle was burning real steady and the flame wasn't like anything I ever saw before. It had a perfect tear shape that was outlined with black. Black like velvet. And the outline went up to the tip of the flame on both sides. The two sides joined together then and made one long high, perfect straight line of black in the air that got thinner and thinner the higher it went until it disappeared in the air. The line looked like it was drawn by charcoal.

So I did. I drew that line in charcoal on my paper. And then the flame. How it was red orange in the middle. Then halfway just orange. Yellow outlined in velvet black on the edge. My colored pencils didn't do it deep enough so I ran to the bathroom and used some water. The colors blurred together deep just like fire. My blood was beating extra strong in my chest when it worked. Wow.

The candle was next, with drips. It was sitting on a rock in a cave. The drips were tear shaped too. I made them red like blood. Not just red, but brown red like real blood. And then a window on the wall of the cave that made it look even more spooky. A candle dripping blood in a cave with a window.

I scooched back on the bed and looked. From there, it was a candle burning right in front of me. I put my hand out and it went into the picture. Into the cave. I could almost put my hand around the candle. Feel the bumps of wax. Smell it burning. I could almost pick it up it was so real.

The blood beating was a buzzing in my chest then. It made me laugh. I made this. And it was so good. And kind of scary.

The picture, it was like a dream—a dream where you don't know what things mean.

I finished the drawing and Gene Autry's voice was in my ears. Singing "Back in the Saddle Again." It was ending and I didn't even know what that program was about. The Great Gildersleeve's shoes were clicking on the sidewalk on the radio now and I didn't know anything that happened on Gene Autry. In that cave, inside my drawing, I didn't hear anything on my favorite radio program and now it was over.

"Davey?" Mom said from the doorway. "Are you busy?"

I jumped 'cause I was just coming back from far away in my head someplace, from those dream things. Dream things I didn't know what they meant.

"Just doing my art homework," I said. My ears were hot like she caught me doing something I shouldn't of.

"Can I have a look?" Mom said in that high voice she always asked in, about how my day went, tucking me in at night.

"Sure," I said.

"Oh my. That's very unusual," she said and pushed her glasses back up on top of her nose. Those swooped up glasses were all the time slipped down.

"I think I'm gonna call it 'Dream Things.'"

She nodded her head and kept looking at the picture. Her eyebrows pulled down, like she was worried or trying to figure out something about the picture. Maybe about me. "Uh huh. Well, it does look like a dream or something. And very real. It's pretty good, honey. I don't think you've ever drawn anything so life-like."

"You like it?" I said.

"Yes. Very much."

Mom turned and looked at me then. Like she looked at the picture. With lines in her forehead. Looking deep. Like trying to see something inside. She took her glasses off then and rubbed the top of her nose between her fingers and put her glasses back on.

"I have something I want to ask you, Davey."

"Okay," I said. Her eyes looked so serious I thought maybe it was something bad. So I watched the little mole in the V of her throat. It was easier than to look in her serious eyes.

She sat down next to me on the bed. Her thigh touched mine. Too close. Again like she was going to say something I might not want to hear. The announcer guy on Great Guildersleeve was talking so Mom leaned over and turned the knob to Off. Then she scooted back on the bed and turned her knees toward me.

"You know that Brew wants to be your dad, right?"

"Right...?" I said. But I didn't really know that. He never acted like he did. I mean he didn't act like he didn't want to be my dad. But he didn't act like he wanted to either. We hardly ever did anything together. Never without Mom. No bike rides to the top of Rocky Butte.

When Robby and Joey were staying with us he took us early in the morning to watch them feed the animals at the zoo. But he never asked just me to go. Never just us two. Like kids when I had the ringworm, afraid to get close to me.

"Well, we've decided to make it legal," Mom said. She looked her eyes down and smoothed her hand on my colored snow flake quilt. "John would like to adopt you and make it official that he's your dad."

Cold. My hands were really cold. And there was this big empty place in my head. I had to take some breaths like I was swimming. My hands went between my legs to get warm.

"But what about Dad, my real dad?"

Mom's face got all over red and she took a deep breath too.

"Davey, your father—Earl—hasn't contributed to your support for over a year." She said his name like it was a bad word or something. "Anyway, he's given his consent for your adoption."

My face was real hot right then and I looked at my "Dream Things" picture. Those things you don't know what they mean.

A candle dripping blood? I wanted to say to Scotty that time, *"Don't go. Stay here with us."*

"What we do is, we fill out some papers your Grandpa Pop drew up for us," Mom was saying, "and then we go to the county court house and see a judge." There were little lines coming down into her lips I never noticed before.

From cigarettes?

She wasn't smiling. "The judge is the one that can make John your dad legally."

How can anybody make somebody your dad if he's not really your dad?

I looked at her eyes. They were so serious it was almost scary. All the misty clouds that make Mom's eyes her eyes were gone. Just solid blue. Like she wasn't my mom at all.

"Would you like that?"

How could I like that? That Brew was gonna make me his when my dad didn't want me anymore?

I just looked at her scary blue eyes and said, "Uh huh."

"I thought you would. It's a very wonderful thing John is doing—to become your father. He agrees to take care of you and support you from now on. Make you his own son, Davey Brugger."

It was like there was this really big room, there in my head, that didn't have any walls. The room was empty. There weren't any chairs or tables. And when I looked, there wasn't a ceiling or a floor either. I was just walking around in the air. There wasn't anything that meant anything there.

Then Mom, she said, "And you can also pick a middle name. You know I told you I never gave you one because people usually don't like the name they're given. So now you can pick one that you like and it will be your legal name."

Her eyes were those misty sky blue ones again and her pretty mouth turned up in a smile.

I could pick a middle name. In that big empty room then, there was a chair. A carved wood one like my favorite one in my bedroom with lion claws to put your hands on and a soft velvet back and seat. Comfortable. So I sat down.

"Uh huh," I said to her again.

~

For the next couple days, names were in my head all the time. Michael, Allen, Richard, even Pop's real name, Ancel. My favorite was Michael but there was one big problem with that name. It was that stupid bully Michael that was in my class since kindergarten.

He was fat and mean with little pig eyes. He always hung out with the big kid bullies under the viaduct. The guys that were mean to Clayton. I just didn't want his name. But I couldn't think of a name I liked better. I guess Davey really wasn't that bad. But it was so neat to get to choose your name. None of the kids I knew got to do that.

There was a big bowl of oatmeal mush in front of me on the robin's-egg-blue table. I didn't like oatmeal very much anyway but I was thinking names and poking at the mush.

Mom was cleaning up the kitchen and Brew already went to work.

"Why so mopey?" Mom said and sat down at the table across from me.

She was in her new white robe. It had rows of fuzz on it too like her old pink one. Mom called it chenille. Her hair was up in pin curls under her white Aunt Jemima scarf tied around her head. Her swooped up glasses were funny. Didn't fit with her no-make-up-morning-face.

"Oh, I'm just thinking of names," I said.

"Have you picked one yet?"

"No. Can't think of one I want."

"Well, Davey you know it would really make John happy if you took his name."

"But I am, Mom. I'm going to be Davey Brugger."

"No, no. I mean, John for your middle name."

Fast-going-down-in-an-elevator. And in my head is that empty room again with no floor. But this time, I'm falling fast through the no floor.

I poked my spoon deep in my mush and the picture in my head stopped.

John?

Of all the great names there are, I have to be John?

"It would really be nice since he's agreeing to be your new dad."

Mom's hand flat on the robin's egg blue table. Like she was reaching to hold my hand. Eight-carat-French-cut looking up at me.

Oh, poop. I don't want to be John.

I didn't take Mom's hand.

Well, it wouldn't be very nice if I said I didn't want to be John.

Couldn't it be some other name though? Damn it.

My ears burny. Brew's cuss word in my head.

I loved my mom though. So it was like eating that oatmeal I didn't like. It would make her unhappy if I said I didn't want to.

My voice got stuck in the mouthful of oatmeal I took, but I said, "Okay."

~

So Mom and Brew, they took me to this new store called Robert Hall to buy me a silk tie and a suit. I never had a suit before but Mom said if I was going to go before a judge, I had to dress up. Brew said Robert Hall was a good place to go because they had swell deals. Some friends of his bought suits there and he said, "They didn't cost an arm and a leg."

~

Now, this was all good stuff. A new dad. A new name. A new suit.

At least Mom, she thought it was good stuff.

~

Inside the courthouse smelled like in the big old Portland library and the building where Pop had his law office. The oily smell of furniture wax from old wood tables, railings, doors and shelves. The glue smell of book bindings from thousands of old books lining the shelves. And the sharp smell of brass polish from door knobs, name plates and spittoons in every corner. They were all good smells. Like we were here to do something important.

Heels of shoes clicked on marble floors, swinging doors swished and people whispered in hallways. And there I was in my new light tan suit and my new grown-out hair slicked down with water and Wildroot Cream Oil Hair Tonic. It all made my skin prickly. I was glad I was there with grown ups. Skin prickly is okay with grown ups there.

I never saw Brew so dressed up. His suit was really swell. Light tan like mine. But the front crossed over and buttoned on the other side. Mom called it double breasted. I never heard of breasts on men before. But the thing was, Brew was all dressed up. He never got dressed up. It was like he really wanted to do this. Maybe he really did want to be my dad like Mom said.

We were standing in a big empty hallway waiting for Pop. For some reason, I had to keep taking lots of breaths.

Mom took my hand and squeezed it. Then she stepped back and looked at me and Brew in our suits, our white shirts and ties and she said, "Just look at my two handsome fellas."

My stomach got all funny and buzzy when she said that.

Pop met us with a cigar in his mouth and just nodded to me. No Old Fraternity Sister or anything. He didn't even take the cigar butt out of his mouth. His big leather brief case was in one hand and after he whispered to Mom and Brew, he took off his hat and pointed with it to some swinging doors.

Even Pop was acting like this was a big deal.

His wet yucky cigar stub landed in the spittoon by the doors with a thunk and we went into the courtroom. Inside, we sat down on a wood bench like in church. There was wood everywhere. Wood wax smell in the air. Wood walls. Wood benches. A wood railing up front and a high wood desk above it.

The judge was sitting up there behind it, all in black. He hollered out something and Pop said, "Here, your Honor."

He motioned for us three to follow him and he went up and handed a folder to a man that handed it to the judge. Paper crinkled like tissue paper when the judge turned the pages in it. Crinkling sound that tickled my skin like the pages were touching me. His big bushy eyebrows came down then almost to the big nose in his red face and the judge looked down at me standing there. Down behind the railing between Brew and Mom.

Right then, I was really proud I was all dressed up next to Brew in his red silk tie and double breasted suit. His Old Spice smell. My new dad. And next to my movie star mom in her gray suit. Her little waist with that cut-in jacket and flared skirt. This really was good stuff after all. I was getting adopted.

The judge just made a grunting noise in his throat though like we didn't impress him at all and took his pen out and wrote something in the folder. Then he picked up a wood hammer and slammed it down on his desk.

Bam. It was over.

~

It was just like my Dream Things picture I was so excited about. I was so excited about it.

Then nothing.

Excited. Then nothing. Excited. Then nothing. I guess that's the hills and the valleys.

Oh yeah, the picture. My Dream Things picture. That happened the next day after the night I did my art homework and Mom told me about the adoption. I couldn't wait to show my picture to Miss Fieldhorn, the art teacher.

Miss Fieldhorn was tall and bony with a man's face. A big jaw and thick eyebrows. She taught all the art classes at school. For the last period Tuesdays and Thursdays, we would go to the art room and she would teach us about art. Most of the other kids didn't like her but for me, she was okay. She was always nice to me.

At the beginning of class, I went up to show her my Dream Things. There was a girl already there at her desk showing Miss Fieldhorn her homework. So I had to wait.

It was another rainy day outside and the art room had windows that went way up to the ceiling all along one whole wall. Those windows made it so light in the art room, it was almost like being outside. Even on a rainy day. Waiting at Miss Fieldhorn's desk, my body was all jumpy 'cause I was excited about showing her my picture. Hard to stand still. So I just looked outside at it raining. Watched the hard rain coming down, bounce up off the black-top in the school yard, so I wouldn't be so jumpy.

There was laughing in the rain. Kids laughing. Scotty and me playing in the puddles. Me singing mud people, mud people. And all the time, the rain coming down faster and harder. A silver sheet of water. A shimmering silver. A glittering silver dress with movie star shoulders and silver white hair. Gramma Jones saying, "You're a real artist, Davey. You make your Gramma Belle proud."

All of a sudden, Miss Fieldhorn said, "Yes?" real loud. I looked down at where the girl was showing off her homework. But she was gone and Miss Fieldhorn was sitting there alone at her desk. Her thick eyebrows pulled down like she was mad. Looking mean. No smile.

My picture on her desk was a big piece of paper. It took up half of her desk. I just started to tell her what I called it but before the words came out of my mouth, she said, "The perspective's all wrong." A big pencil came out from behind her ear.

"But—" I said.

The pencil was really sharp 'cause right on top of the rock, she drew a deep black line and the pencil broke and skidded. Then it dug into the paper and ripped a long slash there.

"This should be a table," she said and she drew another black line down the side of the rock.

"But it's in a cave," I said.

"Well, what's this window doing here then?" and she made black scribbles over the window.

Something was in the way of my voice and my throat was all hot and burny. I tried to say, "It's a dream," but the words got stuck.

She let a big breath out at me and said, "You can't put things in a picture that don't go together." Her eyes rolled up to her thick eyebrows a little bit, the way that Scotty looked at me sometimes. "You confuse the viewer." And she handed the picture back to me. Ripped and ruined.

"Why don't you just take it home and rework it?" she said.

"Okay," I said.

But she was already yelling, "Class, take your seats."

Bam. It was over.

44

Wobbly Table

Outside the courthouse was all granite and marble. Lots of steps. On the steps, Brew stopped. Big breath. Looked out at Portland in the sunshine. His nostrils big and widow's peak up high.

Maybe this was it.

He didn't even look at me inside. Maybe he'd at least shake my hand like he said men do.

But he didn't.

"What-a ya-say we go see the folks?" he said. "Tell 'em the news?"

Mom stopped going down the steps and bent her knee up. Held up her leg in back and looked down. Checked her seam. One hand holding her turned up straw hat on.

"I don't know. How about it, Davey? You want to go see your Gramma and Grampa Brugger?"

That wasn't it. What I wanted. But a day out on their farm after those marble hallways, the wood rooms and spittoons was something anyway.

"I guess," I said. "Right now?"

"Why not?" Brew said and undid his tie without looking at us.

So we started off to where we parked the Oldsmobile. Noise all around. A whistle from a door man that looked like a drum major. Tire screech from a taxi. Fire truck siren. And all the time in my head, a picture of Gramma Brugger's farm out in Aloha. The quiet. It was better than thinking about whose idea this getting adopted really was.

The little farm started at the corner of Johnson, a gravel road. Flat farm land. Only thing you could see across the road from theirs, a white barn sitting at the road a little ways from where we turned. Grapes growing all along the fence of their plowed field til you come to the tall poplar trees on the side of their yard and in front. Leaves like silver money flashing in the windy sunshine.

A cute little house with junipers growing up the walk from the drive-way. Juniper berries I loved to crush with my finger nails and smell. A needle sharp smell like Christmas all year long. Sheds and chicken coops out back. The apple orchard on the other side of the house all the way to the next road.

Brew pulled the Oldsmobile into the driveway at the side of the house and stopped. Let the dust catch up with us.

Where was Gramma? Whenever we pulled in the driveway she was always right away at the door. In the back seat, I watched the front door. The screen door was closed and so was the door behind it. No Gramma.

"Do you suppose they're not home?" Mom said. She was looking at the front door too.

"I don't know," Brew said. A big line down between his eyebrows. "Where would they be? They don't have a car and besides, she's always so busy in the kitchen." He ducked his head, squinting under the sun visor. "She's got too much to do to just leave."

He opened his driver door slow like he was worried. Then came around to Mom's door and opened it for her. All the time, he looked at the house. I climbed out too and we all went up the front walk. Looked in the windows. But couldn't see anything.

Brew opened the screen door and looked through the lace curtains on the door.

"What in the world?" His face all scrunched up.

Then he opened the door.

Grampa Charlie was just sitting in a chair. A big stuffed leather and wood chair next to the wood stove with the isinglass windows on the door. This big grin on his face.

Grampa Charlie was a little guy that everybody thought was cute. Black hair with some gray in it and black eyebrows that curved up over his big dark eyes and made those eyes look like he was always laughing. Most of the time there was some joke going on when he was around. Even if he was the only one who knew anything about it.

And, he couldn't hear anything. He was totally deaf.

In the middle of the living room on the linoleum floor was the big round dining room table somebody pulled there. On top of that table was a little wobbly table sitting in the middle of the big table. On top of the wobbly table was a wood chair. And on top of that under the ceiling light was Gramma Mary.

Gramma Brugger was short too like Grampa Charlie but she was round. Gramma said it's 'cause she's German she was built that way. Almost as round as she was tall. Long white gray hair that was brushed and made into braids every morning and crossed over the top of her head. The gramma that you always see on Christmas cards.

Gramma was sitting up there on that chair on top of the two tables with her chubby arms crossed over her bosoms. Like she was waiting for a bus or something. Like she always sat up there. Like she didn't have anything else to do but sit up there.

"Mary, what in the world are you doing?" Brew said. He almost always called his mom, Mary. But now his face was twisted up red from laughing and his laughing was getting in the way of his talking. You could hardly tell what he called her.

She grinned at him like Charlie was grinning. All innocent. But like she was the only one that knew the joke.

"Well, it's about time somebody got here."

Brew took a big breath and held on to it. Tried to stop laughing. Air coming out in little grunts.

"Mother, what are you doing up there?"

"It's not about what I'm doing up here. It's about what he was trying to do up here," she said and pointed the toe of one of her black old lady lace up shoes at Charlie. That made the little table wobble even more, but her arms still stayed crossed.

Mom told me they call those shoes with their big solid high heels on them, Red Cross Shoes. Bet you could pound nails with those shoes.

"He thinks he's a climbin' up here to fiddle with the burned light bulb," she said. "But I told him he's got another think comin'." You could see in her gray sparkly eyes she was laughing inside. One of them winked and she sharp nodded her head. Her chin saying, "And that's the end of that."

"He just give me that silly grin of his."

Mom was laughing so hard she was staggering and slipping her high heels on the linoleum floor. She had to sit down quick on the davenport. Wipe her eyes. Brew was laughing again too. All bent over. Red forehead all around the widow's peak where I could see.

Gramma sitting up there with her arms crossed made me have to sit down from laughing too.

"Mary, come on," Brew said. "Let me help you down," and he reached his arm up at her.

"Only if you's to change the light bulb, Johnny. I don't want him climbing up here no account." But she uncrossed her arms and started to stand up even before she finished talking.

The little wobbly table leaned all the way in one direction and Mom and me both took a big mouthful of air and jumped up.

Brew had his jacket in his hands. Real fast he threw it down on the davenport.

"Okay, Mother, give me your hand." And just before the little table was going to fall over, he grabbed her hand and one of her solid Red Cross shoes clunked down on the dining table. Her big bottom sat on the edge of that oak table and she slid off and stood up like she did all that every day.

After she pulled her silky house dress straight, her little round fingers caught a wisp of loose white hairs and tucked them under her braids. "There's a pot a coffee in the kitchen." she said. "Would you like some, Marion? I know John would like some and I know Davey would like a Coke."

She always called it Coke. But I knew it wasn't. It was Royal Crown Cola and it tasted different. But it was okay.

Mom said she'd help. So Brew got up there and changed the light bulb, then pulled the chair and wobbly table down. Coffee, some soda pop and a plate full of fresh baked cookies got put on the little table. Their smell was warm peanut butter and cinnamon. Gramma always had a cookie jar full of fresh baked cookies in the kitchen. Mostly sugar cookies. Sometimes peanut butter ones or chocolate chip. But these were still warm. I helped Brew move the dining room table back over to the dining room side and Grampa just sat in his chair and grinned at everybody doing stuff.

Gramma's face was all red and she was kind of puffing when she sat in her platform rocker. "Good thing you come by when you did. I was up there pert near all morning. No telling how long I would a sat up there."

That made everybody laugh again.

"We thought we'd just drop by and tell you the news," Brew said.

Gramma wasn't having any cookies. Always said she ate too many when she was baking them. So she just caught her breath and then picked up her crocheting. "What news is that, Johnny?" Her eyes really looking hard at her thread. Her lips counting.

The house was filled with doylies. On the tables. On backs of chairs where your head goes. She even crocheted the bag she kept her crocheting in.

"We just come from the courthouse downtown Portland," Brew said. Like maybe we went there just so we could have a story to tell his folks.

"My, my. You drive all the way out here from downtown Portland?" Gramma stopped her hand from working her needle and looked at Brew. Her eyebrows way up.

Brew nodded and smiled at his mom. So big the dimples showed in his cheeks.

"We adopted Davey today. He's officially a Brugger now," he said. Kind of loud like he thought Grampa Charley could hear too.

Charley said, "What's that?" real loud.

So Gramma bent over her crocheting to him and yelled, "They's adopted little Davey."

My face got real hot. But Grampa's face didn't change. Still just that big grin.

Then he said, "That's nice."

But that's what he always said so nobody was sure if he heard or not.

"Well, welcome to the family, Davey," Gramma said. And then, "Oh, what am I sayin'? Davey's always been a part of our family. He's one of my favorite grand kids. It's just official now."

My face was still kind of hot so I just drank my pop.

She leaned over and patted her hand on my leg then and quiet said, "Don't you go tellin' the others I said that, now. That's just between us two." Her voice smiling at me.

I looked down at Gramma's Red Cross shoes and clinked the ice in my glass of pop. "Okay," I said.

"You goin' out t'your Aunt Pearl's spread come summer, Davey?"

Before I could answer though, Mom said, "Oh, we didn't tell you. Pearl sold her dairy farm. She's planning on buying something where she can grow a crop instead of having all that work to do with livestock."

I already knew that but my chest still started to tighten up and my throat got hard to swallow when Mom said it.

Gramma, she must of seen that. She always could tell how I was feeling, 'cause right away she said to Mom, "Well then, Davey'll just have to come here this summer." Her pale blue eyes looked at me then. "Course we don't have horses to ride or cows to milk. But we got pigs to feed and chickens. Eggs to collect ever mornin'." She was grinning again like she did sitting up there on that wobbly table. "You can even bring a friend so's you won't get too bored with us old folks." Then she did that nod with her chin again that meant it was all settled.

I could hardly wait to ask the new Billy. Billy Walters.

45

New Billy

It was like I didn't have a brother. 'Cause most the time I didn't. Earl divorced Lou Ella after I left California. Then Scotty moved back to Oregon with him. But Scotty, he was still mad at Mom. She wasn't married to Earl anymore and Scotty thought it was her fault. So he didn't come over very much.

But I never, ever had a little brother. I mean, little Joey was around for one summer. But it was never like he was my little brother. He was Robby's little brother. Really, wasn't anybody's little brother. He could take care of himself.

And I wasn't gonna have a little brother either. Mom wasn't going to have any more kids. Back when Mom and Brew thought there'd be me and Scotty and Robby and Joey, Brew got himself fixed so he couldn't be a dad anymore. I think maybe that was the reason anyway. Maybe not. Sometimes it was like he wanted to be a dad. Sometimes not.

Like when he was around Robby, he did. But not much around me.

After Olive took Robby and Joey away from Brew, it was like he was different. If Mom and him had a baby, maybe he would still want to be a dad. Maybe he never did in the first place. But there wasn't going to be a baby now.

From the first time I met Billy Walters though, I had a little brother. Not really little. Littler than me, but my same age. Not really a brother. But something about him was like a little brother. Or maybe it was me. Maybe I just wanted a little brother.

Most days, I went over to his house after school. Sometimes to see the Baldwins first but then I'd go over to his house. Go out to the teeter totter. Sit there and talk. Wasn't the same as with the other Billy. Billy Rogers and me naked on the teeter totter. I never told him about that. The new Billy was kind of shy. Or maybe I didn't tell him 'cause we were older. But we'd just sit there and talk. Forget it was a teeter totter.

'Cause he was shy, I pretended I wasn't really excited that day I told him about the farm.

"My Gramma Brugger. Out in Aloha. She says I can come out to the farm for the summer," I say and brush some needles off the old teeter totter plank.

"That sounds pretty keen," he says. He's making marks with the bottoms of his tennis shoes in the dirt under the teeter totter and bent over looking at the design they're making.

"She says I can bring a friend if I want." I'm watching his foot print designs too.

We're sitting next to each other near the middle. The teeter totter more like a bench than a teeter totter. His smell close to me. Like bread baking.

He looks up at me like I said something that hurt.

"The whole summer?" he says. His eyebrows and cheeks scrunched toward each other so his eyes squint.

"Don't you wanna go with me?"

"Sure I would, only..." He scuffs his shoes over all the designs in the dirt like he's erasing a blackboard. Erases the tennis shoe marks.

"Only what?"

"Well, I gotta spend the summer with my family in Coquille. My aunts and uncles, grand parents. Always do."

My stomach is all the sudden empty. Like it's rubbing-together-empty.

"Coquille?" I say.

He nods and bites on his lip. "Down south on the coast."

"The whole summer?"

"Yup." His shoulders bump up and down.

Damn hills and valleys. My ears hot.

"Golly," I say.

"Yeah." he says. "I could probly go with you for a weekend though. Before I gotta go." His eyebrows back up.

There's a kind of smile inside me then. Stomach's not so empty. I say, "Better than nothing, I guess."

~

The sun woke me up the first morning Billy and me stayed at Gramma and Grampa's farm. It came in the attic all colored. Red, green, blue. Through the colored glass window under the little peak in the roof. I rolled over to look at it coming through the colored glass. Straw crunch in the mattress under me. Soft warm feathers in like a big pillowcase over me. Feather bed. There's a rooster crowing out back. Maybe singing.

Billy got to sleep down stairs in Gramma's guest room. "He's the guest," she said. She decided. Me up. Billy down. But I liked this better anyway. Crunchy straw. Warm feathers.

I laid still.

No sound now from downstairs.

My hand up by the window. Moved it slow. It turned different colors. Gold and green and blue. Back of my hand yellow. Fingers purple.

I slow slid out from under the feathers. The air is all a sudden cold. Got up quiet then. Pulled my jeans on over my under pants. Tucked in my tee shirt. The wood stairs rough on my bare feet going down. One creaked. I stopped.

Quiet.

Then downstairs I slow open the guest room door. Billy's still asleep. His blond hair smooshed on one side. Neat little ears. Smooth brown arm up on the pillow, bent over his head. Tiny blond hairs on his skin. The room is full of his bread baking smell. Soft breathing. Gramma's clock ticking on top of the lace what-cha-ma-call-it on the dresser.

There's that warm kind of electric thing in my chest again watching Billy sleep. I slow sit down in the chair beside his bed. Slow, slow so it won't squeak. Listen to him breathe. Smell his smell.

I'm waiting for him to wake up. Watching him. And the warm in my chest spreads. Up my neck into my throat. Down into my stomach. Like tickling. It's different than the little brother thing. Nice but it almost makes me dizzy.

There's a noise then out in the kitchen like a chair scooting.

Billy rolls over. His blond eyelashes move like little moth wings. His mouth opens big and his fists pop out of the covers in a stretch. Eyes come open.

"Hey," he says. "What time is it?"

"Don't know," I say. My face all burny.

"Is it time to get up?" Another yawn. Sleepy blue eyes.

"I guess so. I think Gramma's up."

Billy pushes one thumb into the side of his other thumb and it pops. Then he does the other one.

Never saw anybody do that. Must hurt.

He moves a little bit like he's going to get out of bed then. Like maybe in his underpants. Maybe naked.

I try not to look at him anymore. Forget about the warm thing.

"I'll go see if she wants us to do anything."

"Okay," he says.

My legs are shaky.

I hear the covers move behind me. His feet hit the floor.

~

In the kitchen, Gramma said, "Well, hi Davey. Sleep up there all right?"

One of her chubby hands stirring batter with a wooden spoon. A big bowl buried in her bosoms.

"Yeah. That straw mattress is really neat."

She stopped stirring and laughed then. Her gray blue eyes wet and kind of gummy from laughing.

"Mighty home-spun, that mattress. Stuffed the ticking myself. The straw come from right out back. Out where your gramps is plowing today. He's already eat." She looked down at the batter and started stirring again. "Made the Decke too. That's a German word. Means feather bed."

Chimes from the old wind up clock in the dining room came through the kitchen door. Seven o'clock.

The wooden spoon stopped again. "Billy up yet?"

"Yeah, I think."

"We's sure happy you come out to visit us old folks for the weekend, Davey." She looked down at the bowl then like she forgot it was there. "How 'bout you and Billy get some eggs from the chickies for yer breakfast?"

Her cheeks all round and pink. Smiling.

"Sure. Can we?"

"You bet. Just be careful. Put your hands under real slow like and they won't peck you."

Billy's standing in the doorway of the kitchen then in neat jeans. With creases. Looked like his mom must of ironed them. Nice polo shirt. Blue like his eyes.

"Hey, Gramma wants us to get her some eggs. Okay?"

"Sure," he said through a sleepy yawn. Mouth wide open. His white teeth white all the way back. No cavities like mine have.

Be sure you get 'em all, you two," Gramma said on our way out back through the sunshine in the mud porch. "Don't leave none behind."

Gramma liked to tell people what to do. Maybe 'cause she had five kids. But that's okay.

The gate into the chickens' yard opened easy. Some chickens ran around squawking. More jumped down off their perches and ran around making their *Quawk, puck, puck, puck* noises when we went in the chicken coop. Then they ran outside. Poop all over inside.

Billy just stood inside the door like he didn't know what to do or maybe afraid he'd get chicken poop on him.

I watched Gramma get eggs before. She always put them in her apron. Didn't have an apron. So, me showing off for Billy what an old hand I was at this, I pulled my tee shirt out of my pants and reached for a yellow hen. Too fast. Forgot what Gramma said. That old hen just snapped her head out and pecked at my hand. I jumped back.

Billy laughed.

"Ain't funny, McGee," I said.

He turned really red then. "Sorry," he said. "Looks like she doesn't want to let you have it."

"She will if I do it right."

This time I made the sound Gramma makes, "cluck, cluck, cluck, nice chicky," and real slow my hand slipped under the hen and found two eggs. Nestled together. Warm in my hand under her. Like together under a feather bed.

Something was real happy in me then. That smile inside again. Billy watching me put them in the held out bottom of my tee shirt like Gramma put them in her apron.

"Wanna try?"

"Sure," Billy says. "Think I can?"

"Don't see why not. Nothin' to it."

Billy comes over trying to step so he won't step in chicken poop. Fat chance.

"Sure a lot of chicken shit in here," he says.

Makes me laugh. He's laughing too. He reaches out real slow to the rusty red hen next to my yellow one. Tongue between his teeth. Slips his hand under and pulls an egg out like he's done it all his life. He has a big smile. Biggest smile I ever saw on him. Blue eyes wide looking at me. Bites his bottom lip and holds the egg up. Like he's caught a big fish.

I sure like Billy.

He puts it real careful in my tee shirt. So it won't break. Smiles at me when it doesn't. Blue eyes in mine. Then looks down quick. Like he's embarrassed.

We checked all the hens then like Gramma said. Got six eggs all together.

~

After breakfast—pancakes, eggs and some yummy pork chops Gramma said came from last year's pigs, Billy and me, we went out to investigate. Right away outside the back door, Billy took off running to the apple orchard. He can run really fast for a little guy. I chased him out there. All a sudden there's an apple coming at me. Flying at me through the air. Well, remember I don't catch very good. Scotty says like a girl. I put my hands up. My elbows went together. Awkward. But at least it didn't get me in the face. It just thunk landed in the grass by my feet.

I tossed it back and ran closer. I catch better if I'm closer. But in my head, there was a didn't-want-to-be-doing-this. Billy would find out I couldn't catch. And I wished we could do something else instead. The apple came at me again. My hands came up again but it went right through them and hit me in the stomach. By this time, I was bent over though so it didn't hurt much. The apple ended up in my crotch. Lucky it didn't fall on the ground again. So real quick I got a hold of it and tossed it back.

Billy laughed and caught it running. "It'd be better with catching mitts," he said and tossed it back.

An oh-God-let-this-be-over-soon prayer in my head.

We ran around and tossed that apple back and forth a little bit. Then at the old well, in the middle of the orchard, I missed it and it landed on my shoe. Broke all up in pieces.

"I'm sorry," I said. I don't catch very well." My face all hot and me wishing I could hide somewhere.

"No big deal," Billy said. "It's all just fun is all. Not like anybody's trying to win or anything."

I looked down at the apple all mushed up on my shoe and pieces on the ground. Wind blowing through the trees over us. Sun light blinking around us. My eyes started to burn like I was going to cry but I could've hugged him. I was so glad he didn't care.

The old well was all boarded up. Gray wood. Been out there like that for years. I turned away from him. Sat down on the old wood. Head down. Pretended like I was more out of breath than I was and made like I was cleaning off my shoe so he wouldn't see my eyes all wet. He sat down beside me. I could feel his warm. Kind of like sitting on the teeter totter. Different than in the woods though where it's all quiet and dark and mysterious. Smell of dirt and old pine needles. Here, all green and leafy above us. Birds singing. Streaks of sun through the branches and leaves. Sweet smell of apples on the ground. Some rotting. Lots on the trees just starting.

"This place is really swell, Davey."

"You like it here?"

Both of us were taking big breaths from running. Billy's face all pink under his tanned skin. His blond eyelashes flicking up and down. Even sat down, his body was still moving. Shoes scuffing the ground. His butt bouncing on the boards. Like his motor was still running.

"Yeah it's great. What's this thing?" he said, patting the boards.

"Old well. They don't use it anymore."

Grampa Charlie was going in the back door over at the house right then. His grin turned to us for a minute. His grin big enough to see all the way from the orchard.

"My Grampa Charlie. He's deaf. Can't hear anything."

"Nothing?" Billy looked at me. Face kind of scrunched. Like he didn't believe me.

"Nope."

"Wow," he said and looked back at Charlie.

Charlie grinned even bigger and waved. Went in the house.

It was kind of muddy around the edge of the old well. One spot pretty deep mud. Billy jumped off the well. He picked up a stick that fell off one of the trees and poked at the mud. Soft like batter. Gramma's pancake batter.

"Hey we could make something out of this," Billy said. He squatted down and broke off the stick. Used the big end to stir the mud.

Still sitting on the old well, I bent over to look at him stirring the mud. Gooey, thick, and brown.

"I got just the ingredients for you," Gramma's voice came up behind us. We both jumped up. Quick turned around. Thought we were alone out there with only bird sounds and the apple branches moving in the wind.

"When I's yer age, I made some pretty good looking mud pies," she said.

"Oh, Gramma, I don't know if we want to make..."

"Oh, don't be silly. 'Course you do. And I's throwing away a bunch a old spices you could use."

My ears were really hot. I looked at Billy. He was looking at me under his eyelashes. Like he was trying not to laugh. His cheeks all red like it might bust out of him any minute.

"You two just come with me," Gramma said. Her voice kind of high and happy like a little girl.

Billy and me, we followed Gramma to one of the sheds in back of the house. Looked at our shoes. Tried not to look at each other 'cause we would laugh. Didn't want Gramma to hear us laugh.

The door swung open and she said, "There you be. All yours."

Inside the shed on the floor, six or seven boxes and jars of things I always saw in her kitchen. One big box had Mustard Powder written on the side. Another box, Cinnamon. There were jars with Ground Cloves and Cream of Tartar, Cumin, Marjoram and Curry Powder. Stuff I never heard of.

"These here spices 'er gettin' too old," she said. Her voice sounding sad for the spices. "Just like your gramps and me." But then like the German gramma that keeps everything neat and clean, she said, "Time fer new. But just right fer mud pies."

She winked at us and patted me on the shoulder, then turned around out the door.

I hit the dirt floor and started rolling around with my hands on my stomach laughing. Billy was right beside me. That almost made me stop laughing. He was always so neat and clean. And him rolling around on the dirt floor.

I sat up then and looked at the boxes. Then at Billy. Started to laugh again. So did Billy.

Then he said, "Well, why not?"

There were some old pans in the shed too. Even a couple a big old spoons. So we carried the boxes and jars and pans and spoons out to the old well and set up our kitchen.

Billy made two amazing mud pies. One was full of mustard powder. The other had curry powder. One really yellow. One bright orange. I put cream of tartar, parsley and Marjoram in one of mine that turned out kind of light brownish green. The other one was just brown. But it smelled really good. Cinnamon and cloves.

We left them on the old gray boards on the well to bake in the sun.

After lunch that day, I told him about my really neat straw mattress. He never heard of a straw mattress before so I took him up to the attic to show him.

The old white painted iron bed all bars and curlicues was tucked against the wall under the triangle roof. Colors streaming into the wood attic from the little colored glass window in the peak. Bouncing off the old wood framed oval mirror on the wall facing it and landing on the bed. On the straw mattress.

"Wow, this is neat," Billy said.

He moved slow into the room looking around at the old dresser with the marble top under the mirror. At the end of the bed, the home-made cedar chest full of knot holes. A patch work quilt on top. The bare wood beams running along the attic ceiling. Old wood rocker in the corner.

"This stuff is really old," he said. Almost whispering like he was really impressed.

"It's really keen, isn't it? Gramma says this stuff is their old stuff they got at the logging camp when they first came to Oregon."

Billy walked over to the bed and just ran his hand over the feather bed laid out on top.

"This really straw?"

"Well, it's feathers on top. You have to lie down to feel the straw mattress."

His blue eyes looked over at me in the doorway. Like he didn't believe he could do that. Like the bed was really too precious or valuable to lie down on.

"Can I?" he said.

I said, "Well, sure."

Crunchy sounds then. And he laid down on top the feather bed.

"Ah. This is great."

I went in the room and crawled around his feet. Stretched out beside him on the other side under the window.

"Neat, huh?"

His smell was warm and familiar. Kind of like I must of smelled it before. I mean, like I knew Billy for a long time or maybe because it was like Gramma baking bread. How the house smells sweet and rich. I breathed it in. It was clean clothes mixed with mud pies and spices and bread baking.

It made me sleepy.

Billy rolled over. Smiled at me. Blues eyes. Eyelashes flicking up and down. Then didn't.

We both fell asleep.

46

Eva's Bike

Billy laughed when the mud turned yellow from the mustard powder. He had fun tossing the apple and making mud pies both. He didn't think mud pies was sissy. Like the kids at school called me when I played house on the playground with Ina Dean, the ugly girl.

But Ina was nice to me when I had ringworm and I was being the dad playing house with her. What was wrong with that? Maybe because they knew how I couldn't catch. How I was always out in the outfield. Picking up nice little rocks in the gravel instead of waiting for the ball. I was always praying it wouldn't come out there.

Gramma Brugger didn't think mud pies was sissy either. She got us to do it. When I stayed with her before—in the summer after Robby and Joey went back home to The Dalles—she even taught me how to crochet. She didn't think fun things were sissy. There were even pictures of Brew in a white lace dress when he was her little baby. I never saw a boy in a lace dress before. Him in the picture with blond hair—Gramma called him a tow head—he looked just like Mom in her baby pictures. She even taught Brew to crochet when he was a little boy. But Gramma was an old lady, an old German gramma. She didn't even think mud pies was kid's stuff.

Billy knew it was kid's stuff though. Like me, he could hardly keep from laughing when Gramma said we should make them. Maybe he even thought it was sissy. But that's what was really great about him. He didn't care. Poop on the rules.

~

Gramma woke Billy and me up that afternoon. Hollered up to the attic would we takeslop out to the pigs.

Warm apple pie smell filled up the kitchen. Toasty pie crust. Tangy apple smell.

Cinnamon and cloves. Two flaky light brown pies were steaming on little wire racks holding them up over the oil cloth on the table. The air still wavy and hot over the big iron wood-stove in the corner.

"Your mud pies looked pretty good but these from our store of apples, we can eat," Gramma said and laughed. A little lace hanky came out of her apron and she wiped her eyes and then the sweat off her forehead. Her fat cheeks pink and white and red. Like the apple peels in the bucket of pig slop she was handing me.

"Yup. They's good ol' hogs," she said. 'Cause I was looking in the bucket. "Eat most all our scraps."

"You know where the pig pen is, Davey. Just pour this here slop into the trough. No need for more than that. They's always hungry."

Heavy. Almost dropped the bucket when she handed it to me. But Billy, he grabbed the handle too and helped me hold it up.

Gramma let go of it then, "You having fun, Billy?"

Billy's face got all red and he looked down at the bucket.

"Yes ma'am."

Gramma giggled at that.

"You needn't call me Ma'am, Billy. I'm just Gramma Brugger. Gramma to all you kids. So you can just call me Gramma, if you want."

One of her gray blue eyes winked at him but he didn't see. Still looking down.

"Okay," he said.

Outside in back, him helping me carry the bucket, I said, "You don't have to be so shy with Gramma. She's okay."

Billy moved his head back and forth still looking down and squirmed his shoulders around. Embarrassed.

"I know," he said.

The pigs started snorting right away and shoving at us.

"Holy cow, I didn't know pigs got so big," Billy said. "Bigger'n dogs."

"Stronger too," I said.

They were shoving us so hard they almost knocked us off the boards that went over the mud to the trough.

"Boy, this is worse than the chicken shit," Billy said. Laughing at the pigs. Tried not to step in the mud.

"Yeah. But cleaner," I said.

Billy's eyebrows went up. His eyes big.

"Yer kidding."

"Nope. Cleanest animals out here's, what Gramma says. Poop just in their toilets. All the other ones poop all over the place."

Billy almost lost his balance.

"Toilets?"

He held onto the bucket but stuck out his other arm like on a tight rope in the circus. His hand making a circle in the air.

"Whoa. That was close. They really have toilets?"

"Yup. Over by the fence." I pointed at the place in the dirt where the pigs had it all dug up. Then poured the slop in the trough.

He started to laugh.

"I thought you meant they sit on the pot."

Then we were both laughing.

"Can you see that? Fat pig butts all sitting on their toilets?" Billy said.

I got to laughing so much I spilled some slop in the mud.

"Wow, that's keen though," he said quiet. His eyes big and head nodding. His mouth a tight line. "They make their own toilet."

A zing, zing feeling in my chest. Finally did a Scotty-big-brother-thing. Showed him a pig toilet.

"Come on. I wanna show you the calf. Only other animal Gramma and Grampa have out here now."

The pigs were done pushing us by then. Snorting in their slop.

Right away the calf was at the gate to his stall in the shed. Making his baby mooing sound. His thick gray pink tongue licking at my jeans. The shed strong with cow manure smell.

Billy reached in and petted his head. Billy's hand, smaller than that tongue, was all over slobber then.

"Oh, yuck," he said and pulled his hand out. Face all scrunched.

So the calf, he took hold of the bottom of Billy's polo shirt with his mouth and started sucking on it.

"Oh, geez, that's nasty," Billy said and yanked his shirt out of the calf's drooly mouth. "First chicken shit, then pig mud and now cow slobber."

He looked at me, his mouth tight and right away a laugh busted through his lips like a let go balloon spluttering out air. His feet rocked around on the wood grate we were standing on like he might fall over from laughing. My feet started to rock back and forth too and I ended up laughing so hard I fell over backward onto some straw bales. Billy followed me down onto the bales. Now, laughing big. His mouth wide open. White teeth flashing in the sun-going-down shed. He rolled over and punched me. I rolled away from him on the bales. Still laughing. Then I rolled back and bumped into him. Making straw dust float up in the air. He was laughing loud. Tears on his face. He rolled away from me. Then we rolled back together, into each other and stopped. Billy's warm all up against me. His face right there. His nose almost touching mine. I never felt anything like that. In the shed it was really quiet. In all that quiet, the calf made his mooing sound again and a loud slurp. We both laughed right in each other's faces then and rolled and giggled until our sides hurt.

Billy sat up finally wiping his eyes and said, "Hey, a bike. A Schwinn."

I sat up too. He was right. Against the wood wall of the shed. All over dust. A bike. A girl's bike.

"Can't be Gramma's. She's too fat to ride a bike," I said. A giggle was still in my belly. "Can you see her on a bike?"

Both us let it out then. Rolled back on the bales.

I kinda tried to stop laughing but I knew if I looked at Billy, I'd just keep on. So I looked at Billy. Didn't really want to stop.

At last, we just laid still on the straw. Held our sore bellies making sounds like a dying car motor, "ahuh, ahuh." Gramma's dinner cooking smell coming in the shed.

"Can we...can...do you think we can ride it?" Billy said. His voice breathy.

"Well, maybe you can. I don't know how."

Billy quick sat up. Looked at me. His blue eyes big.

"Really? You don't know how?"

I looked up at Billy's face. Straw dust dancing around it in the dim light. A numb feeling in my throat. Something like sad.

"Yeah, isn't that dumb?"

Billy settled back down on one elbow. Looked at me laying on the straw beside him.

"Oh, that's not so dumb."

"It's not?"

Billy's face fading in the dim light.

"No, I just learned this year."

Something like happy then.

"Would you like me to teach you how?"

"Could you?"

Light gone now from the windows. Almost dark. Could hardly see him.

"Can't think why not. Seein' as there's a bike here. Can we use it?"

Dark all around us. Only his voice over me now. Smooth. Never thought about his voice before. Almost like music.

So I said, "Well, I'll ask Gramma. It's kind of late now but we got all day tomorrow." But really what was in my head then was how I probably couldn't steer it or I'd fall off or crash into something. Stuff like that always made me feel so dumb 'cause I couldn't do it and everybody else could.

Billy, he was kind of small and shy but I bet he could do anything he put his mind to. And he wasn't always so shy around me anymore. Didn't really need a big brother to take care of him. But at least he didn't seem to care I couldn't do stuff like that. Didn't make me feel stupid like Scotty did.

"Okay. That's a deal," he said. "We'll take 'er out on the road in front tomorrow morning if she'll let us."

~

"Oh, that's your Aunt Eva's bike," Gramma said at dinner that night. She called it supper 'cause it was small. We ate more at lunch time out here at her farm. "She left it here when she married your Uncle Fred. Had better things to do with her time." Her cheeks got all pink then and she pulled her little hanky out of her apron under the edge of the table. Wiped at her eyes."

"You think we can ride it tomorrow?" I said.

"'Course you can. Uh. You know how?"

"Billy does," I said. "He's gonna teach me." I nodded at Billy.

When we looked at him, Billy's face was really red over the fork full of white mashed potatoes.

"Well ain't that nice."

She slapped her hand down on the table in front of Grampa Charlie who was off dreaming in his deaf world and hollered, "Billy's going to teach Davey to ride little Evie's bike tomorrow."

She wiped her forehead with the little hanky.

"That's nice," Charlie said and grinned at Gramma.

"That's what I said just now," she hollered. "It's very nice of you, Billy," and she nodded her head up and down. Like maybe Billy was deaf too.

Billy was slipped down in his chair almost under the table. His red face hardly above the edge.

"Thanks," he said real quiet.

~

Next morning early, I rolled over in little puddles of color coming in dim from outside. Straw crunching.

Then a creak. Wood on wood rolling sound.

I quick looked down over my feet.

A shadow in the corner. Someone sitting in the rocker. Creak. It rocked forward.

"What the?"

"Just me," Billy said and stood up. Ha-ha-gotcha-smile.

"Geez," I said and sat up.

"I scare you?"

"Yeah, I guess so."

Funny, I didn't scare him the day before when I sat and watched him sleep.

He switched his weight to one leg.

"Wanna ride a bike?" he said.

His body, only a dark curve of his hip.

"Don't you wanna eat breakfast first?"

"Your gramma's not up yet. I got it all cleaned up and out front," he said and sat down in the rocker again. Legs stretched out in front of him. Cracking the knuckles with his thumbs. Like he does.

Quiet.

"Well, I guess we can eat later," I said.

So there it was. I was different than Billy. Wasn't used to having somebody in my room. I tried to turn away from him so I could get out of bed in just my underpants. But I couldn't figure a way. Finally I just jumped out quick and pulled on my jeans and tee shirt. He just kind of laid stretched out in the rocker though like he was watching me.

Shoes.

Down on my hands and knees, I couldn't find my shoes.

"Guess I better wear shoes." That sounded dumb. "Out there in the gravel, you know."

"Yup," he said.

They were under the bed.

Him, still not moving. None of this a big deal for him. Guess it was for me. Somehow, it made us better friends though. Him just there while I put on my clothes.

~

Seemed really early outside. Sun hardly up yet. Still cool. The air smelled good like things growing. A breeze came across the open field from the other side of the road in front of the house. Blew Billy's blond hair up in front.

I said, "You got up really early."

Big smile. Then he caught himself. Head went down.

"Naw, this is gonna be fun is all."

The bike was all shiny and clean by the junipers.

"Looks great," I said.

"Yeah. It is a girl's bike though. Too bad it's not a boy's. But it'll be okay."

He was only about as tall as the bike but he kicked the bike stand back and steered it out the driveway.

"This road's pretty bumpy to start on. Better keep real close to the edge where it's just packed dirt and smooth. That way the rocks won't get in your way."

First he showed me how you push back on the peddles for the breaks. Then he held the bike by the back fender and the seat post and walked along beside me while I peddled forward real slow. The front wheel and handle bars snapping right and left.

"Something's wrong with this bike," I said. "The wheel won't stay straight." He looked up from bending over holding the bike. His jaw tight from the strain of keeping me and the bike from falling over. Blue eyes under those eyelashes flicking up and down.

"It's because were going so slow." His voice squeezed in his throat. "When you go faster by yourself, you'll be able to hold it steady." Then he smiled happy. Like this was really a lot of fun. "First get your balance."

Not sure what that meant but pretty soon, it got easier and he started letting go of the bike. Little bit at a time.

Then I was sailing along by myself beside the road in the sunshine. Wind blowing my hair. Like I didn't have to do anything. Just sit there. A little bit like riding a horse. So I threw one arm up in the air and yelled, "Yahoo."

That was a mistake.

The bike hit a piece of gravel and the wheel jack-knifed. First the seat hit me hard in the crotch. Then the bike fell toward the road and my leg went the other way, flew through the opening between the front wheel and the seat and I was in the ditch. The big problem though was that there was a big patch of blackberries growing in the ditch right there by the road.

I yelled, "Shit."

Well, those blackberry stickers really hurt and so did my crotch. But that wasn't all that hurt. There I was laying in the ditch just like I thought. I can't do anything boys are supposed to do. I get sick on hikes with Scotty, I can't catch a ball and I can't even ride a bike, for cryin' out loud.

"Shit."

But me yelling shit, made Billy laugh. He came running up laughing. Me laying in those blackberry bushes thinking this guy is not so nice after all.

The guy can take care of himself. He's littler than me and shy sometimes but he can collect eggs, ride a bike and catch. He can do everything I can't. And now he's laughing at me.

But right away, he's saying, "I'm sorry. I didn't mean to laugh. Are you okay?"

I really hurt all over but I said, "I guess so."

Billy helped me get the stickers to let go of my tee shirt and jeans. Just when we got one to let go and I tried to get up, another one would grab a hold and try to rip my shirt or get me to bleed. Like they were alive. And my crotch still smarted where the seat hit me. He put his arm around my middle though and helped me get up out of the blackberries. Sat down on the edge of the ditch with me where there weren't any.

"You sure you're okay?" he said again.

His eyebrows down looking worried. Even left the bike laying out in the middle of the road. His hand reached out. The skin of his hand rough and dry but warm on my arm where there was some blood from berry scratches. Somewhere else in me warm and buzzing again. Maybe my chest. Maybe my belly.

This was better than the little brother thing.

~

Those blue eyes started to laugh again though even before he did. He was giggling then and he said, "It did look funny though. You flying right through the middle of the bike. You went one way and the bike went the other way. The bar would a stopped you if you had a boy's bike."

I laughed then too. In my head, it was like I could see it the way he saw it.

PART FIVE

HOW LIFE
IS
HANDED
ON

Cyril Bibby

Who Let You Out?

47

Moon Men

That night when Brew drove us home, Billy and me didn't look at each other. I wasn't gonna see Billy again for the whole summer. How could that be? Why does everybody keep having to go away?

Next to me in the back seat of the Oldsmobile, Billy's bread baking smell was making that burny sad feeling in my throat. If I looked at him. Saw those moth wing eyelashes. He'd see some mopey puppy dog.

I kept telling myself though that Sunny Lea and me, we were going to do a play. But Sunny Lea just wasn't Billy. I kept that in my head though. *Sunny Lea and me are gonna do a play. Sunny Lea and me are gonna do a play.*

~

Craig's dad, Mr. Herman who lived next door, looked like the guy who kicked sand in the skinny guy's face at the beach in those ads for muscles. And he was a soldier in the war. But he was smart too. He went to college.

Brew never went to college. Not even high school. But Earl, my real dad, or Mom, they didn't go to college either. They were older than Craig's dad and Mom said that when Earl and Brew got out of school, they had to get a job right away to support a family. I guess Craig's dad didn't have to.

He had a nice yard. It was always neat and beautiful. Nice flower beds behind the big blue spruce tree in front of his tall white house with the double doors. A white picket fence along our side of his driveway that was always thick with blue gray gravel that crunched when cars drove on it. A double garage. More than twice as big as our little old leaning one.

His back yard was all gardens. A vegetable garden and one with nothing but roses. No platform over a septic tank and grass that always needed cutting. Like ours.

On Saturday and Sunday, Brew in his dirty cords and half-a-hat would be out by our dirt hill burning stuff that he started with a big ball of fire from gasoline that all the kids in our neighborhood thought was pretty neat.

But Mr. Herman in his army colored clothes worked those days out in his gardens. His light brown hair down in vegetables or roses pulling weeds. Listening to the football game or the opera on his radio.

The day I found my cape, he was standing in his driveway when I ran down the black top on Spring Garden into the dusty road in front of his house and our house waving a stick sword and my cape flying out behind me. I was yelling, "I come to conquer. Conquer!"

The cape was an old blue bedspread of mine that got black ink spilled on it. Mom said it just didn't look very nice to have a bedspread on the bed that had ink spilled on it. So she let me have it for a cape.

It had vines and flowers curling around on it that were kind of white and looked like they were deeper down in it than the blue part. They were woven into it so that on the back it was mostly whitish or blue white.

The ink spot was where I tied the bedspread around my neck. So the ink didn't show much. It was a better cape than a bedspread.

That summer all of us kids saw the movie called Broken Arrow. We all loved it, especially Jeff Chandler who was this really neat Indian chief. We all wanted to play something like Broken Arrow when we played outside but playing cowboys and Indians was really for little kids. That's what we used to play years ago. We liked swords and capes and girls in distress. Like they had to be saved from evil doers. So we made our game sound like Broken Arrow but it wasn't about cowboys and Indians. We called it The Broken Sword.

I came running down the black top going pretty fast. My tennis shoes slapping against the black top. Whop, whop. But when I hit the dust my shoes went quiet. Mr. Herman was looking down at his gravel, but when I went by, he just looked up at me and said kind of quiet, "Who let you out?"

I was running fast and kept on going so I could fly down the moo-cow hill. When I got past our house and started to fly down the hill, my ears heard what he said. It was funny.

It was funny 'cause in my head I could see what he saw. This screwball kid with last year's summer jeans too short for him above his high tennis shoes. Wearing a bedspread tied around his neck and holding a stick over his head. Screaming like a crazy person and thinking he can fly.

It was like little Joey always trying not to laugh at himself 'cause he could see how funny he was. That's when I started to laugh. When I saw in my head what Mr. Herman saw, I could see I was a little too old to be running around the neighborhood with a bedspread tied around my neck. But who cares?

I started to laugh the same time I started to fly down the moo-cow hill. It was like at the Penny Arcade down at Rockaway with the laughing lady. Once I started to laugh I couldn't stop. It got louder and higher and I couldn't concentrate on flying. At the bottom of the hill, I just let myself go and fell in the dust. Rolling around in the soft face-power dust laughing. All tangled up in the bedspread. The dust making mud in the laugh-tears on my face and "Who let you out?" in my head. I rolled in the dust until I couldn't anymore. My sides hurt so much from laughing.

On the way back up the hill, it was clear that we couldn't have the Broken Sword be the play that Sunny Lea and me planned to do that summer. We didn't want to have people laughing at us.

~

That year there were two other movies that we all liked, Rocketship X-M and Destination Moon. Sunny Lea and me went to see them both. It was the first time I ever saw a movie about outer space. Both of the movies were really exciting. They were adventures. Like my favorite night-time radio program—I Love a Mystery—that I had to listen to with my new little radio under the covers 'cause it was on after I was supposed to be asleep.

Rocketship X-M is the first outer space movie we saw. On the way home, I told Sunny Lea I thought it had a story like one we could make a play about.

Sunny Lea crossed her arms over her front like she was carrying her notebook and said, "Then I get to be Dr. Lisa Van Horn." Her mouth puckered up kind of tight. She was still mad about having to be Betty's best friend in Henry Aldrich 'cause Robby wanted to be Betty. There's only one woman in Rocketship X-M. Dr. Lisa Van Horn. A swell part for Sunny Lea 'cause she can be so serious. And there are four guys in it. Craig and Gary and me and, since Robby couldn't be there, we would have to let Craig's brother, Dale or Gary's brother, Jack be the other guy. Or we could even have five guys. "You can be the Colonel," she said and looked her blue eyes up at me under her brown eyelashes.

That was funny 'cause Colonel Floyd Graham gets to hug Dr. Lisa Van Horn as the space ship crashes back on earth at the end.

In the movie, they are headed for the moon but they have an accident and end up on Mars by mistake and are attacked by little cave dwelling Martians and have to run for it. Sunny Lea and I don't want to copy the movie, so we changed that part. We start off for Mars and end up on the Moon by accident.

We both like it that Destination Moon had Moon in the name of the movie so our play is going to be called "Off to Mars."

Sunny Lea's next door neighbors have a little boy named Terry who's about the same age as Craig's baby brother, Bobby. There's an old chicken coop in their backyard they don't use any more, so we get all the neighbor kids to meet there so we can tell them about our play. Craig and Dale and their baby brother, Bobby, who's three. Gary and Jack and little Terry, me, and Sunny Lea.

Sunny Lea brings some milk crates and a wooden box to sit on but some kids still have to sit on the floor. There's a lot of noise and arguing going on 'cause some kids don't want to sit on the floor. It's pretty clean. Better than Gramma Brugger's chicken coop. But most of these kids have never been in a chicken coop before and don't want to even get near the little bits of chicken poop that's left around on the floor.

Craig finally holds his littlest brother, Bobby, in his lap and Jack and Dale just stand up and lean against the cobwebby walls. The other kids that have to sit on the floor are okay about it.

When we get started, we tell them all about our play. Of course everybody wants to be in it which is good 'cause Bobby and Terry are so much littler than the rest of us, they'll be good for the moon men that attack us.

Craig says he's gonna ask his dad, Mr. Herman, if we can use their double garage so we can have our audience sit in chairs on the nice blue and gray crunchy gravel driveway and use the second garage for a dressing room and back stage. He's pretty sure we can use it.

So we're all set. We have our moon men and everything.

~

Mr. Herman said okay. We could use their double garage. Craig was so excited, his long legs came crunching through the blue gray gravel and around the fence like a cross country runner. His legs that used to be so short were a lot longer now. Seeing him through our screen door standing on the cement front porch, he was almost as tall as me. He could hardly talk. He kept slapping his chest to get the words out 'cause he was trying to breathe, he was so excited.

I liked plays a lot but Craig was the reason. Well, his mom. She asked me once back when he was the little kid with the short legs and cowlicks, if I wanted to go with him and his little brother, Dale, to see the Portland Civic Theatre. I was so dumb, I thought we were going to a movie.

It was Rumple Stiltskin. And they were real people. We even got to talk to them after the play. For a long time, I couldn't stop thinking about that play. Sitting in the dark with the tall cones of light on real people in beautiful costumes like in my favorite fairytale book. Believing they could really weave straw into gold. That time was why I wanted to do our Henry Aldrich play.

"It's so neat. We're gonna have a real theatre in our garage," Craig said between slaps on his chest. He was more excited about having his garage be a theatre than he was about being in the play.

So right away I got busy. I had to think about all kinds of stuff. What the story was about. What we would say. How everybody would say it. What everybody would wear. How do we make the space suits, for instance? Out of cardboard boxes? If we make something go over our heads, how could we see? What kind of music would make the play exciting like the movie? How can we make the moon men scary? How to make Craig's garage look like on the moon.

48

Outer Space

I called up Sunny Lea and told her to meet me right away in the chicken coup. Except now we called it the Club House. Sunny brought her notebook. Just like school, she wrote everything down. Made a list of all that stuff I had to think about and added stuff of her own. Things like, Do our space suits have hoses on them so we can breathe? or Do Moon Men have feet on their legs or wheels? and What kind of flowers do they have on the moon? I told her it was too much like school. That we didn't need to write everything down. Especially stuff like that.

"Those are important questions," she said getting kind of mad.

"We didn't do that for Henry Aldrich," I said.

"Yes," she said. "And we all know how that turned out." Sounded like Mrs. Pyle the eighth grade teacher bawling out some kid in the hallway at school. "This one," she said, "has to be more Pro-Fesh-Sion-Al." She handed me the list. Made me take it home with me.

What did she think, for cryin' out loud, that I wasn't gonna take this play serious or something? I was gonna make this play perfect. It was gonna be a lot better than the movie. Real people and everything. But I was glad she felt like me about it. What she said was right and it stayed in my head a lot. But sometimes she could be kind of bossy.

~

One afternoon when Mom was at the store I went in the front room to do my favorite thing to do when Mom wasn't home. It was so cool and quiet there with the red silky drapes and thick old carpet. I slow opened the doors of the wire recorder that was a record player too and got out one of the record albums Mom's baby sister, Connie gave her before she went to live in Alabama. Connie loved classical music a lot.

I slid a record out of one of the sleeves in the heavy dark blue album with the bent corners on it. On the front of the album in gold letters, almost worn off, Brahms Symphony #1. *Slow and Very Careful* with the big black disk. It could break so easy. It was as thin and fragile as Mom's good china cups she collected. It didn't look like it because you couldn't see through it but one false move and you could drop it and it would be all over. Of course there's that voice too. *Don't touch things that don't belong to you.* I put the record on the spindle with my hands shaking and it dropped down loud. KLUNK. It always scared me 'cause it dropped so hard. It was like I was sure it was gonna break.

I took off my shoes and like in a serious ceremony, trying to keep my back straight on the bulgy, wobbly cushions, got up on the davenport in front of the mirror over the fireplace and raised my hands. The perfect picture of a symphony conductor from the waist up. Cool, confident, ready. Hair combed.

The music started. Rushing into it at first. Boom, boom, boom, boom. The big deep kettle drum. Like a monster's heart beat. Then slow and spooky. I was Leopold Stokowski. Like in the movie, Fantasia. My hands were conducting my huge orchestra in all parts of the front room. Violins on the right by the record player and behind them the violas and cellos. The kettle drums and percussion behind the mirror over the fireplace. All the clarinets and flutes, trumpets, trombones and horns spread out on the left to the front windows and out into the front yard. My big graceful hands dipping and arching and slow-motion waving in intricate gestures, pointing out the instruments, pulling them in one at a time with the precision of the master musician that I am. The rocky cushions under my feet tipping me from side to side. Almost throwing me off the davenport. The music leaps and the conductor in me responds. My arms take flight and I throw my head forward with the music. My hair falling on my forehead and flying in the air as the music takes off like suddenly soaring into outer space. Sailing out into the stars.

It was just then when it was really getting hard to keep my balance on the davenport that I first heard Sunny Lea's voice in my head again, *"This one has to be Pro-Fesh-Sion-Al."*

Boy, this would really be great music for "Off to Mars." It's perfect.

This is what Sunny Lea meant.

I was so happy, I didn't even wait for the record to end to bounce off the davenport and cross that part of Sunny Lea's list off. Brahms Symphony #1 was going to be the music to blast our audience into outer space.

~

Monday night up in my bedroom listening to the Railroad Hour on my new little Philco radio, I didn't hear Mom at first down at the bottom of the stairs calling me. The springs on my bed crunched then squeaked when I jumped off and went out in the hall.

"Sunny Lea is on the phone for you," she said down there looking up the stairs. Her eyebrows wrinkled down. "Didn't you hear me calling you?"

I fast two at a time ran down the stairs. "I had my radio on."

"Do you have to play it so loud? The Hermans might not like operetta," she said and walked back down the hallway to the kitchen. "I found us our space suits," Sunny Lea said on the phone. "They're just what we need. They've got hoses to breathe and everything."

I was just standing by the driveway window looking at the Herman's blue spruce tree with my mouth open.

The clock was ticking on the mantel.

"Real ones?" I said.

"Well, of course not, silly. But they look like real ones. They're tin cans at the service station. About three feet high with a hose out the top. We could make them look really neat." Her voice sounded really happy. Like she was gonna laugh or something.

"Do they want to give them to us?"

"I don't know Davey. They were closed but it looked like they were going to throw them away. We could go there tomorrow morning, if you want."

"Sure," I said. "I'll come up to your house in the morning."

"Okay," she said. Her voice still all smiley. "See you then."

"Okay. Bye."

Space suits. Wow. Ones that looked like the real thing. I pictured wild weird space suits with tubes coming out in all directions. This play was really gonna be great. Everything was working out swell.

The service station was on Capitol Highway right by our end of the viaduct. I went there sometimes to get free maps for school and every January for really nice calendars that had swell pictures of Oregon—Mt. Hood, Crater Lake.

The service station guy was cleaning the windshield on a 1947 Buick Roadmaster convertible with the rocket ship flying through the circle on the hood. I told Sunny Lea that this was a good sign. Our space suits were gonna be here. It felt like Christmas inside me.

The service station guy must of had to get a job right out of high school too. Like Dad and Brew did. He was pretty young like that. He had on a dirty suit thing zipped up the front, and his hair had what looked like car grease all over in it. Cleaning that windshield, you could see it was combed in one of those new duck tail things in back. A big hunk of gum in his mouth kept snapping and popping. His eyes like bright blue head lights under his black greasy hair.

"What can I do you two for?" he said and clicked his gum loud.

Sunny Lea kind of backed up like she wasn't sure she wanted to talk to him. Then she looked up at him. Her eyes all squinted from the sun. Her nose and forehead all wrinkly. "Well, mister, we were wondering if you were gonna throw those cans with the hoses in them away. The ones by the garage?"

The service station guy looked at us both for a minute. Then his hand, real black under his finger nails, slid into the hair on his forehead and pushed it up off his face. "Well, yeah?"

All this was going way too slow for me.

"Could we have 'em then?" I said.

"That depends," he said slow popping his gum. His hair fell back down to his head lights. "Depends on what you want 'em for."

Sunny Lea gave me a hard look right in the eyes. Like she wanted me to be quiet. Then she gave the service station guy a big smile. Kind of a silly one for Sunny Lea. And looked at him up through her eyelashes which was really not Sunny Lea. "Well see," she said real sweet, "my friend Davey and me are doing a play. The rest of the neighbor kids too, of course." Her voice all smiley. "It's about flying into outer space and we need some space suits. So we thought maybe you'd be nice enough to let us have them. We think they'd make really nice space suits."

The service station guy was popping his gum all this time and kind of keeping rhythm to something with one leg that only he could hear. When Sunny Lea said that he stopped his gum and his leg.

"Whoa Nelly, you mean you guys are gonna get inside the cans?"

"Well, yes. They'd be our space..."

"Hey no way, kid. I'm sorry," he said shaking his forehead hair back and forth. "I couldn't let you guys be doin' that. You'd asphyxiate yourselves and I'd be the one to blame."

We were losing our space suits. So I quick said, "But see, we'd make-"

"Nope kids, I'm sorry. They had petroleum stuff in 'em. Fumes. You'll have to find yourself something else," he said and started to walk away.

Right then, a new Chevy drove in over the rubber cord things by the pumps and a bell rang twice from the wheels running over them.

"Sorry, you guys," he said and went to help the man in the Chevy.

Sunny Lea looked at me with her mouth open and I just shrugged my shoulders. My ears were all hot and my heart was banging away like I was mad or something but I tried not to let Sunny Lea tell.

"Nice try," I said. "But what does he mean we'd afisticate ourselves?"

Sunny Lea closed her mouth and let all her air out. Like a balloon getting smaller and smaller.

In a little voice she said, "I think he means we'd die from the fumes in them."

"Really? Even if we cut holes in 'em for our faces?"

Sunny Lea didn't answer.

My ears were cooling down but it was one of those times again when somebody does something to you you can't do anything about.

"Well, maybe he's right. We wouldn't want to get afisticated, would we?"

"Yeah, I guess," she said. Sunny Lea looked really unhappy though. Her shoulders way down. Her head too. Looking down at her feet as we walked back up Thirty Ninth Street to her house.

I was really disappointed but I was more sorry for Sunny Lea.

"Maybe we could get something like them at the bakery." I said to try and cheer her up.

"Yeah, I guess," she said again. Not even looking up.

"I don't think those fumes would kill us."

There was so much to get ready and already we were having trouble. And even though I had been thinking for days about how to make the moon men scary, I couldn't think of anything that would work.

~

The next time I heard Sunny Lea's voice again in my head, I was in mine and Scotty's upstairs bathroom. Well, not Scotty's anymore. *My* bathroom. It was night time and I couldn't sleep. I couldn't get a good idea for the moon men.

If I borrowed some of Mom's make up, little Bobby and Terry would just look like silly Halloween kids. Not scary moon men. Same with masks. We needed something really different. Really scary.

In bed, almost asleep I all a sudden got this idea. So I grabbed my flash light and ran into *my* bathroom. Ran into the doorway is more like it. Stubbed my toe on it. Then hopped over to the mirror. It was dark in there without the lights on. I turned on the flashlight and put it under my chin.

When I looked in the mirror by the water glass and tooth brush holder, I looked really scary. A shadow going up from my lip made it look like my nose was only half there and a big creepy shadow from my nose was spread out over my cheeks and up to my eyes and made my eye sockets look empty. That was a really scary look for the moon men.

Then it hit me. Our play would be in the daytime. Every time I got a good idea how to do something like in Rumple Stiltskin, it wouldn't work. Like our space suits killing us or like anything we could do with lights wouldn't work in the day time.

I turned on the light and put the flash light under my chin.

Geez. That is really dumb.

Nothing.

I took the glass out of the brass holder and stood the flash light up in it.

Nothing.

This play was supposed to be perfect and I was getting nothing. It was starting to be like me trying to learn to catch the dime. Trying to learn to catch anything. Or learning to ride a bike.

I just stood and looked at myself in the mirror.

Sad looking.

Mad looking.

Prickles in my stomach. Like I wanted to hit the mirror.

Like the time I looked at myself in the same mirror with ringworm. *Frustrated.*

Wait a minute.

Wait—A—Minute. Ringworm. Nylon sock.

I was pretty sure I still had an old nylon stocking of Mom's in my dresser drawer.

I quick ran into my bedroom. Yanked open the top drawer.

Under my shorts. No.

Under my socks. No. Shit.

Second drawer. *Under my tee shirts. Bingo.*

Back to the bathroom. The mirror. I pulled the thigh part over my hair.

My hair. Oh, thank you God. I've got hair.

Yanked the stocking down over my face. Looked in the mirror. Through the tan blur in my eyes, there was this THING looking back at me. Smashed nose. Eyelids drooping way down over slits for eyes. Glowing white forehead and bright white line on top of its nose, leading down to just a crack for a mouth. Like a face made out of wax that got too hot and started to melt.

Pro-Fesh-Sion-Al.

~

There was still too much to think about. So Sunny Lea and me, we got together in Craig's garage to work on the first part, the part where the Colonel Floyd Graham tells Dr. Lisa Van Horn his idea to fly a space ship to Mars. It was in her laboratory so we didn't need anything there except a card table and chairs and a lot of bottles of chemicals and stuff.

It was the part that Sunny Lea would be really good at. Like she always was in real life. At school anyway. Just serious and listening. Just serious and listening was who Dr. Lisa Van Horn was and so was Sunny Lea.

But she wasn't. Sunny Lea started doing all kinds of weird things that morning in Craig's garage. Talking loud. Banging the table. Picking up bottles and walking fast around in circles. Laughing and joking while the Colonel was trying to tell her his plan.

Finally, I stopped telling her the plan. Stopped doing the play and asked her what she was doing.

"I was just acting," she said.

"Oh," I said. My face was all warm. "Could you be more like you are—well—in school?"

She looked her blue eyes straight at me. Not blinking and her face kind of red. "What-a-you mean, like at school?"

It was like I had something in my throat. "Well, serious. You know. Quiet and serious?"

"You mean I shouldn't say anything?"

"Well, maybe you should.. umh," I said, still something in my throat, "just listen."

"Well, how do they know I'm just listening?"

"They?" I said.

"The people out there in the driveway."

"Oh," I said. "Well, if you nod your head they'll know."

She nodded her head.

We started again. Me telling her my plan to take a space ship to Mars. Sunny Lea put her elbows up on the card table. Some of the bottles rattled. I got nervous then wondering what she was gonna do next. But she put her hands together like she was praying but with her fingers spread apart and touching. Like a spider on a mirror. She leaned toward me on the other side of the table and got that serious look on her face like she did when she was watching a science movie at school about finding uranium in the desert or something. Her blue eyes just half open and wrinkles thinking in her forehead.

When I came to the end of a sentence, she nodded her head and her hands tipped forward too. "Uhm hmmm." she said real soft. Then again, "Uhm hmmm," tilting her fingers. Like she was really listening hard to the Colonel and figuring out what chemicals she could make to get the space ship where it was going.

She was perfect. *Pro-Fesh-Sion-Al.*

49

Moon Flowers

As it turned out, the service station did help our play though. The week before our play, I had to change my Chevron calendar I got from the service station from June to July. I flipped the page over and there on my bedroom wall was a beautiful picture of Mt. Hood. July.

It made a little tickle in my chest 'cause, in the picture, Lost Lake was in front of Mt. Hood. But a lot more important was what was growing in front of the lake. Moon Flowers. That's what they looked like. Tall long flowers shaped like long skinny, moon colored parachutes. Milky white little blossoms down by the green stems and getting wider and creamier the higher the little blossoms went. Ending in a glowing creamy dome of blossoms at the top. Like stretched out parachutes. Moon Flowers.

I thought Sunny Lea's question—"What kind of flowers do they have on the moon?"—was dumb at first. But here they were growing right in Oregon. I told Mom about them and asked if we could go camping on the weekend up at Mt Hood so we could get some for our play next week.

Mom said what she always said when I asked something like that, "Ask Brew."

So I asked Brew.

He said, "Why not?"

So we were going to Mt. Hood to get Moon Flowers for our play. It made me giggly. I didn't tell Sunny Lea 'cause I wanted to surprise her. That was what made me giggly.

~

I woke up in my sleeping bag by the lake real early. My hair felt kind of wet and when I touched the outside of my sleeping bag it was wet too. Mom and Brew were sleeping in Scotty's tent on the other side of our gone-out campfire and there was hardly any light in the sky up above through the tall fir trees. Some bird was hooting. Maybe an owl or a dove. The air smelled like wet wool, dirt and fir trees.

I pulled the top of the sleeping bag over my wet head and went back to sleep.

By the time I heard anything again, it was crackly coming through the feathers of the sleeping bag. I pushed the warm fluffy bag off my head. The fire was burning beside me and Mom was making scrambled eggs at the little gas stove set up on the picnic table. I could smell coffee. Warm and cozy. Yum.

Mom was in her jeans with the big rolled up cuffs and the red and white checkered collar coming out around the neck of her dark blue sweater. Her beach and woods out-fit. Her swooped up glasses flashed and her dark red "eight carat French cut" sparkled in the sun when she flopped some eggs with the spatula onto a plate.

"Hi Sunshine. Sleep well?"

"Yeah," I said in the middle of a yawn. "Where's Brew?"

"Well, he said he was going hunting." She twisted her mouth as she scooped up some more eggs and dropped them on a plate. "But I don't know what he was talking about. He didn't bring a gun and it's not legal now anyway."

Mom and me just that minute sat down at the picnic table when Brew came back to our camping place limping from his old maple tree wound.

"Hurry up and finish your breakfast," he said grinning his dimple at us. "I've got something to show you."

So after we ate and washed up our dishes, packed everything back in the car, the three of us started on a hike around the lake.

It was already warm and the sun made the air smell all piney. On the right of us the water on the lake made slapping sounds against the bank. There was a lot of stuff in the path 'cause you could rent boats to row out on the lake so not too many people hiked around it. Brew kind of went ahead of us and picked up branches and stuff out of the path. So I started helping him. One time I stuck my hand right in the middle of some nettles and got little stingy spots all over my hand and arm. Mom and Brew said the prickles would go away but it didn't feel like they would. I was looking down picking up a branch when I heard Mom.

"Oh, how bea-u-ti-ful."

First I looked back at her to see what was bea-u-ti-ful and saw she was looking ahead of us on the path. I turned around and there they were. Moon Flowers.

In a clearing, growing along a little scooped out back-water part of the lake with Mount Hood huge like heaven towering into the sky behind them were thousands of moon flowers. It was like a kind of misty dream. The sun shimmering off the creamy white flowers.

"Wow," I said. "I wonder if it's all right to pick some?"

Mom looked at me with her eyebrows arched up over the top of her glasses. "Well, isn't that the reason we came up here?"

"Yeah but they're so beautiful, I feel kind of funny picking them." I had this empty place in my stomach since I started to think about it.

"Well," Brew said, "I think if you pick some over to the side. The ones hiding behind the bushes over there." He pointed at some ferns over to the left side of the path away from the lake part. "So you don't mess up the picture for other people, it'll be OK."

That surprised me. It sounded more like something Craig's dad, Mr. Herman, would say than the man who attracted neighbor kids to his bon-fire with gasoline fire balls. But he always surprised me. Like when I couldn't find my wonderful old fairytale books and found out he gave them to my cousins and didn't even ask me. One minute he was in dirty cords and half a hat and the next minute he was all dressed up in a suit and tie wanting to adopt me. I gave up a long time before that hoping he'd ever understand me. Then he said that. And he even cared enough to go out early looking for my moon flowers.

Even so, I only picked five. I just felt too bad to pick more. And we took them back to our camping place and put them in water.

~

On the day of our play the driveway was full of people sitting on chairs in the blue gray crunchy gravel. My stomach was doing summersaults inside me. Everything was ready but my hands and arms were all jerky. Every time I said anything to anybody, my eye would see my arm jerk out funny or my hand would shake when I went to do something.

I just hoped I could keep my voice from jerking like the rest of me.

The Moon Flowers that I surprised Sunny Lea with were each in a coffee can full of water "back stage." They looked a little limp. But they were okay for just one time on the moon. Little Terry and Bobby, the Moon Men, had their nylon stockings and some empty squirt guns that would be their deadly ray guns. Sunny Lea and me decided to just have all of us that were going in the space ship wear sweat shirts and sweat pants like they did a lot in the movies. Space suits were too much to worry about and we didn't want to get afisticated.

Sunny Lea had this great idea too that we have a drawing for a door prize. So we bought an *Oh Henry* candy bar that we were going to give to the winner after the play. Mom thought it would be good for me to welcome everybody in our audience and announce the play after we had the drawing. So when everybody was there, we had our drawing. Then I went out and stood in the opening of the garage and said, "Welcome." But I couldn't think of anything else I was supposed to say and I was still all jerky, so I went back stage to Craig and Dale's portable record player and lifted the needle to put it on the Brahms Symphony #1. My hand was all shaky though and the needle didn't go down steady like it was supposed to. There was a loud zip noise and the record started in the middle of the booming kettle drum's monster heart beats.

I heard someone go, "Ugh." I looked up and saw Sunny Lea standing there with her hands over her ears. Her face was all screwed up like someone squealed their fingernails on a blackboard. I made my mouth shape, "Sorry" and went to the doorway to go "on stage."

Everything else went pretty good though. The whole audience clapped real loud at the end of Sunny Lea's and my first part. Her "Uhm hmmms" were perfect.

When the garage door closed after the first part of the play, all the neighborhood people stood up and clapped. From the inside of the garage though, through a crack in the door, I could see some people starting to walk away. They thought it was over. Then I heard Mom's voice out in the driveway saying loud, "There will be a short intermission before the second act." The people turned around and came back.

I told Craig and Gary to grab a coffee can and Sunny Lea and me grabbed the rest of them and we took the Moon Flowers out and set them around on our moon. Right away we opened the garage doors before any more people thought about going away and started the second part.

Finally we were there. On the moon. When we all came out of our space ship, I saw that Gary and Craig had left the wrong side of their coffee cans out toward the audience. *Maxwell House* and *Chase and Sanborn* didn't seem much like the moon but the rocks and dirt around on the garage floor looked real good and especially the moon crystal.

Craig found a big quartz crystal in a chunk of rock up at their cabin on the Zig Zag River on Mt. Hood and that was right in the middle with moon flowers all around it.

Everything else in the moon part of our play went real well too. That is until the little Moon Men came out of their caves "back stage" to chase us. They were really scary with the nylon stockings pulled over their faces. But the stockings weren't the nightmare. And from then on the play was really a nightmare.

It was like Henry Aldrich all over again. Little Bobby and Terry had filled their squirt guns with water and they tore out of their caves more like little kids having fun than scary moon creatures. They were not only chasing us with their deadly ray guns like they were supposed to but they started squirting the audience. At first the audience thought it was funny and was laughing. But then they started ducking the squirts and then *not* ducking the squirts and getting all wet. Bobby and Terry didn't pay any attention to where their squirts were going. People's glasses were getting sprayed so they couldn't see. Some got it right in the eyes. Ladies' make up was dribbling off and they had black smudges under their eyes. By then half the audience got up out of their seats knocking over their chairs and backing away in the crunchy gravel so they wouldn't get squirted. And they weren't laughing anymore.

As the moon men chased Sunny Lea and me by the garage doors again, I grabbed the door handle and pulled them shut. Ending there was all we could do.

One of my favorite movies was called *Always Leave Them Laughing* and we had already passed that point.

When we got the audience back in their seats, I went to get the door prize. There was only half of the *Oh Henry* left. Robby and Terry ate the rest. So Mrs. Baldwin only got half a door prize.

~

So much for Pro-Fesh-Sion-Al.

~

Sunny Lea and me, we felt pretty awful but I did learn something that day in Craig's garage. I was gonna do real plays someday. Just not with little kids.

50

Bibby Babies

For fifth grade I got "Crazy Lady Faely." That was kind of mean. Crazy Lady Faely. But that's what the kids called her 'cause she cried a lot. It was strange to have a teacher that cried a lot.

The story was that Mrs. Faely was going to have a baby but the baby died. She had a hard time getting over that. So she cried a lot. But besides that she was kind of strange anyway.

She was klunky. She had big feet and walked like a man. Most of the time she left her goulashes on all day. Open and flopping. She wore plaid wool skirts a lot too. Those made her look like a man who played the bagpipes but left the bagpipes at home. Her hair was dull brown and came straight down to her shoulders then cut off all the way around straight like it was chopped off. Her face was lumpy. The one thing she did do that was like a woman was her fingernail polish and lipstick. But they were as red as a fire engine. Her fingernails looked like curved eagle claws on fire. And her lipstick made you really notice her lumpy face.

Mrs. Faley was very serious. Never smiled.

On the first day of school, she clumped into the class room with her goulashes flopping and wrote her name on the black board. But everybody knew who she was. She was "Crazy Lady Faely." Everybody knew that.

Then she sat down at her desk and started to tell us what she would be teaching us in fifth grade.

What I didn't know when class started that day was that fifth grade was going to be so different for me than fourth grade when I had ringworm on my head. But by the time class ended that day I was sure this year was gonna be pretty different.

With everything Mrs. Faely told us about fifth grade, we did a little bit of what she was going to be teaching us. We read a little history and talked about it. Did some fraction problems and read some social studies. By the time we got to the Big Announcement, it was late afternoon. Last period. She told us she was going to read a chapter every Monday in last period from a new book and we would spend the whole week after that in last period talking about it. The book was called *How Life is Handed On* by Cyril Bibby.

Without any warning, she said, "How many of you have had either your mother or father explain to you where babies come from?"

My hand went up before I even thought about it. I looked around the room then to check out how many of us there were.

I was the only one.

My stomach all a sudden was really empty and there was that fast going down in an elevator feeling. My arm started to drop back down. Chest to go tight. But then I saw how everybody was looking at me. Some kids had their mouths dropped open. Some had little "o" mouth question faces, heads to one side, eyebrows up and Stephanie and Betty who always sat next to each other were covering their mouths trying not to giggle. But something was really clear in all their faces: they envied me. I never saw that look before. It was like I just won a race or something.

Oh my Gosh, I know something none of the other kids know. And it's something important. Adult. Something I've known since I was seven years old.

All them knowing that I know is powerful. This knowing that I know. My whole body is glowing happy like I'm running naked in the sunshine. Riding Star fast with no barns to run back to. Finally catching the ball that wins the ball game. It makes me warm all over. Not just happy. Powerful.

That old tight chest feeling is gone. Feels like gone forever.

I just wish Billy was here. Billy didn't get Mrs. Faely though. He isn't in my class. It would be so great for him to be here though. This is better than knowing how to ride a bike any old time.

Something almost as good as Billy being there happened though. The big man in class, the big shot, Leslie, was looking at me too and it was clear from his look, he had lost some of his big shot stuff to me.

After school, on my way off the playground, he comes after me.

"Hey, Davey. Wait up."

So I wait up.

"You goin' home?" he says.

"Yeah," I say and start walking to Multnomah. Trying to look normal. Like he has me wait up for him every day.

That's all he says though. And it's all I say. He just walks beside me.

It's kind of weird.

Leslie is short. A little shorter than me but really strong looking. Not gangly me. He has muscles on his arms that really show. Even when he's not making them show on purpose like he does sometimes when the girls are around. There's this really neat vein too, running down from his shoulder over the smooth curve of his arm muscle to the inside of his elbow. His hands are big for his size and kind of square like a boxer. So is his chest. And he's all the time moving his sharp little steps like a boxer. Even walking beside me, it's little spurts of run-walk. His hands dancing in the air.

But the one thing about him that is really great is that he can draw. I mean really draw. I've seen his pictures. Mostly big cats. Tigers, cougars, leopards, panthers. And they look real. That's really something. How he can just make them on a piece of paper with a pencil so that they look alive. I wish I could do that.

I'll bet that stupid art teacher, Miss Fieldhorn, doesn't rip his pictures with her pencil.

So we're walking to Multnomah and he says, "Your mom really told you how people do it? I mean, make babies?"

"Yeah," I say kind of like Scotty's Jack Armstrong. Arms swinging, chest out. "A long time ago when I was seven."

"Wow," he says. His face kind of red and his green/brown eyes kind of checking me out from under his light brown hair. Like he doesn't know whether to believe me or not.

When we get to 35th in the middle of Multnomah, he says, "Well, I'll see ya," and goes up the hill to the right where I always go down the hill and across the railroad tracks.

"Yeah. See ya," I say.

That was strange. The big man in class. I mean, last year I walked home with stumbley ol' Clayton. But that was because he's my friend and maybe a little bit 'cause nobody else wanted to walk with me. But this was very strange. Just because I know some grown up stuff?

~

Billy and me, we could only see each other at lunch time or sometimes at assemblies in the cafetorium since he wasn't in my class and rode the bus home after school. So the next day at lunch, I ran down the hall right after the bell let us out of Crazy Lady Faley's and waited outside his class room.

We were best friends now.

I threw my arm over his shoulders when he came out and he said, "What's up?" Like always. Then he jabbed me in the ribs tickling me like he did sometimes.

I'm really "pokelish." It made me jump and take my arm off from around his neck.

He laughed because he knew he could make me jump like that and 'cause I did jump. Then he threw his arm over my shoulders and we wobbled back and forth down the hall banging our butts against each other all the way to lunch.

"So you were the only one that put your hand up?" he said when we sat down at the table with our trays. Some kind of gray tuna casserole, a bun, an orange and a little carton of milk.

"Yeah. I couldn't believe it. I thought there'd be a lot of us." The tuna casserole was too salty. "Yuck. Salty," I said.

"Yeah. Good thing we got milk."

I took a swig of milk. There was a picture fast in my head of how the other Billy a long time ago made it come out of his nose. Tried not to laugh. Anyway, that was when we were just little kids. Who needs to think about that.

I watched my new best friend eat.

"So, did your Mom tell you?" I said.

Billy's eyelashes fluttered and he looked down at his tuna casserole. "My dad," he said. Red coming up from his neck a little.

"Oh," I said. "That was better than your mom though, right?"

"I guess," he said and pushed some casserole around on his plastic plate. "Except he got all embarrassed telling me."

He put some of the casserole in his mouth and looked his blue eyes at me. Chewed.

I didn't tell him that I had a dad that couldn't even give me a good night kiss when I was five.

"It was last summer when he drove me down to Coquille. He got so nervous he could hardly drive." Billy looked down at his plate again and chuckled. "All I wanted to do was get out of the car."

"Last summer?" I said.

I said it a little too loud, 'cause his head snapped up with his face scrunched and he quick looked over his shoulder at the kids eating at the table next to us.

"Yeah?" he said in a kind of loud whisper.

I tried to do the same whisper. "Wow, I was seven when my mom told me."

His blue eyes opened really wide then and I saw that same look in his face that I saw from all the kids in my class.

"Really?" he said.

I guess I thought about it before, but right then I thought my mom was really something.

~

That first afternoon Mrs. Faely read us the first chapter in Cyril Bibby's book, *What is life?* But then for the next month the book was all about animal babies, cats and rabbits and frogs and even a duck-billed platypus baby. Nothing much happens like that first day until we get to the chapter called, "The Mother's Part." Chapter four.

Mrs. Faely is at her desk reading the chapter to us and when she gets to the part about people her lumpy face starts getting all red and I think she's embarrassed to read about what people do to have babies. But I'm wrong.

She's reading, "The mother does much more than just lay eggs." Her eyes are getting red too and then there are tears coming down her cheeks. "She also protects and feeds the growing embryo baby," she reads. But her voice is all bumpy sounding. Like a car running out of gas. Chugging and almost choking. "until it is ready to be born." It's then she closes the book on her desk and puts her head down on it.

All of us look around at each other. Leslie looks at me. He nods and shrugs his shoulders. Like this is what we've all heard about. A teacher that cries. Stephanie and Betty start to giggle, Hee Hee. They giggle at anything. But then even they stop 'cause of the quiet in the room. It doesn't seem like the thing to laugh at. The class is never this quiet.

Mrs. Faely looks up then. Her lipstick and eye make-up all messy. "Why don't you all take a little recess to go to the lavatory." Her voice all raspy. "Just five minutes."

When we are all back in our seats and Mrs. Faely is reading again, she reads the word, vagina, for the first time. But nobody gasps or giggles or anything. We're all just sitting there listening to what she is reading. Maybe everybody's asleep. But no. Just then, we must of all grown up or something.

~

But I'm wrong again. Three weeks later, it's chapter seven, "Coming Together." Mrs. Faely is reading along how fish fertilize eggs and all of a sudden the book changes to Rabbits. "The male places his penis in the vagina," Mrs. Faely reads and there are some gasps, then snorts and Stephanie and Betty aren't the only ones giggling.

Mrs. Faely keeps reading though. Like she doesn't hear any of the kids. "The penis becomes rigid, and this makes it easier for it to be placed in the vagina."

There's a loud scraping sound and I turn around and see Leslie. His legs out stiff in front of him under his desk. His knees had come up and hit the bottom of his desk and scooted it. His face is all red and his mouth tight like he's holding back a big laugh.

Then the kids start to laugh at him.

"Class," Mrs. Faely says loud.

Leslie sits back up and Stephanie and Betty cover their mouths. There's a lot of throat clearing and everybody looks up at Mrs. Faely who's sitting at her desk. Her fire engine mouth tight. Not reading. Waiting.

She finishes reading about rabbits and then she reads, "In humans, also, the penis is placed carefully inside the vagina."

It's like in a movie where the film stops and everybody freezes. But right here in this class, everybody that is frozen, is looking at me. Like their faces are all frozen asking me if that is true. Like I'm the authority, the only one in the class who really knows. Before I even think, my head is making this big nod. Like I'm on stage in a play and they have to see my head move way to the back of a huge theatre. Not just out in to the driveway like Sunny Lea's nods, but as far as you can see somebody's head nod.

As soon as my head moves, the faces in class un-freeze. They are saying, "Wow," and "Really?" Their eyebrows are up and, of course, Stephanie and Betty have their hands over their mouths. Michael, the kid that I never liked, has his tongue out so far I bet I could see his tonsils, saying "Ughhhh."

But even as my head nods, something is different with me too. Right then was the end of my special time. Right then, I'm not the only one who knows anymore. As soon as my head moves, nods the Big Nod, my power is gone. Now everybody knows what I know.

I can't hear Mrs. Faely reading any more or the kids around me in the class. All I can hear is the no-sound in my head. I lost that important thing that I had. That power. My whole body is buzzy and empty.

Then through the no-sound, I hear Mrs. Faely's voice reading Cyril Bibby, "One big difference is that sexual intercourse usually takes place only between a man and a woman who are very much in love with each other."

In my head, like it's far away from me somewhere, there's this picture of sitting at the old kitchen table with Mom before we got the robin's egg blue dinette set. It's a spring day, Kitty is rubbing around my legs and Mom's saying, "This is only possible between two people who love each other very much."

51

Toreador Song

Billy and me, we didn't have such a hard time saying goodbye that summer after fifth grade when he went away to Coquille again. We were good friends then. He was my best friend. My buddy. And I was his. We'd see each other in the fall.

And I had a job. A paper route. I started that even before the summer vacation. Gary's dad got me started on weekends. Saturday I met him at his house at four in the morning and we took off in his car. It was always cold then in his old Plymouth and the car smelled like the heater. Kind of a burning wire smell and the smell of old newspapers and cigarettes. The smelly old Plymouth rattled into the dark morning led by the two yellow beams from its headlights. At the newspaper station, we stopped and picked up piles of that morning's Oregonian. Then the car smelled even more like newspaper but fresh ones. Ink and wet grocery bags.

Together we used some old pliers to break open the wire from around the stacks of papers. Then, while he drove to the start of the route, I rolled the papers and tucked one end of the paper inside the fold at the edge of the roll like he showed me, so they wouldn't come undone when we threw them out the windows. By the time we started the route, the car was hot and stuffy. Hard to breathe with the heat and newspaper smell.

Gary helped his dad most times during the week and I did on the weekend. Sometimes Gary would come during the weekend and sleep in the back seat or suck on his all day sucker. Sugar Daddy was his favorite. I got to know Gary better then—when he was awake.

Both Gary's mom and dad had funny names. His mom's name was Winnie. Laury was his dad's funny name. Laury looked like President Truman. He always wore a hat and wire glasses and looked like just about anybody you'd see on the street with hardly any chin. He was supposed to be a Mormon too but he smoked cigarettes and drank coffee every morning in the car, so he wasn't really a Mormon. He said of the two of us, I was the best helper. That wasn't hard to figure out though since Gary was asleep most of the time.

One time when he was with us on the weekend, Gary told me his Mormon cousin, Alicia, was going to come for a little while in the summer from Salt Lake City. So we'd have another girl in the neighborhood to play with. Sunny Lea and Donna were enough girls in the neighborhood, if you asked me. But Gary said she was nice and I would like her.

By the time school was out for a while, the old Oregon Journal—the afternoon paper—sold out to the Oregonian and Laury put my name in with the manager at the station and I got my own afternoon paper route. But somehow, I missed Laury's old hot car and four o'clock in the morning paper throwing.

Christmas had been really neat that year 'cause I got a bike like I always wanted and a bee-bee gun. Ever since he found out I was in the 4H Rocks and Mineral Club, my Uncle Lloyd, Brew's older brother who owned the agate shop in downtown Portland, started giving me neat rocks for my birthday and at Christmas. Quartz and amethyst, and thunder eggs—neat things like that. That year he gave me a piece of rock with real garnets sparkling in it. Almost as neat as the things in Mom's jewelry box. And Pop, he surprised me with a dog. A wonderful white Alaskan dog called a Samoyed.

Crazy Lady Faely told me that the Samoyeds were ancient Alaskan dogs that the Chows and Huskies were bred from. 'Cause he was a boy dog, I couldn't call him Lassie like I wanted, but Mom said I could call him Laddy. So I did.

But most important was I got a bike so I could have a paper route and make some money. I didn't have to carry a piece of linoleum around the neighborhood and charge people to watch me tap dance on it like I did when I was little or pull up flowers from our yard and try to sell them. I could make some more money too, delivering papers everyday by myself. Not just on weekends with Laury. I was gonna start buying my own clothes as soon as I got to seventh grade.

So that summer with my new bike I started my own paper route. After dinner one Monday night I was listening to the Voice of Firestone up in my room. On top my colored snowflake quilt, I was just staring at the ceiling, looking at that dark spot in the ceiling tiles that was still there over by the door to my room. A man with a big voice was singing something called the Toreador Song from Carmen. Some kind of opera about a Spanish bull fight. But that song was so exciting, I could almost hear the crowds of people there yelling and see the bull fighter flashing his cape. Almost getting stabbed by the bull. The tune just stayed in my head too after I heard it.

One night after that, I was drying the dishes for Mom and humming it. Mom was standing at the sink with her arms up to the elbows in soapy water and she started humming with me. Pretty soon she got really going with it like a Spanish dancer and raised a soapy fist out of the water and was flinging dish suds around over her head and stomping her white strap shoes on the kitchen floor singing, "Toreador-o don't spit on the floor-o. Use the cuspidor-o. That's what it's for-o." She was snapping her fingers over her head and twisting around the kitchen until she really broke herself up.

She got me laughing so hard I almost dropped a dish. "Is that what the song means?" I said.

"I don't have the faintest idea," she said. Her face all red and laughing. "It's just the only words I know to it." She wiped her hands on her little waist apron then took off her swooped up glasses all steamy from laughing and wiped them on her apron too. "Where'd you hear it?"

I told her I heard it on the Voice of Firestone when this guy was on with Rise Stevens.

"Oh," Mom said, "he must have been from the Metropolitan Opera. I think that's where Rise Stevens sings Carmen. She's supposed to be the best."

Well, I couldn't forget the tune or the big booming voice of the man who sang it and the only words I knew were what Mom sang. So every day when I was out alone delivering my papers, I sang "Toreador-o don't spit on the floor-o. Use the cuspidor-o. That's what it's for-o" as loud as I could. My voice booming as big and opera sounding as I could. I was getting pretty good on my bike. A lot better from that time Billy taught me out at Gramma's farm. So when I got going with the song I snapped my fingers over my head and smelled my arm pits like a Spanish dancer does while I was riding. Sometimes one of my paper route customers would hear me and clap. It made me embarrassed they saw me acting goofy, but happy too that they clapped.

One day on my way home from my route, I was riding by Gary's house revving my bike up for a zoom down the hill and singing my Toreador song big as I could when Gary and this really pretty blond girl stepped out of the gate in his back hedge. I could feel my face get all hot and red. My heels just went backward hard on the pedals and my bike screeched sideways and stopped big, digging up grass in front of them.

Gary said, "Davey, this is my cousin Alicia from Salt Lake. Ali, this is Davey, our opera singer in the neighborhood." Gary's fat cheeks had a big grin in the middle. No Sugar Daddy around his mouth like he usually did though.

I was so embarrassed I could hardly look at her. But when I did. She was beautiful. Blond hair, almost white like Gary's but long curls, almost like Shirley Temple but not such a little girl. Blue eyes like frozen water from Lost Lake with Mt Hood huge like heaven towering into the sky behind it.

"You have a beautiful voice," she said. Her smile made a dimple on one side in her cheek. The frozen water in her eyes melted.

Something in me did too.

~

It was a long time since Sunny Lea got us all together after dinner for Kick-the-Can. She was always good at getting us all excited about playing that. But that night was warm and stayed sunny late and there was something soft in the air like little chick feathers touching your skin. So Sunny Lea got us all together. I think Sunny Lea wanted to see who Alicia was.

The two of them were really different. Alicia with her white blond hair and ice blue eyes. Cool and quiet. And Sunny Lea more like us boys. Always wanting to run and jump and get things started. Serious in school but liked to laugh. Her dark brown hair flying and her dark blue eyes flicking quick from serious and deep in thinking to laughing out loud.

We played until it got dark so I got to see what Alicia was like.

Sunny Lea saw me watching her while we were playing Kick-the-Can and said kind of like she was mad at me, "She's so girly."

But I liked that. She was kind of shy and not very interested in playing games. More like me. Not like Sunny Lea who could beat any of us at games. It was fun to have someone to play with more like me and besides she was really pretty. Like Gary said, I liked Alicia.

I didn't think I'd get to see her that much though 'cause I still had to deliver my route in the afternoons.

~

Around that time the manager at the station told me about my prize. I was getting a lot of subscriptions for the paper 'cause I wanted to win the prize for getting the most. And I won.

The manager announced the contest about a month before. He told all the paper boys. "Paper carriers," he called us but in the afternoon, we were all boys. Men with cars did most of the morning routes. He told us that whoever got the most new subscriptions to the paper would win a prize. That we could pick out a prize from a catalogue. When I saw that catalogue, I knew what I wanted and I knew I was gonna win.

See, the Journal sold out to the Oregonian 'cause they didn't have enough subscribers, so the Oregonian needed to get a lot of people taking the afternoon paper to keep it going. Every day on my route, I went to all the houses around my regular customers. Not everybody was home but I got at least one a day. It all started when I went up to this house that had Gambini on the mail box. A winding path through a nice cut lawn with happy little cement gnomes standing along beside it. A big jolly man as big as Santa Claus opened the door. But he didn't have white hair. He had almost no hair except real black around the edges and red laughing cheeks.

After I asked him if he wanted to subscribe to the new afternoon Oregonian, he winked at me and laughed. "Oh, you're the singing paper boy, aren't you?" He didn't wait for me to answer though. He just said, "Well, anybody that loves opera has to be my paper boy." Then he just signed up and I thanked him.

But it got me thinking about other things to sing. I went next door to Craig and Dale's a lot to listen to records. Craig had Peter and the Wolf that I liked a lot and Winnie the Pooh. One time when I was over there listening to records on his portable record player, Craig played a record of a guy singing Faniculi Fanicula. That was the theme song to Pepper Young's Family too that I used to listen to on the radio during the day when I stayed home sick from school. Well anyway, that tune started going through my head then. So I made up words to it that sounded Italian and started singing that on my route too. Then I kind of made up words to another song I heard on the Voice of Firestone. A song sung by a barber named Figaro. I just sang his name a lot like the guy on the Voice of Firestone did. Pretty soon, I had lots of opera kind of songs I sang and people were signing up for subscriptions every day.

So I won.

The manager asked me then what prize I wanted. I told him I wanted the Selections from Carmen with Rise Stevens.

His big football coach face got all twisted funny like I was speaking a foreign language and he didn't understand and he said, "What?"

I told him again real slow and tried to make it more English that I wanted the 45-speed-album-of-records-of-Selections-from Carmen.

Again he looked all weird. His face all red and scrunched up. So I showed him in the catalogue the picture of the record album.

He said, "Are you sure? Nobody ever asked for that before." He looked at me like I had ring worm on my head. That was a look I knew.

"Yup," I said. "That's what I want."

He let his air out and his chest kind of caved in. "Well, Okay," he said. "We'll have to order it."

I was so excited, I jumped up and down and said, "Yes, yes, yes." Now I could learn the real words to the Toreador Song.

The manager was still looking at me like I was some weird kind a kid.

52

Tennessee Waltz

After listening to Let's Pretend, Buster Brown, and Armstrong Theatre of the Air like I did every Saturday morning, I went up the hill to see Gary. Well, really to see Alicia.

I went in Gary's back gate on Spring Garden and there she was sitting in the swing hanging in the apple tree. A little wind was moving the leaves and the air smelled like ripe apples. I watched her barely swinging like the breeze was pushing her. Her pretty pale face looking down the yard at the old dried up garden where I put some of Mom's jewelry that time.

She looked over at me standing on Gary's old cracked and broken sidewalk and from under my feet it felt like the ground shook a little. Probably just remembering the earthquake there.

"Oh, hi Davey. I didn't see you there."

"Hope I didn't scare you," I said. "I just came up to see Gary." My eyes wanted to look down at the ground. See what it was doing. But I wanted to just look at Alicia as long as I could. Her white blond hair. The hair on top lifting a little in the breeze. Sweet apple smell. Those ice blue eyes.

"Oh, Gary went back to bed. He went with Laury to deliver papers early this morning." Her cool blue eyes looked down at her flowered dress and her hand brushed something off her lap, even though there wasn't anything to brush off, then smoothed the soft cotton over her knees. The thick white blond curls fell forward hiding her milky cheeks. "He was sleepy when he got back home."

"Oh," I said.

The ropes holding the swing creaked like horse tack on the limbs of the apple tree every time Alicia moved a little in the swing. My eyes finally looked down at the broken sidewalk 'cause I didn't have anything else to say.

"It's a really nice morning," she said.

"Yeah," I said and looked up. "Fresh." I took a big breath. That apple smell. It tasted sweet in my mouth and then cool in my throat.

321 - Part Five: Who Let You Out?

"Un huh," she said. Then stood up out of the swing and straightened her skirt. "We could go for a walk. If you don't have anything to do." She wasn't much taller even though she was standing up. "I still haven't seen much of the neighborhood." Her blue eyes flashed at me from under the apple leaves like clear water catching the sun in the woods. "Would you like to show me around?"

"Uh, sure." Nobody ever asked me anything like that before. It was kind of weird. Show her what?

But then she walked to me and said, "In Salt Lake we live in the city. It's a big city. I've never really been in the country before."

It made a lot of sense then and I could spend a lot of time with her showing her stuff. Just us. Nobody else.

We went out the gate onto Spring Garden and walked down the hill. Not exactly together though. For some reason, I walked almost on the other side of the road at first. I showed her where I lived and showed her Craig and Dale's house next door. Told her how we used their garage for a theatre. Before I thought about it, we were walking together. We walked slow down the moo-cow hill talking. She laughed when I told her what we called the hill and pointed over to Sunny Lea's cow munching grass. I told her my favorite thing used to be to pretend I was flying down the hill and how we all got sick drinking the creek water at the bottom. Our feet made soft puffy plopping sounds walking in the deep face powder dust in the road there and the Scotch Broom popped seeds that rattled in the brush.

We climbed the other side of the hill and went all the way down to underneath the viaduct on thirty seventh street then up Capitol Highway by the Chevron station and back up thirty ninth street by Sunny Lea's house. Talking, talking, talking.

She told me about where she grew up in Salt Lake City and how different it was than Multnomah. She had a really nice voice. It was like some kind of music. Kind of like she was singing a soft song. Nice to listen to.

We passed Sunny Lea's house and were almost back to Gary's again. I could hear Craig and Gary up by his house hollering to each other. Probably organizing a softball game in Mr. Coleman's field across the street from Gary's.

Alicia turned and looked up at me, "We have a really famous choir at our Mormon church. You sing so well I think you could probably sing with them if you lived there. Where did you learn to sing like that? I mean, opera?"

I could feel my face getting red. My heart beating in my throat. I was just fooling around when she heard me sing. It didn't sound that good. "Oh, I don't know," I said, "I just sing. I didn't really learn how. Besides, I was just being silly when you heard me."

Her dimple and her smile went away. "It didn't sound silly to me. It sounded really good," she said. She reached her hand down between us and took a hold of my hand. She stopped me walking and looked her eyes into mine. "I mean it," she said.

Her hand felt really warm in mine and soft. My heart started hitting my ribs then. Real steady. When she looked at me that way, so serious, straight on, no smile, it was like she was saying something more than what her words said but I wasn't really sure what that was.

Then her eyes went up over my shoulder looking at something. "I wonder what they're doing here," she said.

There was always a vacant lot between Little Terry's house and Gary's but now it looked like they were building a house there. It looked like the basement was all finished and the floor over it was finished too with two-by-fours sticking up all around it. Like they were getting ready to build walls.

"Let's go look," she said. Her clear blue eyes flashing back at me behind her. Her pretty white teeth smiling against the color now in her checks. She squeezed my hand. Pulled me into the weedy yard.

This was a lot better than going up the hill and having to play soft ball.

We went around to the back of the foundation and new floor where there were a couple of cement stairs down between walls to a door that was closed.

"What-a you think is in there?" she said in a whisper.

I shrugged my shoulders. I really didn't care. But going into a dark new basement with Alicia felt neat. Kind of scary. New scary. But neat like playing in the woods naked. Smoking naked on a teeter totter. It was something I knew I wasn't supposed to do but really fun. It made me all buzzy inside like one minute I wasn't alive, just walking around asleep, and the next minute I was wide awake—wide alive.

We went down the steps. Her hand was squeezing mine. Her breathing loud in my ears between the cement walls. I turned the door handle and the door just swung open. There was a cool smell that came out. Cool like shadows and cement. A sidewalk after it rains but all closed up. And it wasn't dark. There were windows covered with paper on top of the walls. Light coming through.

We went in. Her hand still tight on mine. The cool wasn't just a smell but a feeling too. Like the new cement. You could feel it wet in the air. And new wood smell mixed in. Piney and cool and cement feeling all around us.

There were some two by fours and other wood stacked on the new cement floor. And a closet. The door was open to the closet where there were cans of paint and cans of building stuff and a chair. The paper dim, light falling on it. An old wooden chair covered with paint smears and dribbles. Oil cloth on the seat under the old drips of paint.

Alicia let go of my hand and went in the closet and squatted down looking at the paint cans. Her skirt touching the cement dusty floor.

"Color Base," she read. Her finger tracing a line on the can under the words. Another can, "Linoleum Paste, contractor grade."

My legs were kind of shaking from the rest of me being all buzzy so I sat down on the chair seat.

Her face looked around at me smiling. One dimple. She was still squatting and the edge of her flowery skirt made a line around her in a circle on the cement dust floor. She patted her hands together dusting them off and stood up. Then she came over to me. Her cool blue eyes almost black in the dim basement. She looked down at me in the paper filtered light. There were no sounds from outside, no soft-ball game yelling and nothing in the basement to make noises. Just cool cement quiet. She sat her legs across mine in my lap and put her arms around my neck. Her head came down real slow and her lips touched mine. Soft and cool.

A soft and cool kiss. It was a long kiss. A kiss that I went somewhere else in. Fresh peach ice cream on a hot day.

In our neighborhood there was this really nice guy, Mr. Coleman, who had a pick-up truck and lots of times, always in his railroad engineer's cap and over-alls, he'd take us for a ride. Craig and Dale, Gary and Jack, Sunny Lea and Donna and me all bouncing along in the back of his pick-up. He had barns where he kept gladiola bulbs that he grew and sold. He had peony farms too and other places where he grew turnips and stuff. But my favorite was his peach orchard. Sometimes we'd go there and help him pick peaches. One time afterward at his house on a hot day, he brought out his ice cream freezer and made peach ice cream for us all on his big front lawn. That's the way kissing Alicia tasted that day in the cool cement basement of the new house. Fresh peach ice cream on a hot day.

There was something else too besides taste. It was like being in a movie. Everything black and white—dim paper filtered. When we kissed again, my arm went around her waist and then up her back and felt her smooth skin between the thin shoulder straps of her summer dress. *It was Susan Hayward's skin above her evening gown at a cocktail party. She was just playing with me like she did with most men. But she didn't know that this man was different. I was just playing with her and her heart would be broken when I left her for another glamorous movie star.* My eyes opened just a little then in the next kiss on her neck and I saw her white blond hair. Blurry from between my eyelashes. *It was Barbara Stanwyck's movie star hair falling on the lapel of my tuxedo. Her smoky voice in my ear and her movie star body pressing against me in the chair. Me, a grown up and all dressed up in a tuxedo.* That's what Alicia's kisses were like too.

I couldn't get enough of those kisses. Lips as smooth and soft as movie star lips. Kisses that tasted like peach ice cream. Peach-ice-cream-tuxedo-movie-star kisses. The more we kissed the more I wanted to kiss Alicia.

So then it's like an hour or so before we come out of that door again and up the basement stairs into that weedy overgrown lot. The sunlight so bright we can hardly see. Her hand still tight in mine and her lips all red and puffy. My legs really sore.

Baseball yells are coming from up the hill. She quick looks up there over her shoulder. Her face all pink. And we say we'll see each other tomorrow. Like the bright light makes all our kissing kind of wrong or something and she goes off through the weeds to Gary's house.

~

So then it's Saturday night. Saturday night is bath night. I asked Mom, one time when I was little, why and she said 'cause we went to church on Sunday we needed to be clean. So we took a bath on Saturday night. Mom stopped taking me to church when we moved to Multnomah with Brew but Saturday night is still bath night.

I close the bathroom door and run hot water in the tub. My own special tub that has feet underneath with claws on them. I like the water as hot as I can get it without it hurting me. Pretty soon the bathroom is filled with steam. The mirror over the sink is all foggy and so is the window. As I'm taking off my blue jeans and tee shirt, Patty Page's voice starts going through my head. "I was dancin' with my darlin' to the Tennessee Waltz when an old friend I happened to see."

The bath room with the door shut is all echo-y when I start to sing. It's a lot better than singing outside on my bicycle. I can even sing soft and my voice sounds like it's coming through a microphone. My skin is all wet from the steam even before I step my feet into the hot water in the tub. Still singing, I slide my bottom down the curve on the back of the tub but have to hold my breath when it hits the hot water. Then lay back against the smooth curve and sing again. "I remember the night and the Tennessee Waltz."

Steam is going up in tall jets into the bathroom off the water in my tub and my eyes close soft like I'm in a nice dream. All around me in the steam is the orchestra, the music in the background of my song, and the bathroom is filled with my voice singing *The Tennessee Waltz.*

My hands slip over my skin under the hot water like my skin is made of silk. It's so smooth. The skin between my legs, the creases under my knees and the crease in my fanny going down to that little puckery soft spot feel my fingers. They make my skin all bumpy for a minute. Almost tickly. Then it smooths out to silk again.

It's then my Thing starts to get hard. Singing my song and dreaming, I don't feel it at first. Then it's really hard and I feel it.

It happened before. Like when I pooped in the bushes when I was in California with Scotty and those times with the naked mannequins in the store window.

See, a while back Mom and Brew thought I should learn to swim so they paid for me to go to the "Y" every Saturday for a couple of years. I would go down to Portland on the bus and go to the "Y" to swim. We always swam naked which was nice and a rule then at the "Y." I guess they thought it was more natural or something. Anyway, it felt nice to have the water swishing by your naked body but I wasn't very good at swimming and the teacher was always yelling at me and making me feel stupid in front of all the other guys. So one day I went down to Portland but I didn't go into the "Y." I went for a walk instead. In a street that hardly anybody went to on Saturday mornings I passed this building that had all these naked mannequins in the window. The window guy was changing their clothes or maybe they were mannequins for sale but one thing was clear. They were all naked. Men and women and kids all standing around in groups with no clothes on. I tried not to stare 'cause I didn't want anyone to see me. But I went around the block and went by the window again. By this time, my Thing was really hard. It felt good, kind of all tingly, but a little painful too.

Like now.

My Thing is all hard and tingly and the water is cooling off. So it's time I get clean and get out of the tub. But my Thing does feel good. I don't really want to get out so I start there to clean myself. I trap a little soapy warm water in the skin over the end and close the skin up with my fingers. I swish the water around inside a little. And right away, my whole body is goose bumpy. It's like somebody is tickling every part of me at the same time. I stop and take a big breath. The tickling changes to a nice soft feeling inside my skin everywhere. Wow.

I just lay back and close my eyes. Pretty soon, I swish the water around again. More goose bumps. I stop and feel that sweet rush inside my skin again. I do it until it hurts a little bit and I feel kind of ashamed. Like when I open my eyes the light makes it feel kind of wrong or something. Like what the sunlight did to Alicia and me after our kissing. I don't know why I feel that but I make myself get up and let the water out of the tub.

Maybe this is part of what Cyril Bibby was talking about in his book.

Maybe I really didn't know as much about this as I thought I did.

But why didn't my Thing get hard when Alicia and me were doing our movie star kissing?

Maybe this is what Mom and Bibby both meant when they said, "This is only possible between two people who love each other very much."

~

I run water to clean out the tub and *The Tennessee Waltz* comes back in my head and I start singing again.

53

Petty Girl

The little maple tree that Brew planted survived another summer. It was bigger now and there was a lot more shade under it. Billy and me were laying under the tree in the grass with Laddy and looking at Brew's new *True Magazine*. True: a man's magazine.

We looked forward every month to the center fold. The Petty Girl we called her. Every month there was a picture, a whole double page drawing by George Petty, of an almost naked lady. She usually had white blond hair and really long legs. There was usually some story in the magazine about flying saucers too but Billy and me were just interested in looking at the Petty Girl together.

Billy was back from Coquille where he spent the summer and we had just a week or so before sixth grade was gonna start. We were laying in the cool grass under the maple tree talking when the mail man came by in his African safari hat and shorts and gave me our mail—some envelopes and Brew's new *True Magazine*. We laid it on the grass and quick opened the magazine to the Petty Girl. Even Laddy stuck his nose in the centerfold.

There she was. The Petty Girl. Her white blond hair in thick curls coming down to her sun tanned naked shoulders and billowing around the white telephone receiver she was holding up to her ear. A tiny red and white checkered bra just barely covered her little breasts and her real short little red and white checkered shorts didn't cover the little round cheeks on her bottom that you could see 'cause she was sitting kind of sideways. One of her really long tanned legs was bent like one foot was resting on the rung of a stool that wasn't there. You just had to pretend it was there. The other leg was stretched out all the way to her red high heel shoe, showing her pretty little knee with a dimple in it. Her blue eyes looked out at us from the page like cool water in a mountain stream. Her face tilted forward, laughing and her white blond hair falling on her pale cheeks. It was Gary's cousin, Alicia, all grown up. Or it looked like her anyway.

Alicia was back in Salt Lake City. She spent just two weeks with Gary and Jack and his family in Multnomah. And Alicia and me went to that basement almost every day and necked. A couple of times the guys that were building the new house were working up above, so we couldn't go in the basement. Then there were times we couldn't sneak away from Gary and his brother Jack. But most early mornings when Gary went back to bed after his dad's route, we could.

The last morning, the day before she left for Salt Lake, I met Alicia in Gary's backyard and she took my hand and kissed me right there. Right there in the morning sunshine with the ripe apple smell all around. Right out there in Gary's back yard under the apple tree, she pulled me up to her and put her open mouth on mine and kissed me hard. Right out there, just like she didn't care who saw. Just like she wasn't, and Gary's mom and dad weren't even Mormons. It was kind of like a dream or something.

Just then Gary's old screen door slammed though and Gary was on the back porch. Jack came jumping down the creaky back steps like he might go through the boards any minute. I quick broke loose from Alicia and turned around but I couldn't see from his face whether Gary saw us kissing. He was just standing there looking out in the backyard at us. Not smiling. He didn't have Sugar Daddy on his mouth. His face was clean and his hair was combed.

"You ready to go to the Ward, Ali?"

Alicia looked her blue eyes at me usually cool as mountain tops and they were pink around the edge, even warm looking and watery. "I have to go to church, Davey." Her eyes looked at me like she was already trying to see me all the way from Salt Lake City. There was an empty feeling in my chest from that look and I couldn't swallow. The wrinkles in her forehead said she was sorry, but that was the last time I saw Alicia.

Until now.

At least that Petty Girl centerfold was how she would look someday.

~

Billy could tell something was up with how I was looking at the Petty girl.

"Pretty neat, huh?" he said. Question marks in his eyebrows.

I didn't answer him. Just stared.

Billy knew me pretty well by now. After all, he was my best friend. He knew something was going on. "What's up?" he said. "You look like this is somebody you know, or something."

"Well. sorta," I said. My face was all hot but he was my best friend so I had to tell him. I didn't keep secrets from Billy. Most of the time, anyway.

His mouth was wide open and he almost choked. "No way," he said. "She's just a drawing."

Laddy rolled over and rubbed his back on the grass, kicking his legs in the air.

Billy shooed him away and I just stared at all-grown-up Alicia.

"Well, isn't she?"

"Yeah, I guess," I said. "She just looks like Alicia. All grown up."

Billy was laying on his elbows tucked under him with his chin on his fists. He pushed up and turned his wide blue eyes at me.

Those blue eyes with the moth wing eyelashes.

"Who's Alicia?"

So I told him about Gary's cousin. How she came to Multnomah that summer, about us finding the basement, and how she sat on my lap in the cool quiet paper lit closet.

"No lie? She really sat on your lap? Put her arms around your neck?" came out on his breath like he could hardly believe it.

My face was really hot then. I felt like I was burning up, I was so embarrassed. Billy didn't even have a girlfriend and here I was telling him all about necking with Alicia. And Billy's face was getting all red while I was telling him, but I kept on talking like I couldn't stop.

"Then we started kissing. We kissed a lot. Like movie stars kissing. She even let me put my hands all over her little bosoms."

Billy's mouth clamped shut and he bit his tongue. "Owey. Her titties?"

"Billy, that's not nice." For some reason that made me kind of mad. My throat got dry and I could feel my heart beating by my ears.

Billy, on his belly in the grass, reached one arm underneath the front of him then and kind of scootched around on his hand.

Then something weird happened.

My Thing got hard.

It never did when I was necking with Alicia. Well, maybe a little bit but when I saw how excited Billy was getting. His face all red and his hand going down there, how great he thought it was what I did with Alicia. My thing just went boing. Rock hard.

Then Billy rolled over and pushed his hands between his legs to keep his Thing down.

That was when something else really weird happened to me. It was something like that going down fast in the elevator but it was something like flying down the moo-cow hill too. It was a good feeling and it hurt too. I rolled over to Billy and we started to rassle and laugh. Kind of like we did in Gramma Brugger's hay, but pretend fighting. He punched me and I punched him back. Then my arms went around him and I could feel Billy's arms around me and we rolled into Laddy. Laddy barked and jumped out of the way and we both laughed even harder.

But then we were pressed against each other.

We stopped rassling.

Just pressed against each other and we stayed that way. Our arms around each other. I felt him hard against me. I could hear his breathing. Feel him against me. But everything else was gone. Laddy, the maple tree, the grass. Only Billy.

Billy looked away from me then like he didn't want to look at me. He broke away and got up. He looked down at Laddy. "I think I better get going," he said. "Mom wants me to do some stuff today."

I said okay and he said "See ya."

I laid in the cool grass under the little maple tree a long time not thinking of anything. Then I rolled over and looked at the clouds. Big white ones floating in the blue sky. The sky was never that blue before or the clouds so puffy and white. Laddy's fur was smooth through my fingers. Soft, white and so smooth. That's when I fell asleep.

54

Boy Scouts

Sometimes, I hated Scotty 'cause he went to live with Earl and didn't live with us anymore but most of the time I wanted to be like him. He was strong and handsome and he knew stuff. He knew how to get along in the woods all by himself. That was pretty neat.

One morning after sixth grade started, I got ready for school and went downstairs to have breakfast and there laying on the robin's egg blue table was Scotty's picture on the front page of the Oregonian. "Hardy Scouts Conquer Snow at Chilly Winter Camp," the headline said. He was standing tall and straight flapping out a blanket in the air with snow falling all around him.

My real dad, Earl and Scotty, they moved back up to Oregon when they left Nevada City and Earl got married again. They moved into her house up in Sylvan, just outside of Portland.

"Sky High," the paper said. "Setting up camp, Scotty Williams, one of six Portland Boy Scouts who chose the year's three coldest days to camp out on Mount Hood just south of timberline in blizzard conditions. (Story on Page 9.); *additional pictures on wire photo page."*

All those summers of Scotty gone glumped up in my throat and my eyes got all watery turning to page nine. On what the paper called the wire photo page, I could hardly see Scotty's smiling face peeking out of his sleeping bag as he "emerged" from his tent, 'cause my eyes were so blurry. I wiped them on my sleeve and read the story of the six Boy Scouts on Mount Hood.

That's my brother who I never see anymore. I missed him so much and it was so neat the things he did with his picture in the paper I wanted to show everybody. And looking at him made me so mad.

~

At lunch recess after his class that day, I met Billy. My arm went over his shoulders like usual and we headed for the cafetorium. When we got our lunch and sat down at one of the long metal tables, before I even opened my little milk carton, I looked at Billy sitting across from me and said, "Let's join the Boy Scouts."

Billy looked his blue eyes up from his tuna casserole, blinked his moth wing eyelashes at me and said, "Sure. Why not?"

Just like that, Billy and me went to the next troop meeting in the basement of the Presbyterian church in Multnomah and signed up. I always wanted to ever since that time in our upstairs bathroom I watched Scotty putting on his Scout shirt with the red and yellow neckerchief and his shiny gold tenderfoot badge. Combing that thick red hair of his.

I guess Mom knew how much I wanted to be in Scouts 'cause the year before Billy and me joined the regular Scouts, she became a Cub Scout den mother for me when the other lady quit and nobody else would do it. I always had fun at our Cub Scout meetings but Mom hated them. She struggled through a den meeting every week in the basement at our house. Every meeting she had to think up something for refreshments that the guys weren't interested in anyway until one Tuesday afternoon when it snowed and Mom couldn't get to the store. All there was in the house to give us was hot chocolate and cinnamon toast. The guys went crazy for it telling Mom what a great den mother she was and how they never had anything so good. Mom just stood there in our basement on that cold winter afternoon shaking her head listening to all us guys in our snow wet clothes go on about how neat it was to have cocoa and cinnamon toast while we wolfed down the delicious hot sweet cocoa and toast dripping with melted butter and sprinkled with sugar and cinnamon. Her eyes blinking behind her swooped up glasses. Her jaw hanging there. She couldn't believe she had been trying so hard and these guys went nuts over so little.

The other thing she hated about being a den mother was that she always ended up having to finish all the guys' projects that they were supposed to make. For half a year we were supposed to do projects that had to do with the Philippines. But the guys just goofed off at meetings, punching and rassling like that's what they were there for. Just a time for best friends to hang out together. But she stuck to it 'cause she knew I wanted to be a regular Scout one day. Mom and me ended up spending a couple of weeks sewing Manila rope together like little braided rugs to make sandals that rubbed your bare feet raw when you wore them.

She even got Brew to help. For the big presentation at the pack meeting, Brew ended up making the entire rice patty model the guys were supposed to make during the meetings. So Mom was really relieved when

I told her Billy and me joined the Scouts and she didn't have to have anything to do with it.

The day after the troop meeting Billy and me were drilling each other on the Boy Scout Oath at lunch when we got the word that Mr. Halverson, our principal, called a boys only assembly for the sixth, seventh and eighth grades for the period after lunch.

So after we ate, me and Billy, we went out to the playground for the rest of the lunch recess. We walked slow down to the woods behind the portables hanging on to each other and bumping our butts together like best friends did, still saying the Boy Scout Oath and Law over and over together so we'd have it down by the next troop meeting. "On my honor I will do my best to do my duty…"

When the buzzer went off, we ran back up to the building and joined the crowd of guys pushing and shoving in front of the cafetorium. All the tables were put away and folding chairs were set up for the assembly when we went in. This was a big deal. It was the first time Mr. Halverson called an all boy assembly since I started at Multnomah.

Mr. Halverson was a really stiff man. He hardly ever came out of his office and when he did, he never smiled. Always in a dark pinstriped suit and vest with a tie so tight his face was red like it was choking him, he walked like his long arms and legs sat in a chair most of the time. Like he tried hard not to move them very much when he walked.

Billy and me sat in the third row close to the stage. There was a lot of scraping chair sounds and kids still pushing and yelling and jumping around. Putting their hands on seats to try to save them for their friends and getting their hands sat on. The old smell of casseroles, tuna and macaroni and cheese and other stuff was in the air. Like it never really went away.

Pretty soon, the noise started to die down and you could hear Mr. Halverson's shoes click on the wood floor coming down the side of the room. He stopped in front of the little stairs that went up on the stage and then he lifted his foot up slow like it was hard to do and went kind of jerky up the steps. There was a tall wood thing up on the stage that he walked up to and put the papers he was carrying on it. He looked down at the papers until everybody was really quiet. Then he looked his red, choking face up and aimed his eyes above us at the back wall.

"Today," he said and then stopped and cleared his throat with a grinding sound in the microphone. He reached his long fingers of both hands up to his suit lapels and grabbed them like he was hanging on to keep himself up straight. "I have something very important to talk to you about."

It was kind of weird 'cause it was like he was talking to the back wall instead of to all the guys sitting in front of him on folding chairs. But then he stood there like he forgot what he was going to say. We all waited. The clock on the back wall made those loud clicking sounds as the second hand clicked around in a circle over its face and somebody giggled 'cause we were waiting so long.

That got his attention and his head snapped in that direction. "Something serious," he said. His voice sounding like it was coming through his nose.

Then we waited again and listened to the clock.

His eyes went down then to his papers and he said, "I have noticed, when I have had the occasion to visit the halls of our institution, that you boys tend to be quite demonstrative of your friendships with each other." His eyes went back up to the back wall again and his face seemed to get redder like his tie was getting tighter. "Friendships," he said and again he made that throat grinding sound in the microphone, "are not a bad thing, mind you. But I want you to understand that the effusive behavior between you boys I have witnessed here at Multnomah Grade School could be misconstrued."

Again the clock. His eyes jumped down to his papers and back up to the wall. "When men hang on to each other—with their arms wrapped around each other, it means only one thing."

The lunch in my stomach right then moved like I must of eaten it too fast. One big lump of macaroni stuck down there and gurgling. And I could feel heat around my shirt collar. Smell Billy's baking bread smell next to me.

"It means homo-sexu-ality." Mr. Halverson said. His choked up red face all scrunched like he was cussing. "It is when a man wants to be with another man instead of a woman."

The casserole smell in the cafetorium was making me sick. Like black walnut milkshakes were bubbling up in my stomach and I wanted to get up and go to the boys' room. But I could see out of the corners of my eyes no one was moving. Everybody was just staring at Mr. Halverson.

"It is a disease, a sickness. It is a, a perversion," he said to the wall, his nasal voice getting louder and louder.

The second hand clicking on the clock got really loud too. It was like it was moving around snapping inside my head and all I could hear was the clock. Then over the clicking in my head came Mr. Halverson's twangy voice. His eyes were looking right at us guys then but Billy and me were so close to the stage I could see it was like he was looking right through us all. Like he was seeing something only he could see, a ghost that followed him around or like in one of my really bad dreams when a cog gets stuck in your head and you can't get out of the dream. His face was all red, scrunched up and choked looking. And his forehead was shiny with sweat.

"I want you all to know," his twangy voice said coming out his nose, "that this behavior in my school must stop. Not just because I will not tolerate it, but because I have the greatest confidence that none of you wants to be thought of as a depraved and corrupted pervert that hangs out in men's rooms thinking only of having sex with another man."

One of Mr. Halverson's hands dropped from his lapel then and exploded in the microphone when it hit the wood thing. There was sweat running down his face and he closed his eyes. Then he opened them again and picked up his papers. His shoes clicked across the stage in time to the clock and he disappeared behind the drapes.

~

There was no sound in the cafetorium except that stupid clock.

Two men having sex. How? Bibby never talked about that.

My eyeballs were hot. And my throat all dry like I couldn't swallow.

Then some chairs scraped and guys were getting up.

Billy and me got up too without looking at each other. We walked out to the hallway trying not to touch each other in the crowd.

"Well, I'll see ya," Billy said looking down at the tile floor.

"Yeah," I said.

And Billy made his way through all the guys and was gone.

~

After that, I thought about what Mr. Halverson said in that assembly a lot. Somehow, I knew what he was talking about but somehow, I didn't. I didn't know what it had to do with Billy and me but after that Billy and me were different. I was kind of afraid to be friends with him 'cause it might mean I was sick. I guess Billy felt the same way.

The night of the next troop meeting, I got my Scout shirt on and stood in front of the bathroom mirror thinking of Scotty while I combed my hair. Tried to look as grown up as he did. I looked at my old brown hair that was flat and dead looking. Like a wet dead rat. Not alive like Scotty's. Not shining like the wound copper wire in the back of my old radio. I tried out different faces. Trying to make my freckle face look like a real man. Not like a girly boy. Puffed up my chest like the guy that kicked sand in the skinny guys face so I would look different than me. And waited for Billy. Waited for Billy to come by on his way to the Scout meeting like before. He never showed up.

Finally, I walked down the moo-cow hill and got to the Presbyterian church basement after the meeting already started. I felt that old tight feeling in my chest again when I walked in. From where I came into the meeting, Billy was sitting by himself on the other side of all the seats filled with Scouts.

As far away from me as he could get.

55

Mister Nichols

'Cause of the snow we'd been having, I looked out my bedroom window one morning at the end of January to see if I needed a sweater and it was Spring. Next door there were patches of gold light all over the Hermans' green front yard and yellow and purple crocuses were peeking out of the ground around the Blue Spruce tree.

"It's Spring," I said to Mom in the kitchen downstairs.

At the stove, she was dishing up some really thick oatmeal I didn't much like. She was standing there, in her white chenille robe with her hair in pin curls under the white scarf tied around her head, banging a spoon against the pan to shake off the sticky oatmeal.

"Don't be fooled. You better wear a sweater."

I wasn't gonna let her spoil this sunshiny day for me. "But Mom," I said, "it's sunny and warm out."

"Right this minute. But it's January," she said peering at me with her head back through the glasses that had slid down her nose like they always did. "It's not Spring yet."

The oatmeal needed half a bowl of milk to loosen it up to the point that I could eat it. And Mom was wrong about the weather. The sweater made me too hot all the way to school.

At my locker in the hall, I had just taken off the sweater and hung it inside when Miss Wilson called my name.

"Hello Davey. I was wondering if you knew that the school has hired a new music teacher."

Her big smile was about all you could see of her in all the pale milk color of her skin and outfit. She almost disappeared against the walls of the hallway. She was dressed as usual in her off-white knit dress and skin colored lipstick.

I told her I had heard we were going to have a new teacher for music class.

"Well, that's not all. Mister Nichols, uh, that's his name, Mister Nichols, wants to start a choir and I told him what a lovely voice you have."

She stopped talking and just looked at me like it was my turn to say something. Somebody slammed a locker door right next to us and she jumped. I couldn't think of anything to say. So, way after when I should of said something, I finally made myself say, "Oh, really?"

"I suppose you can remember Nichols, can't you? Pennies, dimes, and nickels, ha ha." Her off-white face was getting pink. "Well, you might want to stop by the seventh grade class room and introduce yourself. It's right across the hall from your sixth grade class. Or I could take you in and introduce you." Big smile then. Her teeth just more off-white. "You do have a beautiful voice. Well, ta tah." She waved her little off-white hanky that just appeared from nowhere and clicked off down the hall to her fourth grade class room.

~

Billy and me didn't always have lunch together since Mr. Halverson's talk, so when the bell rang for lunch recess, I took a deep breath and crossed the hall to Mr. Nichols' class room.

At lunch one time, there were some girls giggling about a new music teacher but I never saw any new adult in the hallway or anything so I didn't know what he looked like.

When I walked in, the class room was empty except for a man who was wiping the blackboard with his back to me. He had on a dark blue blazer and gray slacks. His hair was wavy and black. I walked up to the desk and cleared my throat. But before I could say his name, he turned around.

In front of me behind the desk and framed with the midnight blackboard behind him was the most handsome man I ever saw. Like Mario Lanza, my idol. He slapped his hands together, dusting them off and a cloud of white chalk dust rose up from his long tanned fingers. Then his fingers landed like feathers on the desk in front of me. Strange for such strong hands. I never saw hands like that. A gold ring clung to the little finger of his right hand. The finger nails were trimmed neat and dark pink against the olive skin of his fingers. They rose to heavy veined hands that were strong and masculine but beautiful at the same time. Crowned by brilliant white French cuffs. I didn't think you could get a shirt that white.

I was just standing there in front of him still with my mouth open about to say his name and he said, "Yes?"

My eyes went up to his face then. The collar next to his tanned face was as white as the cuffs. There was a faint dark tint on his skin of whiskers that were shaved smooth and his mouth was in a smile like a laugh he was trying to hold back. Like he thought I was funny or something. Or he had a secret he wasn't going to let me know. It made his cheeks dimple.

"Miss Wilson," I managed to get out. "Miss Wilson said I should-"

"Oh," he said and he smiled even more so that his white teeth showed. They were as white as his shirt. "You must be Davey Brugger."

"Uh huh," I said. Maybe it was because it was so warm for January that my hands were all sweaty. Maybe because I was nervous. But I really liked this teacher.

Maybe Miss Wilson did too and that was why she was so jittery when she told me about him. Why she wanted to introduce me. So she could spend more time with him. I could sure see why.

"I'd love to hear you sing some scales," he was saying. "Why don't you come by tomorrow during lunch and I can listen to you."

"Okay," I said. But I didn't move.

Mister Nichols picked up a folder off his desk. Those smooth tanned hands with their perfect finger nails moving like they were performing acrobats doing a ballet in the air under their white cuffs. One curled around the handle and opened the desk drawer. The other flicked the folder into the air making a flash and in one clean motion slipped it inside the drawer. Then both hands slid the drawer closed with a smooth swish click.

The end.

His dark brown eyes looked up at me again like he was surprised I was still there and his white teeth smiled.

I quick looked down at my feet and turned them around. Then I walked right out of his class room really fast.

~

It was hard to sleep that night. Every time I turned over, I'd wake myself up 'cause his dark chin, his tanned hands or his French cuffs were there and I was singing scales for Mister Nichols.

Finally, about five thirty in the morning, I got up and started looking for what I could wear for going to see Mister Nichols at lunch time. My old tennis shoes and jeans just weren't right. After taking everything out of my dresser and putting it all back, I spotted my old suit hanging in the back of my closet. It was the suit Mom and Brew got me at Robert Hall to get adopted in. The suit wasn't right for school either. I'd look like some kind of weirdo. But maybe the pants would still fit. They did if I loosened my belt and pulled them down low on my hips. There was a sweater in my dresser that was long enough to go down over my belt so it didn't show I was pulling my pants down low and looked good with my white shirt. One pair of regular shoes was all I had. They were pretty tight but they'd do.

By seven o'clock, I went into the bathroom to look in the mirror so I could see what I looked like. I tried jumping up to see what my pants looked like. But even when I jumped up and down I couldn't see all of me in the little mirror over the basin. So I climbed up on the edge of the bathtub.

"What on earth are you doing?" Mom said behind me.

I almost fell off the bathtub.

"I was just trying to see my pants," I said.

"Well, it sounded like the house was falling down. Were you jumping up here?"

I just looked at the little mole moving up and down on her neck. My face was all hot and when I said it again, "I was just trying to see my pants," it sounded really stupid.

She pushed her glasses up on her nose and stepped back to take a good look at me.

"Well, they look pretty nice and I'm glad you're wearing a sweater. It is still January. But why are you all dressed up?"

"You know," I said. "I have to sing for the music teacher today."

She shrugged her white chenille shoulders.

"He just wants to hear you sing. You don't have to put on a fashion show for him."

She turned in the doorway and headed for the stairs like all this was a bunch of baloney.

"Mom," I said, "this is really important. I want to sing in the choir. And he dresses real nice."

She stopped at the top of the stairs and looked at me for a minute. She smiled that little soft smile then that always made me really feel good. Like I was special.

"Okay," she said and started down the stairs. "Come on down and have breakfast or you're going to be late."

~

All morning in class my head kept going to bad stuff and then good stuff. First I saw myself opening my mouth to sing for Mister Nichols and nothing came out. I was having trouble with my voice anyway. Sometimes I'd be talking along and it would crack and my next word would land down on a bass note I never heard myself make before. So I wasn't sure what would come out when I sang for him.

But then I started to daydream that I sang so well for him he decided to give up teaching and leave Multnomah to take me on a world tour singing in all the big cities. London, Paris, Rome. Just me and Mister Nichols.

Right in the middle of this daydream, I heard my teacher Mrs. Owens say, "Davey what is the matter with you today? Did you hear the question or did you just decide not to join us?" Her magnified eye balls were staring at me through her big glasses. Our noses almost touching. And all the kids were giggling in the back ground.

Then the lunch bell went off.

I promised Mrs. Owens I'd get myself together after lunch recess, stood up and pulled my pants down so they touched the top of my shoes, then headed for Mister Nichols' class room.

Mister Nichols was sitting at the spinet piano playing. It was a really nice tune I never heard before. Then one of those wonderful hands reached up and turned the page on a little piece of music on the music rack. It was like he was just reading it like a book.

That's something I would really like to do. Learn how to do that. But Mom and Brew just didn't understand. I asked them for a piano all the time. We finally got a Hammond Chord Organ. They said they thought I would like it but really it's what they wanted. It had buttons like an accordion for the left hand. It sounded like an accordion too.

Mister Nichols came to the end of the music and then he saw me. Big smile. White teeth.

"Ah, Davey," he said. "I was just looking over some choir music for next year."

"It was nice," I said. Then it was like I was gonna choke and I cleared my throat.

Mister Nichols reached up again and took the music off the rack and laid it on the top of the piano but he stayed sitting on the bench.

"Come on over and let me hear you sing a little."

His hands ran up the keys then and came down on a chord.

It was like I couldn't feel my legs. But he asked me to go over to him so I had to get them to work. With my first step my legs started to shake. Then I was beside the piano but my legs were still shaking.

"Now I'm just going to play a simple "C" scale. Like this…" and his hands moved over the keys, like they did in the air that first day…"and then you sing the same thing. Okay?"

His hands made the notes come out of the piano with such power then, I had to sing. There was no choice. Sounds came flying out of me like I didn't have anything to do with them.

His black curly hair nodded quick and he flashed those white teeth at me.

"Good," he said. "Let's try it a little higher."

Again the notes just rang out of me.

"Wonderful. You have a good sense of tone. Do you read music?"

I shook my head, "No."

"Well, we'll see if we can't rectify that," he said.

He sat back on the bench and pulled one leg up. His beautiful hands curled around his knee. He rocked a little back and forth.

"You have a really nice voice, Davey. I would like to have you in the choir next year. We're going to do some great music."

Then he stopped himself rocking and looked up at me. A crease between his dark eyebrows.

"Would you like that?"

Again, my voice came out like the singing did. Like he had more control over it than I did.

"Yes," I said. Too loud.

"Good," he said with almost a laugh and started rocking with his hands around his knee again. "I'm also going to arrange for you to be in my regular class too. That way we can have some time to work on your music reading."

That's when the daydream started again. It was coming true. I could see us touring the big cities. Just Mister Nichols and me. There was Big Ben, the Eiffel Tower-

"Oh, so you've already met."

It was Miss Wilson's voice and my day dream popped like in a cartoon.

There she was in Mister Nichols' class room. But she had on colors. She had on a light blue sweater and a navy colored skirt. Even a pink and blue silk scarf. I never saw her like that. She didn't disappear against the walls. She looked kind of pretty.

Mister Nichols undid his knee and stood up.

"Oh, hello Mary," his tanned face was saying. "Yes, Davey here just became a member of next year's choir."

His hand patted my shoulder and I could feel my face getting all warm.

"Well, isn't that grand. I knew you could use that lovely voice of his," she said.

Her blue eyes were really looking at him and her face was getting a little pink again like yesterday.

"But I just came by to see if you'd like to have lunch together."

I could feel his warmth next to me.

"Why yes, what a wonderful idea," he said. "Davey and I are all finished here. Right, Davey?"

Again the hand on my shoulder.

I quick looked up at that handsome tanned face.

"Yeah, I guess so."

But he wasn't looking at me. Those brown eyes and smile were aimed at Miss Wilson. Like they really liked what they were looking at.

I looked my eyes down at my feet and like yesterday got them to walk really fast out of his class room.

56

Billy's Secret

"So before we all head out tonight," Alan Fox, our Scout Master was saying, "I want to say once more, plan to be at Camp Fair Weather this summer."

Alan Fox was a hairy man. His legs below his Scout shorts were covered with wooly blond hair. It popped out like little wires too over his neckerchief in the hollow of his neck. Like he must be covered all over with that thick wooly hair.

He reached down and scratched the fur on his leg. "Start making plans now and let us know at the next troop meeting."

It was the first time I heard anyone talk about summer Scout camp except some older Scouts saying how much fun it was swimming and canoeing at the lake or hiking the cape that stuck out into the ocean. But that night the Scout Master and assistant Scout Master showed slides at the troop meeting and told us all about the camp down at the beach. Slides of guys climbing a rope, eating in a place they called the "mess hall." But it didn't look messy. There was even one slide upside down of guys sitting around a campfire singing. That looked really fun.

In my head I imagined a slide of Billy and me there at Fair Weather sitting by a campfire singing and laughing.

We were dismissed and I looked over at Billy. Billy just looked down at the floor like he didn't want to look at me. Then there was a lot of noise. Everybody talking loud. "I'm gonna go." "Can't wait til summer." Hard clangs. Metal on metal sounds the chairs made. Banging and scraping. All us Scouts folding and stacking them up in the corner.

Billy acted like he couldn't hear me over all the noise when I followed him out of the church basement door but then he looked back over his shoulder and said, "Davey, I can't."

I wasn't sure what he was saying. So I said, "What-a-ya-mean?" running to catch up to him out the door.

"I can't-go-to-camp-Fair Weather-this-summer," he said then. Shaping each word with his mouth like maybe I was deaf.

He looked down at the sidewalk then. His eyelashes almost on his cheeks so I couldn't see his eyes. Again, like he didn't want to look at me.

"How come?" I said walking with my shoulder almost touching his now.

He quick looked up at me, then back to the sidewalk. "Well, you know I go down to Coquille every summer."

"Yeah, but can't you take a couple weeks to go to Fair Weather?"

This was bad news. Billy was still acting kind of funny but I was sure that would change down at camp. I had all these pictures in my head of Billy and me at Camp Fair Weather. Swimming in the ocean together. Hiking the cape. Sharing our canteen of water.

He was still looking down and kicked a rock into the street in front of the drug store with his tennis shoe. Then he stuck both hands in his pockets and hunched up his shoulders like he was trying to move away from me.

In my head I saw Mr. Halverson. His red choked up face sweating.

"There's something else I gotta do." Billy was still looking at the sidewalk.

"Oh, yeah, what?" I said. "Don't you want to go?"

He quick looked up at me again and his eyes stayed up this time. "Sure I do."

We were up to the viaduct now and you could see all the houses down over the edge from the lights in their windows. The moon was really bright shining over the other side. Lighting up the viaduct and making a dark curved shadow down on the rail road tracks.

Billy turned to look out and I stopped a little ahead of him and leaned on the cement railing.

"So why can't you take a couple weeks?"

"Aw, geez," he said and stopped walking. He leaned against the railing beside me and looked over the edge shaking his head.

There was a little wind but it was warm. Even though it was only March, Spring blossoms were coming out early in some of the trees already. They made the air smell sweet. Made everything kind of like a nice dream.

Billy bent down and picked up a little pebble off the sidewalk and dropped it over the railing. Watched it. I tried to watch it too but it was too dark out.

"I have to have an operation."

"What?" I said. I must of heard him wrong.

Then he looked his face right at me and said, "In the hospital."

I didn't hear him wrong.

This was not a nice dream.

His eyes were in the dark but there was light from the moon coming over my shoulder and I could see little silver flashes where his eyes were. Silver moth wings moving up and down. Then he looked back down at the railroad tracks.

"You know when you're a baby your testicles are up inside you?" he said.

"What?" I said again.

It was like he was talking a foreign language.

I heard Scotty in my head say, "Stupid."

"You know," Billy said like everybody knows that. His face turned to me again, "Your balls. When you're born, they're up kind of in your stomach and later they come down."

"No," I said, "I didn't know that."

I didn't. And I didn't care what Scotty said. I didn't know that.

"Well," Billy said and looked his eyes down where you could see the curved shadow on the railroad tracks, "mine didn't come down like they were sposed to. So I have to go in the hospital and the doctor is gonna go up in me and bring them down to where they're sposed to be."

My stomach was like when Scotty and me were little and he used to sock me really hard. All of the air went out of me.

"Wow," I said. "That's scary."

Billy just kept looking at the shadow.

"Aren't you scared?" I said.

"I guess I was," he said. "But the doctor said when I get older I can't have any kids unless he does that. Someday I want to have kids."

A car drove slow over the viaduct behind us. Lights filling up the sidewalk. The tires sounding like pulling up stuck down tape.

"So that's why you can't go to Fair Weather this summer?" I said out into the dark the car left behind.

"Yup," he said. "Come on Davey. Let's go. It's getting late," and he started down the sidewalk ahead of me, walking home.

~

The first week at Fair Weather that summer, I missed Billy. I always did when he went away for the summer though, so that was nothing new.

But there were so many new things to do at first, I kept wishing we could do them together. The five mile hike into camp would of been shorter. Talking in our sleeping bags would of warmed up the three sided cabin the first night. And even if it was funny that the camp counselor pointed at me after breakfast that first morning in the mess hall and said, "You're a volunteer," washing dishes would of been more fun if Billy had been there.

After a while I didn't think of Billy so much though. Gary was there and even big ol' clumsy Clayton. Gary was getting so fat he didn't like to hike much and Clayton didn't know how to swim, but we had lots of fun canoeing and stuff. It wasn't until I got back home on Sunday afternoon and found the letter from Billy waiting for me that I thought about him being gone and him having to go in the hospital to have his testicles operated on.

The letter said how he wished he had come down to Fair Weather with me and how next week he was going into the hospital to be cut open.

I quick looked at the date marked over the stamp on the envelope.

Billy was in the hospital right now.

It was like somebody turned on a hot water faucet in my eyes. Hot water was filling up my eyes, trying to run over and my stomach tried to push a sound out my throat so hard it burned. That sound jammed up against my Adam's apple and I bent over and almost coughed it out.

I was too old to cry.

I was not gonna be that ninety pound weakling that cries.

But the doctor was cutting Billy open down there right now.

That was the first time I ever talked to God except in church or at night before I went to sleep. Sitting in my bedroom on that Sunday afternoon, first I asked Him not to let me cry but the picture of Billy being cut open down there hurt so much it was like I was the one being cut open. I tried to stop crying 'cause I didn't want Mom or Brew to hear me being a baby but it just made my throat hurt more. God just had to help Billy out. He had to make it go all right. Billy was my best friend. God just had to not let the cutting hurt too much. And He had to get him well. Billy wanted to have kids.

It wasn't until the next morning, talking to God most of the night, that something in my head said Billy was okay.

Billy came home at the end of the summer and when I told him on the phone we had the new *True Magazine*, the man's magazine, he came right over to see the new Petty Girl. When I saw him on our front porch through the screen, I just pushed the screen door open, jumped out the front door and hugged him. There was that baking bread smell from him warm against me that I almost forgot the summer was so long.

He looked really surprised. He was laughing but there was a kind of funny look on his face like he was saying, "What the heck you doin'?"

I stopped right away and headed out to the maple tree with Brew's magazine. There was a funny feeling in me like after I took Mom's jewelry and that old "men shake hands" thing in my head. I mean, they don't hug, stupid.

Laddy was really happy to see Billy too. He jumped up and put his paws on Billy's chest. That can be pretty scary to people who don't know Laddy though 'cause he's so big. Billy just pushed him down. But Laddy still wanted to show Billy how happy he was and stuck his nose then almost his whole head between Billy's legs.

Billy took in a big breath and backed away fast. But I had to pull Laddy away and tell him to lie down.

I was so embarrassed Laddy was pushing his nose in there, I didn't ask Billy if it hurt and didn't ask him anything about his operation. We just laid down on the grass and opened the magazine. There was the new Petty Girl. Blond like always. This time in some sort of see-through outfit that looked like she was a marching girl in a parade or something. Red, white and blue cowboy kind of boots with gold tassels and a red, white, and blue marching band hat with a gold pompom feather high up on front. She was stretched out on a red, white and blue striped pillowey thing like elephants put their front feet up on at circuses.

Billy just kind of looked like he wasn't looking. Like he wasn't really interested. Then he rolled over and bent his knees up with his feet in the grass. Looking up at the sky, he rested his ankle up on his other knee and folded his hands under his head. He was quiet. Laying on my belly and propping my head up with my elbows, I just watched him.

It was a warm day. The sky was all blue. No clouds at all. Just leaf shadows on Billy's face. The maple tree above us was big now. A real tree. Not the little skinny thing Brew planted a long time ago and we used to swing on and make him mad.

"I've only got one," Billy said. His eyes squinting up at the blue.

I pretended I didn't hear. Just pulled my elbows down under me and rolled to my side in the grass. Looked at him.

"Did you hear what I said? I've only got one ball," he said.

Laddy started rolling on his back in the grass, really waggling around scratching his back. Then jumped up on his feet and shook himself and sneezed.

Those blond eye lashes of Billy's looked over at me and fluttered when he said, "They only found one. The other one dried up the doctor said."

The grass felt cold almost wet all of a sudden.

Because Billy was here and he looked okay, I never thought that maybe everything wasn't okay.

"You mean they could only bring one down?" I said.

"Yup," he said and closed his eyes.

The maple leaves made a swishing sound above us and Laddy got up and walked slow across the yard and went around the corner of the house heading into the backyard.

My eyes followed Laddy. "Did it hurt when they cut you open?" I said.

"Naw," his voice said. Too loud. Like it wasn't really his voice.

I looked back at Billy. "How about kids?" I said.

Billy let out his breath. Then it was his voice again. "The doctor says maybe. I just have to wait and see."

His body rolled over toward me, his knees up and his arms wrapped around his chest. Then those blue eyes opened and a little laugh came out of his mouth.

"Sure looks funny though. Just one."

My head got kind of dizzy then 'cause I had a picture.

I took a breath and said quiet, "You gonna show me?"

"No," he said right away. His eyes laughed blue straight into mine and he didn't move away. No fluttering eye lashes. His eyes just wide open.

I got this funny idea he really did want me to see.

He was pulling his mouth down in the middle. Trying not to smile. But the corners were going up. Like he couldn't help it. He kept looking his eyes into mine through those steady moth wings of his.

I let out a little laugh and said, "Come on let me see."

My body kind of wiggled to him and he jumped up laughing.

"NO. Come on, Davey." Still grinning. Ready to take off. Like a wind-up toy all wound up ready to move.

Then his left foot sprung out toward the road and I scrambled to my feet. But by that time he already started running. Even if his legs were shorter and he couldn't run as fast as I could, he already got a head start on me. His tennis shoes had already kicked up dust to where the black top started going up Spring Garden.

His laughing was coming out jerky and he was starting down the hill to the Baldwin's house. But something was burning like fire in me. Down below my belly and climbing up. I really wanted to catch Billy. I ran after him down the hill. Past the blackberry bushes. But the ruts in the road tripped me and I went flying head first, almost fell down. It made me laugh at myself. A kind of jerky giggle. I could hear Billy laughing big in front of me like he was winning this game but I was closer now. Then he jumped off the road and down into the field that stretched all the way over to the road in front of his house.

I had to catch him before he got home.

The edge of the field was in front of me. This is where I always landed in my dreams on my little flying platform with all my soldiers behind me. I jumped from the side of the road into the air and almost flew like I did in my dreams. I landed in the tall dry grass right behind Billy. But I kept on going down. It wasn't like my dreams. My legs just folded underneath me. My arms went out and my hands grabbed a hold of Billy. Well, really, his pants. And they started to come down. Billy went down with them, trying to keep them up. We were down in the dry grass and Billy was squirming and kicking his legs and wiggling around on the ground, holding his stomach because he was laughing so hard and gasping for air from running and holding his pants so they wouldn't go down over his hips.

All around us was the crunch and beer smell of dry grass.

Billy was fighting to keep his pants up and laughing so hard it made me pull on them even more. His shirt came out of his pants. That's when I found out he was ticklish. Every time my hand went for the top of his pants, he laughed harder. So I just started tickling his stomach. His smooth skin on my fingers. Like the silky red drapes in our front room. His head was rolling back and forth on the squashed grass and tears were coming out of his eyes and I could smell his bread baking smell real strong under me.

My chin landed, thunk, on his chest when he bucked up off the ground from tickling. For a minute in my head, I was riding Star and my fingers dug again into Billy's smooth belly. It was like we were going crazy. Both of us laughing so hard we couldn't stop. His face breathing hot on mine, rolling back and forth laughing and tears going down his cheeks. Crazy.

Then his laughing changed and it started sounding like little short sobs.

His voice squeezed out, "Davey, stop. Please stop."

His voice sounded like maybe he was hurt. Whimpering. Like when Laddy got hurt.

I rolled off him and he stood up.

The sound coming out of him was like laughing and gasping and crying altogether.

I watched him from where I was sitting on the ground. My heart beating against my chest. Breathing fast. Calming down.

He slow straightened the top of his pants, watching me out of the bottom of his eyes. Like he didn't trust me but he didn't want me to see him watching. Or maybe he was still playing the game. He tucked in his shirt and buttoned the top button of his pants that was undone. Then he made a loud grunting sound and jumped sideways. He started running to his house, like he thought I was gonna chase him again.

He was still playing.

I stood up in the grass and he turned and looked at me. Then laughed big, like he won and waved to me before he turned again and ran up on the road by his house.

Inside me, it was like I was gonna laugh too. But I didn't. I just sat back down in the crunchy grass. There was a warm in my stomach that went all the way up to my chest and tears were in my eyes even when I was really happy.

I pulled on a piece of long dry grass. It broke off. Then I bit the end off and chewed it.

"Thank you God that Billy's okay," I said.

57

Lord's Prayer

So here I am, a seventh grader, singing in the school choir. This weird kid who a few years ago stole his mom's jewelry, who still has nightmares, sleep walks, tries to pull his best friend's pants down and talks to God whenever he feels like it, like He's his best friend or something.

The choir is the best thing that ever happened to me. I love to sing. I love singing in the choir. But even I think I'm kind of weird.

The kids make fun of me when I stay in the class room at lunch time learning new music. "Hot house flower," "Pansy," they're whispering in the hall when I go past them. It is kind of a weird thing to do when everybody else is out playing. But there's this piano that I can pick out notes on. A lot better than a stupid chord organ. It's really great. And so is Mr. Nichols. He helps me a lot with the music.

I still can't take my eyes off his hands. They conduct the choir. But they are like magic hands, with their hypnotizing movements in the air, casting a spell on me. Showing me what I really want—to be a singer.

When school started again this year though, he was wearing a wedding ring. He must of got married. Miss Wilson doesn't come by for lunch anymore.

Sunny Lea is in our class too. It's the first time we ever had a class together. She doesn't like Mr. Nichols though. She thinks he doesn't like her either. When she sang scales for him, he didn't put her in the choir.

I've even got to like the old casserole smell of the cafetorium where we practice on the stage. That smell is there all mixed up with the dust from the old wine colored velvet drapes and the grassy rope smell from all the ropes back stage and over the stage that close the drapes and lift things up and down.

Nobody else from our neighborhood is in the choir. Not even Gary who took piano lessons for years like I always wanted to. Even helping me learn Here We Go and The Indian from his first book Teaching Little Fingers to Play didn't help him out. Gary just can't carry a tune. So he didn't bother to try out for the choir.

This year was the first year at Multnomah we had an honest-to-gosh Christmas concert. Mr. Nichols had us do it at night after dinner so all the parents could come. The choir started singing *Angels We Have Heard On High* in the hall in front of Mr. Halverson's office, then we slow walked into the cafetorium still singing and down both sides of the audience. In the program I even got to sing the solo in *Silent Night* with the rest of the choir singing in the background. We sang it with only candles to light the stage and there was Gramma Jones. Her filmy white nightgown and silver hair just like last time. Sitting there in the candle light... Maybe not.

When we all came back from Christmas vacation, Mr. Nichols asked me if I would like to sing a solo all by myself at our Spring concert. Of course, I told him, yes, I wanted to. So he told me to think about a song to sing.

I still went to the bible school in the upstairs of the Presbyterian church in Multnomah too. It was kind of fun, we did a lot of singing and I got to get out of class during last period every Monday. About this time our teacher there, Mrs. Mc Beasley, announced that we were going to have a graduation ceremony at the end of the year. Mrs. Mc Beasley is a big jolly woman with round red cheeks. She looks like Mrs. Santa Claus. She isn't big like Gramma Brugger. Short and big around. I mean she is tall big. With white fuzzy hair. Talking about the graduation ceremony to us all in class made her cheeks get even redder. She said we would have a procession and music and even diplomas.

She was so excited about it, we started that day to learn a hymn called *A Mighty Fortress is Our God* that we were all going to sing together as a choir. I was going to get to be in two choirs. And here I said being in one choir was the best thing that ever happened to me. This was better than best.

We spent the whole period working on A Mighty Fortress and then when class was over, Mrs. Mc Beasley's red puffy cheeks asked me to wait after class because she wanted to talk to me. Maybe I was too loud or something. I was so excited about all the singing, maybe I was sticking out too much, not blending like she kept telling us to do.

Her big Mrs. Santa body turned around in the doorway after everybody was gone and looked over at me sitting there waiting. She said, "Well, David," with a frown and looked down at the linoleum. Kind of like she was trying to find the right words.

Right away, I said, "I'm sorry if I was too loud. I just love to sing and singing in two choirs is so exciting."

With a jerk, her head came up. Her hair was a puffy cloud sitting on top a mountain. Her blue eyes got really big then and her head went back. She erupted like a volcano. A big "Ha ha" came out of her dropped-open mouth. It was the loudest laugh I ever heard. Mrs. Santa must of learned that from her famous husband.

"That's not why I kept you after class, "she said. "I love your voice. It is a little loud considering everyone else is so shy but no, keep it up."

My shoulders that were way up and tight, like when I get nervous, came down and I felt a giggle in my throat but I didn't let it out.

"The reason I kept you was to ask if you'd sing a solo at our graduation ceremony."

My giggle turned into a laugh and came out. She laughed with me then.

"Really? Well, sure. I'd love to sing something. You really want me to?" She nodded a big nod. "Certainly."

I was really gonna have to think again about that best thing that ever happened to me thing.

She sat down in one of the desks that looked way too small for her and nodded at me again.

"Well, you be thinking of what you'd like to sing for us."

I didn't tell her I was already trying to think of a song to sing at the Spring concert.

Wow. Two choirs. Two solos. Wow.

~

That week the song came to me. It was a song I could sing for the school concert and for the bible class graduation. I was listening to the Great Gildersleeve on the radio and Birdie, Gildersleeve's black housekeeper sang it. She was my favorite person on that program except for Gildersleeve. He reminded me of Pop. I only heard Birdie sing one other time when she sang *Were You There When They Crucified My Lord?* but this was even better. This time she sang *Ave Maria.*

Birdie had this deep rich voice that made you feel like when your skin touches velvet or something. And most of all it was full of that feeling like she was talking to God and she knew he was listening.

I could do that.

It was perfect. That was the song I wanted to sing.

After rehearsal the next day I went up to Mr. Nichols to tell him about *Ave Maria.* He was talking to this new kid from New York, Thomas

Thomason. His name was an echo. He was always hanging around Mr. Nichols. Almost as handsome. Dark wavy hair. Muscles. And he could sing. Right then, he was being really friendly with Mr. Nichols. Making him laugh and stuff. Like the kid wasn't even a student. Like they were the same age or something.

Being around this guy, I always got this funny feeling in my stomach I didn't like. Kind of jittery. And something about him made me mad. Why did he have to be so good looking and, even if he was, why did he have to have a good voice along with it? It wasn't fair.

And the way he was standing with Mr. Nichols. His legs spread and his hips pushed forward. Like he was something special. Like he knew how good looking he was. He looked too old to be in seventh grade too. He had to shave already. One thing for sure, he always made me feel like a little kid, he was so sure of himself.

Thomas Thomason stopped talking and they both looked at me.

I opened my mouth to say something but the guy was just standing there with Mr. Nichols. I mean, he didn't walk away. He sure thought he was something.

"Yes, Davey?" Mr. Nichols said.

I wasn't gonna get to talk to Mr. Nichols alone. I had to give that idea up. But my tongue didn't want to work right.

Finally, I said, "The song. The song you wanted me to think about?"

Those really white teeth were smiling and said, "Oh, yes. Have you decided what you want to sing?"

Why couldn't I talk to him alone? This just wasn't the right time to tell him or talk about it. But I already started and I was feeling really stupid.

"*Ave Maria*," my mouth said.

"Ah. Schubert or Bach-Gounod?"

Oh, my gosh. Could this get any worse? There were two Ave Marias?

I started to shrug but then I could see how I would look in front of Mr. Nichols and the new kid and said, "Schubert. I think."

Mr. Nichols' dark eyebrows came together and the echo kid kind of leaned in like he could help Mr. Nichols.

"Well, Davey, it's not an easy song." Mr. Nichols said. "I had thought you'd pick one less difficult."

From the look on his face, it was clear that he thought I couldn't possibly sing that one. But 'cause he thought it was too hard for me was all the challenge I needed.

"Well, I know the song." I said. "I just have to work on it a little."

His pulled down eyebrows went up. "Oh. Well, I guess it's okay then." His warm hand was on my shoulder.

Ha. And the echo kid thought he was so special.

"Go ahead. Give it a try."

Mr. Nichols' face smoothed out and the white teeth smile came back. So did a smile from Thomas Thomason. Like he had something to do with it.

~

On Monday after bible class, I told Mrs. Mc Beasley. Her reaction wasn't what I expected. Her eyes got really big again like they did before she laughed and then she sucked in air like the opposite of "old man winter" and breathed out so quietly I almost didn't hear, "Oh, no, David. That's Catholic."

For a minute, I couldn't think right. Like I got really dizzy or something. Catholic? Why is it Catholic? Throckmorton P. Gildersleeve isn't Catholic. Birdie his black maid isn't Catholic. Is she? What is she talking about? Mary wasn't Catholic.

This time my tongue really wouldn't work.

Maybe that was the reason in my head to sing it. Was I still Catholic? One thing was sure. Mrs. Mc Beasley didn't like Catholic.

She was looking at me funny. Maybe she was figuring out I was a weirdo.

But all of a sudden she was smiling her big round cheeks at me and saying, "Why not *The Lord's Prayer*? It has the same kind of accompaniment and I can get the church accompanist to work with you on it."

"Well, I guess," my voice finally said.

At least, I knew the words.

She tried to jump up from the desk she made look so little. But her hips stuck and almost took it up with her. "I even have a couple copies you can take with you." And she ran to her gray metal file cabinet.

Twenty minutes later, I left the church with copies of *The Lord's Prayer* by Albert Hay Malotte and the phone number of the church's piano accompanist.

~

Myron, the accompanist, was a tall skinny man who was going to Portland State College and majoring in music education. He used his hands like he thought they looked like Mr. Nichols' hands—full of magic. But they didn't. His long bony fingers looked more like they were attached to wrists that were on ball bearings. They could really play the piano but when they weren't on the key board and me sitting on the piano bench beside him, his hands whizzed through the air like lethal weapons. When he talked, I always felt like I had to duck. His hands flying around. Then they would always end up limp. Just hanging from his wrists. So dramatic.

His face was really pale and he hardly ever smiled. Vitalis or some other smelly hair tonic was so thick in his slicked down hair that when I left his house, I could still smell it for hours.

When I told Mr. Nichols that I was going to sing *The Lord's Prayer* instead of *Ave Maria*, I didn't tell him I was working with Myron on the music even though he warned me that it was just as hard as *Ave Maria*.

I was really gonna show Mr. Nichols I could do it though. Then he'd see I was the one that was special.

~

Going to Myron's house twice a week was really helping. There was so much accompaniment, I kept wanting to come in before Myron was finished with his part. It didn't seem natural to wait so long. I wanted to say the words more like when you talk but Myron would fling his hands in the air and tell me this was singing not talking and I would duck and start the song over again.

But I still wished he'd play those parts faster so I didn't have to wait so long.

Pretty soon, I was learning to count though. But it was like learning to dance in gym class. If I was counting and looking at my feet, I forgot to dance. Now, if I was counting, I forgot to sing.

"You have to count it enough times," Myron said, "that eventually it's a habit and you don't have to count any more. But now COUNT." And a hand whizzed by my head dangerous as a skater in a roller derby.

That day when I came out of Myron's house, someone was coming out of the house across the street. Right away, I saw the big shoulders and muscly arms. The black wavy hair. It was Thomas Thomason the echo boy from New York. He waved at me and came jogging over dribbling a basketball.

Him standing there in front of me, legs spread. King of the mountain. The veins in his arms running over the muscles were making me feel jittery. Like I wanted to look at them but I didn't want to 'cause I couldn't show that I was interested in how he looked. His whiskers and handsome face making me feel like a little kid. But how did he get to look like that and still be my age? And to top it off, he could play ball.

"Hey, Davey, so you know Myron, huh?" Like he found out something secret about me. He punched his basketball hard against the black top. Shifted back and forth from one leg to the other. Then pushed his hips forward. Like Billy Rogers' mean friend Frank from when I was little.

"Yeah," I said. I wasn't gonna let him know why I was there.

"He sure can play the piano, huh?" He winked and gave me a big smile like he knows everything without me telling him. Maybe even something I don't know.

"Well, see ya," he said. Then took off running and shooting imaginary baskets.

Off to tell Mr. Nichols, I'm working with Myron, probably.

~

Sunny Lea and me stopped on the viaduct one day like we did on the way home from school. I was telling her that I had to go down the street on the other side of Capitol Highway by the Chevron station to work with Myron.

"I just don't like Mr. Nichols," she said, brushing her bangs off her forehead hard like they were what she didn't like. "He's just so mean."

"I don't know why you think that," I said. "He's always really nice to me. I'm learning a lot from him. Getting to sing a lot too."

She looked down over the railing like she didn't hear me.

"He told me he was going to put some stuff on my fingers that tastes terrible if I didn't stop chewing my finger nails."

I looked down at her fingers holding on to the sparkling cement railing. Her finger nails looked a lot longer than I ever saw them. Longer than when we did our play and she did the Doctor think thing with her fingers in like a prayer.

"Well, it worked, didn't it?"

"Yeah," she said, making her blue eyes tight slits at me. "But he only said it 'cause he doesn't like me. I called him Mr. Five Pennies."

"What?"

"Oh, my grandmother said it would make him laugh. So I called him that the second day of class. He didn't laugh. I did but he didn't. He just thought I was a smart-aleck."

So I didn't tell Sunny Lea again how much I liked him. We just walked to the end of the viaduct and I crossed the highway to the Chevron station.

"Good luck at the concert," she said.

"Aren't you gonna come?" I said.

"Sure, I am. Me and my gramma."

~

When I told Mr. Nichols I was gonna sing the *Lord's Prayer* for the bible class graduation too, he thought it was a good idea.

"You can think of that as a 'dress rehearsal," he said. "But if it doesn't go well, you'll be sure to let me know ahead of time, won't you, Davey?"

He said it more like he was telling me instead of asking me. His dark eyebrows were together and his black wavy hair nodding close to me.

My air came in all at once and my throat got really dry when I tried to answer. "Yes," came out all jagged.

His eyebrows still looked worried so I said, "Myron will help me."

"Myron?" he said and his eyebrows went up.

I hadn't told him about Myron. Thomas didn't either, I guess. The down elevator was back in my stomach again.

"The church accompanist," I said, trying to stop the elevator.

"Oh," he said. His eyebrows back together. "Did you plan to have him —I mean, do you think he would accompany you at the Spring concert?"

The elevator stopped with a jolt.

"I don't know. Would that be okay?"

The picture I had then of Myron at the Spring concert made me kind of embarrassed. His flapping hands. So dramatic. But he would help me count. I would be safe with him at the piano.

"Of course that would be okay."

Mr. Nichols straightened up and his eyebrows went back up where they belonged. White teeth smile.

"I have enough to worry—uh, to do at the concert. That would help me out."

There was a warm feeling in my chest. I was gonna do Mr. Nichols a favor. And most of all, I was gonna make Mr. Nichols proud of me.

"I'll ask him," I said.

~

Myron was really happy when I asked him. "Of course," he said. "I'd be delighted."

It was the first time I ever saw him smile. At least that looked like what he was trying to do when his really red lips straightened out thin in a line and his oily hair nodded. He was so surprised he forgot to wave his hand in the air.

~

The Monday afternoon of our graduation ceremony at bible school it rained. Not just a little rain that we called "Oregon mist" but it really poured. All us kids got there soaking wet and in the church there were only a few people in the pews. By the time we started, only about a quarter of them had people in them. Of course, not very many parents could come on a Monday afternoon anyway. But all that rain didn't help.

I was kind of glad though because the graduation could really just be a "dress rehearsal" for me to sing the *Lord's Prayer*. But by the time I was supposed to sing my stomach was a mess. "Butterflies" is what Mrs. Mc Beasley called it. Oh you've just got butterflies, she said. Her red cheeks laughing. But my stomach felt more like a hornet's nest.

Near the start of the program was where I was supposed to sing and that was good so I wouldn't have so much time to worry. I stood in the choir room that we called "back stage" waiting and started real quiet talking to God. I asked him to make the song good. Make the counting a habit like Myron said. I was deep into talking when a hand zoomed by my head and the breeze brought me back.

"Break a leg," a voice said and Myron's tall bony body zipped by me into the church and sat down at the piano.

What a weird thing to say. Just like Miss Wilson. Myron was weird.

I walked out on the stage-platform-place at the front of the church counting and the next thing I heard was all the people clapping. Myron's arm was around my shoulders leading me back to the choir room.

His pale face looked at me there and said, "Perfect."

But I had no idea what happened. The whole time up there was blank in my head.

The rest of the kids were coming in and putting on the white blousey things we were supposed to wear for *A Mighty Fortress*.

They were whispering things like, "Good job" and "You did great."

I guess I must of.

But it wasn't much of a "dress rehearsal" if I couldn't even remember singing the song.

~

The week went by and then it was Saturday night, the night of the Spring concert. My stomach was a little like it was on Monday but more excited this time than nervous. More like going to the circus than having to take a test. After all, I already sang it for bible class.

Then I did something I shouldn't of. I looked through the crack in the velvet curtains out at the audience. The first thing I saw was Mr. and Mrs. Baldwin sitting in the front row. I staggered away from the curtains. Oh, God. There were people out there I knew. The hornet's nest was back.

I couldn't help myself though. I went back to the curtains and looked again. Beside them, Craig and Dale were sitting with their parents and next to them, Gary and Jack and their mom, Winnie, and their dad, Laury, that I delivered papers with. Sunny Lea and her gramma were just sitting down next to them. Behind them Mom was sitting with Pop and my cousins, Margo and Katy with their little brother T.P. and Aunt Ethelyn and Aunt Pearl.

Oh, my God. At least Scotty wasn't there or Gramma Brugger.

Brew wasn't there either. At home I heard Mom and him arguing about it. He said, "I don't want to listen to a bunch of kids caterwauling." Oh, well. That was Brew.

Myron came up to me then and said, "You all set, Davey?" Then he looked his pale kind of skeleton looking face in the half dark up to me close. "What's the matter? You look like you saw a ghost."

"There are people out there I know," I said.

I felt like I did the day Gary's broken sidewalk came up and hit me in the head in the earthquake.

"Uh oh," he said. "You really shouldn't have looked, you know. Well, when you go out there you'll just have to do what I do, I guess."

"What's that?" I said. Maybe he had a magic pill or something to make this feeling go away.

"Well, when the lights go down and all you can see is their little white faces sitting out there, just imagine they're all on toilet seats."

Then for the first time since I met him, he laughed. His voice making high hee hee sounds.

In spite of the hornets in my stomach, I almost laughed too.

"And remember I'm right out there at the piano with you. And you have nothing to worry about anyway because you sound great." Then his hand was in the air like a helicopter taking off.

That helped.

Well, at least I knew the words. I wouldn't forget the words. But this time I had to wait. I was going to sing before the choir did, so I could have time to get with them. But not at the first part like the bible school. Waiting made me want to jump up and down. So I quiet talked to my other best friend.

Finally it was time.

With the spot light on me, all the people out there did look like they were sitting on toilet seats. I felt a kind of giggle in my belly where the hornet's nest had been. That was better than bees though.

That's when I started hearing the music. Really hearing it inside me. It was a deep vibration somewhere between my chest and my stomach. And the words were like the prayer I said last time in the choir room. But now I didn't have to be quiet about it. My throat opened up and the sound poured out of me. It felt fantastic. Like a laugh feels good. It just came out like Mrs. McBeasley's laugh. Like a wonderful volcano in me erupting. The sound rushing up from that place inside and billowing out. Big sound. Wonderful sound talking to God.

Then I saw Billy.

For a second I didn't hear the piano and then I didn't know where the count was. So I just came in singing again. There was a little hiccup in the piano but then everything was like it was supposed to be. I closed my eyes and I was sitting in Billy's field again after his operation.

"For Thine is the kingdom, and the power and the glory forever" came soaring out of me like I was gonna fill the whole huge cafetorium with it. My chest felt like it could hold the whole universe, stars and planets, sun and moon.

"Amen."

I opened my eyes and it was over. There was a sound like ocean waves booming up on the beach. People were clapping. It was better than when Gramma Jones cried. It made me feel like I was floating up off the stage— flying. But for real. Not just dreaming.

~

Backstage when the concert was over, Myron said, "Good, Davey. You forgot to count once but I don't think anyone noticed." He smiled for the second time I ever saw. But his lips weren't stretched this time. It was just an easy smile.

That was better even than his laugh. It was real.

I was thanking him a lot for saving me, when Mr. Nichols came up. I was so glad I really sang the song and made Mr. Nichols happy that I remembered I should introduce Myron to him. Then I went "out to meet my public" as Mr. Nichols said I should.

Mom and Pop saw me first. They came over and Pop made that sucking through his teeth sound that he did like he was trying to get some stray cigar tobacco out of his teeth or something. He looked down at me with a smile twitching on his mouth.

"Well, Old Fraternity Sister, you haven't lost the knack, have you?"

I wasn't sure what that was supposed to mean but by then cousins and aunts were there and everybody was hugging me. Saying how great I was. Then they were gone.

Miss Wilson came out of the crowd and shook my hand and said, "Wonderful. I never knew you had such a BIG voice."

That made me warm happy all over. Wow.

About that time, Mr. Nichols came over and put his arm around my shoulders and said, "Good Job."

His body pressed up against my side. Warm. His arm hugging me to his smell that was like oranges. That hug was almost better than the people clapping.

It was then I saw Billy trying to get up to the front through all the people in the audience. He had just pushed by a family with a lot of kids when he saw me with Mr. Nichols. He stopped and looked at us for a second. Forehead all scrunched. Then his eyes looked down and he turned around and left.

My stomach was like when Scotty used to punch me. I got a lump in my throat. But Mr. Nichols still had his arm around my shoulders so I couldn't run after Billy.

~

A few days later on lunch recess I was telling Billy how I wanted to be a singer. How great it made you feel to sing a solo. And how everybody thinks you sound great.

He didn't even look at me when he said, "I don't know why you want to do that. You don't have that good a voice."

58

Fair Weather

At least Billy was gonna come to Fair Weather for two weeks that summer. I was really glad about that. But he was still acting funny. Acting like we weren't best friends. Sometimes he came by to go to the Scout meeting. Sometimes, I'd be waiting and he didn't. Around Mr. Nichols, he was really weird. Like Mr. Nichols came up to me in the hall and asked something about the choir and Billy looked down at his feet as if he didn't want to look at him. Not being shy like he used to be. Billy was really over that now. More grown up ever since his operation. It was more like he didn't like Mr. Nichols. Like Sunny Lea. But he never said anything.

At Fair Weather though, we could get back to being really good friends again. We'd be together having fun for two weeks.

The one thing I didn't count on was the alphabet. See, everything we did in Scouts was always by our last names and Billy's started with a "W" and my new one started with a "B." It would have been better if I was still Williams. B's and W's were never together.

We had rides going down to the coast and of course we were in separate cars. When we got out to get all our gear together for the hike in, we were put in alphabetical order. So Billy was way behind me as we followed ol' hairy Alan Fox, our Scout Master, on the five mile hike. And when we got in Camp Fair Weather, Alan Fox assigned us to different cabins. Billy was way on the other side of the woods from me.

At the mess hall though, I forgot all about Billy. That's where the camp counselors met us all. They divided us up into groups and assigned each group to a counselor in charge of us and he was gonna show us where our cabin was. I just got assigned to a counselor and was standing with my group just breathing in the salt air and moss smell when this guy with sandy hair and big shoulders and chest came over and put his hand on my head and ruffled up my hair. Like Brew and Earl used to do when I was little.

"Hi little Brother."

Scotty.

The last time I saw him was at his graduation from Sylvan. Now he was in high school. Looked more like college. Another year and he would be. He hardly looked like the brother I saw off and on before that. Camping out in the woods near his house where he lived with Earl and his new step-mom. Or teaching me to sing a duet with him, *All God's Children Got Shoes.* Or coming over to our house, being silly on our wire recorder. Him being Rank Face, private eye, looking for his prize case of green bananas. Me doing the sound effects. Mom, the blond gun moll.

Funny, I didn't mind at all when he messed up my hair there at the mess hall. He was the handsomest counselor there. And he was my brother. Not the counselor I was assigned to but that didn't matter. He was gonna be the number one life-guard on the lake that summer and he was my brother.

~

Tommy Benson was in the cabin with me 'cause he was a "B." Of the five other guys in our cabin, Tommy was the only one from last year. He was just as white as last year too. Whiter than me. Like he never got tan. The black socks he always wore with his shorts made his puffy legs look whiter and his nose was always wrinkled up trying to hold on his thick glasses that had clear frames when they were new but were kind of yellowish now. Tommy was kind of a geek but he liked to laugh. That made it fun to be around him.

Pretty tired from my KP duty in the mess hall the first night there, I was late getting out of bed the next morning. Tommy and me were the only ones left at the three sided cabin when I was making my bed up for morning inspection. He just got his shirt on and was pulling up his pants when he suddenly yanked them down with his underwear and mooned me.

I grabbed my old Donald Duck camera Earl bought me for Christmas a long time ago and took a picture of his bent-over, wriggling naked white behind. That made him laugh like he couldn't stop. His brown hair in his eyes and his glasses falling off. I never saw anybody's face get so red from laughing. He was still laughing when we got to the mess hall for breakfast.

Billy was sitting with the group from his cabin when I found him after breakfast. Since we had some free time, I told him I'd like to show him stuff around camp. He was still being strange though. Real quiet. Not talking. Hardly even looking at me when I showed him the bridge made out of knotted ropes and the rope climb.

We practiced crossing the rope bridge. My shoes were wrong for it. The hard soles kept slipping off the rope you had to walk on. My foot slipped once and I went down all the way. My foot through all the ropes and my crotch landing on the walking rope. I looked pretty silly. One leg hanging through all the ropes. It hurt like a sun-of-a-gun. But, at least it made Billy laugh.

He had on tennis shoes so he could walk across without even hardly holding on. He started being a little bit more like he used to be then and we took turns on the rope climb. Shimmying up to the top knot about fifteen or twenty feet up. Billy was good at that too. Like he was at bike riding and catch. He went right up the rope without stopping at the knots like I did. I took a picture of him at the top.

By the time we walked out to the ocean through the damp salt smelling pine trees on the sandy path near my cabin, we were laughing together about kids at school and stuff almost like old times. We found a big old black rotted log that washed up on the sand and sat down beside each other looking at the ocean moving up the beach and out again in the fog.

It was chilly but I could feel his warm next to me.

Then Billy stretched out on the log and took a big breath of foggy air and slow let it out. Like he was letting out something more than air. Something he collected over a long time and held on to. Something he wasn't talking about.

"Sure is nice here," he said.

A wave crashed and sloshed on the wet gray sand.

"Sure is," I said.

The waves were making a swooshing sound in a rhythm like an orchestra. Gray and white moving stuff blending against the white sky over them. Seagull silhouettes hollering up in all that white. Everything like in a black and white movie.

Maybe now was a good time I could ask him why he was acting like he was. We were alone and being best friends again. He would probably tell me now. But it was so peaceful. Maybe it was just good enough the way it was. But I really wanted to ask him. Maybe I would.

"Well," he said and sat up, "I better get back to the guys."

There was an old tight feeling in my chest then. Like cinching up a belt.

"Really?" I said. "How come?"

"Oh, I told 'em I'd help 'em 'canvas the area'—get our camp cleaned up for inspection. Our counselor is kind of a jerk. Wants it 'neat as a pin' he said yesterday."

Billy stood up and stretched and cracked his thumbs like he always did. Those blue eyes looked down at me on the log. But I couldn't see inside. No smile.

"See you tonight at the Pow Wow?"

"Yeah. You bet," I said trying to sound casual.

My chest was like somebody dropped a rock on it.

~

The Pow Wow was a kind of show put on by the Order of the Arrow. The Order of the Arrow was a special group of Explorer Scouts that knew a lot about Indians. Scotty was in it. They did Indian dancing and stuff. They made their own costumes and traveled around doing their dances for people. Scotty even went all the way to a big show in Saint Louis, Missouri to dance with his group.

Fair Weather had a kind of theatre outdoors under some big pine trees. There were wooden seats like in a high school basketball gym. Each row got higher up on metal braces the farther back they went under the trees. Billy and me and a bunch of us got seats up close to the platform down in front 'cause we got right over there after dinner. But it was just like at school with guys trying to save seats for their friends. Pushing and shoving and hollering to their friends that got there late.

All of a sudden though, all that stopped and everybody got real quiet. A big bass tom tom started a slow heart-beat like something exciting and kind of scary was gonna happen. Down both sides of the bench seats down front, naked bodies came dancing slow and quiet to the drum beat. Well, at first they looked naked 'cause all that most of them had on was a strip of cloth in front and behind their butts.

I was so surprised, I tried not to gasp but I could hear air being sucked in all around me. Nobody expected this. Real slow the lines of bodies all about Scotty's age, sixteen to eighteen, made their way down to the platform and danced soft up the steps to the stage.

Up there, you could see why they were so quiet. All of them had moccasins that looked like they were made out of soft leather. Some had a few feathers in their tied-back hair or pieces of silver. Bones or sea shells in rows covered some of their chests but not their backs. Mostly though, it was like there were twenty naked men dancing around on the platform in front of us.

I kept trying not to notice. But I had never seen twenty naked men before. It was hard not to notice.

They were all tall, lean guys and their hairless chests, and round curved butts, and muscles at the top of their thighs making a dent there, were beautiful as they danced. Their smooth hip muscles flexing strong underneath their tanned skin. Like muscles of young wildcats. Like those animal pictures Leslie in fifth grade used to draw.

Beautiful.

But I kept telling myself not to think that. This was serious. They were Indian braves.

The show was the story told by the Indians about Lewis and Clark coming to the North West and how they welcomed the two white men. Two Scout leaders played Lewis and Clark and as they were led onto the stage, the dancing got bigger and faster. Through the swirling bodies, I saw Scotty. His face tense and concentrating. Then all the dancers started to chant and shake bells. Their chanting was more like grunts and moans than music but it was very dramatic. Their feet started to hit the platform harder in time to the drums and bells and I lost Scotty in the fast moving bodies. They twirled and circled, their arms almost to the ground dragging their bells, then up into the air. Strong naked legs bending and springing. Feet stomping. Hai ya ugh. Hai ya ugh. Muscled arms shook the bells like they were shaking the life out of them. Like wild animals shake their prey in their teeth. And the grunts changed to whoops. Arms flashed into the air over their heads. Bells jangled. And something like electricity filled the air over the stage.

It slid over us in the audience and vibrated through the wooden seats under us. Guys started bouncing in their seats and stamping their feet. The excitement got so strong all around Billy and me, it was like everybody was gonna jump up and start dancing. I couldn't help it, my body was bouncing too. The dancers' steady stomping feet, the tom toms, the whoops and grunts and bells kept getting louder and stronger until in a huge crash, it ended.

We all jumped up then, hollering and clapping. Billy beside me was yelling and slapping his hands together over his head.

~

Back at the cabin in my sleeping bag that night, I had a hard time going to sleep. There were still naked bodies dancing around in my head.

Just when I was finally about to go to sleep, somebody was shaking me. It was Tommy.

"Do you want to see the show?" he said close to my ear.

"What show?" I said and sat up trying to clear my head. "I thought we already saw the show."

All I could see was the black outline of Tommy's head against the dim light of the sky behind him coming in the open side of our cabin.

"No not that show. A private one." he said and stood up. "I'm going. Wanna come?"

"Okay," I said.

So I jumped up and pulled on my jeans and slipped into my shoes without socks to follow Tommy's scrunchy footsteps through the loose sand in our campsite.

"Where're we going?" I said as we got to the trail through the pine trees and salal.

"Just the next campsite."

Tommy's body was warm next to me in the damp woods. He turned and I followed his dark shadow through the trees.

"This is kind of weird."

"Yeah, I guess," he said over his shoulder. "I just heard about it too."

We walked into the clearing of the next campsite. Just three big tents around the edge of a cleared area. A dim glow was coming through the canvas from just one tent and some shadows were going in through the flaps in front.

Tommy walked right up to the tent and held the flap open for me and I ducked under. It was so dim inside when we first got there, I could hardly see anything. The only light was coming from a candle making a little crackling sound on a box between two bunks. Guys were coming in the flaps every once in a while and kind of lining up around the walls of the tent. The only bunks were the two bunks in the middle by the candle.

It was like one of my bad day dreams. Strange and scary. It made my stomach empty and nervous and my head was confused. What kind of show was this?

On the bunks, a guy was in each of the sleeping bags. Just lying there staring up at the top of the tent. My eyes were getting used to the dimness and I could see movement under one of the sleeping bags. The sleeping bag was unzipped and just kind of draped over the guy inside like he just pulled it over himself but it had been open before we came. The other sleeping bag in the flicker of the candle just looked smooth.

Somebody cleared their throat—one of the shadows lining the walls. It made me jump, it was so loud. 'Cause there wasn't another sound in the tent except the candle or the scraping sound when somebody rubbed against a canvas wall. We all just stood there waiting for something. Like in the dark backstage waiting for the curtain to go up. But this was more eerie. Nobody even whispered.

When there wasn't any more room to stand around the walls of the tent, the guy in the unzipped sleeping bag nodded to someone standing next to the flaps and that guy bent down and closed them, snapped the flaps together.

Then we waited some more. The air getting warm and heavy.

Creepy quiet.

I was looking around at the guys. The candle light coming from underneath their chins made shadows go up their faces. Spooky. They all seemed older than Tommy and me but it was hard to tell with all the weird shadows. Billy wasn't there. Scotty wasn't either.

Then there was movement in the middle of the tent. In that bunk where the sleeping bag was unzipped, the guy threw the top of it off him.

He was naked.

Not with a cloth over him like the Indian dancers.

Stretched out. Legs spread. Stark naked.

In his hand was his hard boner. And he was rubbing it. Like nobody else was there.

I had to swallow. But there was nothing to swallow. My throat was hot and dry.

This was the "show."

All these guys were here to watch him play with himself.

I just stood there too though. Watching.

I couldn't not watch. My eyes were stuck on what I was seeing. Like a big part of me had nothing to say about not watching.

Then real slow the other sleeping bag opened. Now there were two guys jerking off. And all of us still quiet and watching.

Around us, there was something in the air again. Like that thing that was electric at the dance. That thing that makes the air crackle. It was like a smell but it slipped down over us and I could feel it on my skin. Embarrassment too. Like this was dirty and we shouldn't want to watch. But we did.

Watching made the blood in me beat stronger 'cause it was something we weren't supposed to do. And everybody wanting to watch made the blood beat warm right under my skin. Everything was sharper, clearer. The smells, the sounds, the way things looked. Like until then I was going around asleep and this made me wake up.

But this was not like when I was little and the other Billy and me and Frank ran around naked in the woods. Having fun. There was something serious about this. Not just fun. Nobody was smiling.

The watching was making me warm all over my body. My underpants started getting really tight and I could hardly breathe. It was good and bad at the same time. I was ashamed it was so exciting.

When it was over, nobody said anything. We just all went out of the tent into the cool salty air not looking at each other. Tommy and me went back to our cabin and got in our sleeping bags without saying anything.

59

Cape Fire

My brother, Scotty, talked to our counselor the next morning and they traded places for the day. Scotty was taking us on a hike.

"I want to show you something I saw a couple days ago. That's what we're gonna hike to. My favorite place down here," he said to me while I was putting stuff in my backpack for the hike. "Cape Fair Weather."

The fog was gone and the sun was out warm and bright. Only a few big white clouds sat in the edges of the sky. The rest was solid blue. It was a great day for a hike. With a backpack on though it got really warm climbing up the steep trail on the mountain behind the mess hall. And, like always, it was hard keeping up with Scotty. He was older and stronger and more used to hiking like this.

Every time some of the rest of the guys wanted to rest, Scotty got this disgusted look on his face. It almost made me laugh. It was that same look he got years ago when Mom insisted that he come with us to see Santa Claus. Or like on our hikes in Nevada City. His jaw went tight and his lips bunched up. He squinted his eyes and let out a big sigh like why did he get involved in this?

The weather changed though when we got to the top. No blue sky 'cause we were walking in the clouds and the trail flattened out under a dark roof of tree branches that stretched out in a long almost straight line on top the cape and out into the ocean. It rained or dripped from the trees above us the whole way. There was no blue. We were walking in those big clouds sitting on the edge of the sky.

Tommy and me walked together some times. But then he looked his squint-holding-his-glasses-on at me like he wanted to talk about last night in the tent. So I moved up ahead. Walked with somebody else.

The time wasn't right.

Then, walking along quiet like that, I started to have shadowy pictures in my head of inside that spooky tent and I looked at Tommy to say something and he just started talking to somebody else. Like he didn't want to talk about it either.

When we got there, the end of the cape was on fire. Little puffs of smoke—gray, black and white—were coming out from under the waxy green leaves of the salal growing there in the rocky dirt down over the edge. It was like the cape was alive and smoking a pipe full of wet tobacco. Blowing the smoke out through the rocks over the ocean spread out below us.

This was what he wanted us to see, Scotty told us. It was the roots of the salal on the end of the cape smoldering.

Down in the damp rocky dirt there were little bits of stuff glowing red-orange. Like a campfire that's almost gone out.

"I don't know how long it's been burning, but I saw it a couple days ago," he said. "I'm not sure but it looks like it must grow at the same rate of speed as it burns."

There were some "wows" and "reallys?" from the guys and some others just grumped, "We came all this way for that?"

What he told us was hard to believe, but I could see why he wanted to show it to us. I never saw anything like that before. It was almost as good as seeing a volcano or something.

"Well," he said, "we better start back." And there was that disgusted look again mixed up with a little smile creeping onto his mouth that looked like Pop. "At the speed we've been hiking, we'll be lucky to make it back for dinner."

So we all turned around to hike back and I was alone with Scotty.

"Don't think they appreciated this," he said. "Maybe you and me can come back up here on Sunday. See if it's still burning. It's about the only time I'll have free while you're here."

"That'd be great," I said.

I was just glad I'd get to see him at all. He was always so busy doing something else. Even when we weren't at camp. But today he was treating me like I was special. Like I was the only one there that could keep up with him. Appreciate what he did. Maybe on Sunday I could even talk to him about last night.

~

As it turned out though, we climbed up the face of the cape from the beach down below on that Sunday. It was a really steep climb over jagged rocks. I got scared stiff at one place just hanging onto some weeds on the side of the cliff to keep from falling all the way down. Like that time with Brew and Uncle Lloyd in the Tillamook Burn, me crawling on a log over a ravine.

Scotty got disgusted with me. Like he did when anybody couldn't keep up with him. Either in the woods or in his ideas.

Anyway, he was mad at me, and we couldn't tell if the roots were still burning so I didn't talk to him about the "show" in the tent that night.

It was like the salal roots smoldering. Hot inside me. But there wasn't anybody to talk to about it.

It just wasn't something I could talk to Billy about.

PART SIX

Changes
1952

60

House Warming

I couldn't see why they wanted to move away from our great old house on 37th. Away from all my friends. Away from all the great places there, the woods, the moo-cow hill, our theatre in the Herman's garage. Those things were what made our neighborhood our home. But in the summer before eighth grade, Mom and Brew found a new house for sale that they wanted to buy.

The house was one of those dumb new houses in Vermont Hills that looked like the toys they made out of cardboard during the war. It didn't look like a house. Ours looked like a real house and besides I couldn't even imagine moving away from Multnomah to that place with no trees and little side-by-side houses. It was the worst news I ever heard in my life.

After Mom and Brew told me, I walked out of the kitchen like I was sleepwalking in one of my awful dreams, those crazy daymares. Through the hall by the boogie man closet and up the old stairs with the worn carpet. At the top of the stairs in Scotty's old room on the ceiling were the glow-in-the-dark stars. Just shiny spots in the day time. But that did it. The tears started coming out of my eyes.

This was not right. I was not the one that leaves. That's other people like Scotty and Earl.

I wished I was sleepwalking. But I wasn't. This was real. I just laid down on my bed and cried. Socked my pillow and let the crying out the way I did the singing. Damn Charles Atlas and his ninety pound weakling. Damn Pansy and Wallflower and Mama's Boy. Damn. Damn. Damn. Let everybody hear, for all I care.

Pretty soon, there was something wet and cold on my hand. It wasn't tears. I opened my eyes and looked down. Laddy was pushing his nose against my hand. His white curved plume wagged back and forth in the air real slow. He was such a good friend. He didn't care if I cried. It didn't matter to him if I was a cry baby. He just wanted to cheer me up. I sat up. Then I reached out and patted him on the head and his tail speeded up. Like I turned an electric fan up a notch. It was funny. But it didn't stop the tears.

Brew said our house was old and drafty. Hard to heat. And we were at the bottom of the hill—"Down in a gulch," he said—where all the water drained. Mudnomah.

But this was our home.

Then Laddy's big tail started going high speed and right then Mom came in my bedroom door.

Most of the time Mom looked happy. Like nothing bothered her. Sometimes she looked worried. Like when I got hurt or something. But now her eyebrows were down and her face didn't look soft, like usual. And that look that made me feel special was not in her eyes. She just looked mad.

"Is it really this upsetting to you that we want to move?" she said.

A big gush of tears came then. "I won't even be able to go to the same school."

She was in her gray suit that had the big cuffs with the buttons on them and the crinoline petty coats that held the skirt out like an umbrella. A red and white poke-a-dot scarf covered up the little mole on her neck. Her arms in their grey sleeves hugged her chest.

She took a big breath all of a sudden that lifted her elbows and her eyebrows came tight to together and pushed her new red turned up glasses down her nose.

"I thought you didn't even like that school."

"That was last year, Mom. I'm in the choir now and we have Mr. Nichols."

All the words were rushing out so fast it made me kind of hiccup through the tears and snot going in my mouth.

"And there's Sunny Lea and Billy, and Craig and Dale, and Gary and Jack. None of those kids will be at that dumb new school."

She let her breath out and dropped her arms.

"I can't keep up with what you like and don't like. What you want and don't want. I didn't know you felt so strongly about your school."

Her arms flopped like the scarecrow in the Wizard of Oz. "I'll talk to Brew," she said.

It was the stinking trombone all over again. They never paid any attention to what I wanted. Like it didn't matter. And I always pretended like it didn't. I said I wanted to play the saxophone so there was a trombone under the Christmas tree that year. All because Mom heard a trombone quartet on the radio playing the Flight of the Bumble Bee.

Forever I wanted to play the piano. Like I did out at Gramma Brugger's farm. Finally when I thought I was gonna get one for Christmas, what did they end up getting? That Hammond Chord Organ. It was delivered on Halloween.

Now they had a Hammond Spinet Organ and they both took lessons.

She did talk to Brew though and they decided not to buy the house in Vermont Hills. But he still wanted to move.

They found a house on the other side of Multnomah close to school.

The old railroad tracks that used to go under the viaduct and behind the school toward Portland were made into a road now. They called it Multnomah Boulevard. The house Mom and Brew wanted to buy was just a little ways up the new road in the opposite direction I used to go home from school.

It was a beautiful house with a waist high stone wall in front. Fall flowers called Basket of Gold blooming all along the top of the wall and tumbling over the edge. The house sat up on a hill with a garage underneath the house. No more "down in the gulch." A stairway climbed halfway up the hill to a winding sidewalk that curved the rest of the way up to an enclosed porch with a peak roof on top. The front of the house on both sides of the porch and over the driveway had small square windows in rows all the way from the floor to just under the roof. Brew called them French windows.

Next to the yard on one side was a big open field with blackberries growing and a really nice house was next to the yard on the other side. In the back were two stone walls making terraces on up the hill like Billy's back yard and on the bottom near the back of the house was an outdoor fireplace and a patio.

It was a really nice house and I already made so much of a fuss, I was ashamed to say anything bad about moving. So before school that fall, we were packing up all our stuff and getting ready to move.

On the day we were gonna move, Brew went to get the truck he rented and Billy came over to help us load it. Loading it took almost all day but we finally got it done. Brew and Mom and Billy and me were really tired. It was like when we did our show. There was all that practicing and getting ready. Then the day comes and you're all excited about finally doing it. Then it's over and you're kind of numb.

All of us standing in the front yard looking at the truck kind of numb. That's when it hit me. We were really leaving. It seemed like it was the first time in my life that I was the one leaving.

I looked over at Billy and my eyes got all hot. Billy looked down like he always does.

Then Mom's eyes went around to us all and she said, "Well, did anyone forget anything?"

We hadn't been paying attention to Laddy but just then he came up the little hill beside the house strolling into the front yard from the basement door in the back. His big fluffy tail moving in slow motion. In his mouth was his dog dish that we had left in the basement. He never picked up his dish in his mouth before. But now it was the only thing left in the house and he was not about to leave it behind. He kind of lazy walked up to the back of the truck and spit it firmly out onto the ground. Clunk. Then he looked up at us all standing there. He had that look on his face that he always did when things were going okay with him. His black spotted tongue hanging out a little. His mouth stretched from one ear to the other in what anyone would say was a smile.

We all laughed and I hugged him. My hands full of his long white hair and his wet tongue licking my ear.

When I stood up, Billy was looking at me. Our eyes stuck together and that rock hit me in the chest again.

"I guess that about does it," Mom said.

Billy said he'd call me that night and come over soon. Brew thanked him for coming over to help us. Then Mom and Brew, me and Laddy all got into the truck and headed for our new house.

~

The first couple weeks in the new house were lonesome. I couldn't just go outside to see my friends. But Billy and me talked on the phone more than we ever did before. And when I went to see the Baldwins, they told me that Laddy came to see them every morning like clockwork, on his rounds of the old neighborhood. I didn't know 'cause Brew and Mom had lots of things for me to do at the new house to keep me from being "mopey," unpacking boxes, helping to move furniture and take stuff up the steep new wooden stairs to my bedroom and the "guest" room.

The new house did have a really neat yard. There were a lot of plants around in the flowerbeds beside the house. A lot of peonies and a lilac bush. In the back of the house by the fireplace was a camellia and by the back door a daphnia that smelled really good. Instead of hanging out with my friends, I started digging in the flowerbeds, cleaning them up and pulling weeds.

Then school started. Eighth grade.

A week after, Brew brought home a TV set. This was our first TV. He put some old chairs of Gramma Brugger's down in the basement and hooked up the TV there. It was so much better than watching TV with all the other kids in the window of the appliance store across the street from the school. Now we had our own and I could invite friends over to watch.

Mom and Brew's anniversary was on a Saturday that fall. That morning Brew and me were in the front room. Brew reading the paper and me just sitting in a chair looking out our new front windows. Sitting up on a hill, we had a nice view of the valley across the road in front of the house all the way to Barbur Boulevard on top of the next hill. Trees in the valley and up the other side were turning color. All red and gold in the slanted sunlight.

While I was looking, a truck pulled up and parked in front of our wall and two guys in coveralls got out. I got up and went close to the windows trying to read what the truck said.

"Brew, there's two guys--"

Brew jumped up and put his finger over his lips. His widow's peak pulled down on his forehead. Then he quick ran and closed the two doors in the front room that went into the hallway by the bathroom and the kitchen where Mom was fixing breakfast. Then ran tiptoe to the front door and opened it. Put his finger over his lips again to the two guys.

They came in real quiet and unplugged the spinet organ. Then picked it up like it was a coffee table or something. There was a little trouble getting it out through the porch but it finally went down the walk and into their truck. Then I saw through the windows what was coming on wheels up the winding sidewalk. A church model organ with a big separate speaker, foot pedal board and bench.

A sound came out of me even though I was trying to stay quiet.

Brew put his finger up again and said, "Shhh."

The two guys were quiet as burglars. They got it all set up where the spinet had been, beside the big windows, smiled at Brew and tip-toed out.

Brew went around to the doors and real quiet opened them. Then he sat down again with the newspaper.

"Honey," he said kind of loud.

There was no answer.

"Honey," again.

"What?" Mom's voice said from the kitchen.

"Would you come in here for a minute?"

Brew's voice sounded like he was singing. His face was kind of red and scrunched like he was trying not to laugh.

"I'm busy," her voice said, kind of mad.

"Just for a minute." He looked at me and snorted.

Her white chenille bathrobe came through the door and she stood with her hands on her hips. She was not smiling.

"What?"

Brew just turned his smiling face toward the organ.

Mom's face looked up at the organ across the room too.

There it stood between the windows and the fireplace in all its glory. The new Church Model Hammond Organ. Polished dark reddish carved wood with little arches like tiny church ceilings. Two full keyboards like stair steps across the top and a huge pedal board under the carved wood bench. And a speaker as tall as I was.

Mom's jaw dropped open. She gasped and said, "Hupfff," as her jaw closed. Her breath blew her upper plate—her only false teeth—half way across the room with the power of a strong armed pitcher throwing a fast ball on a really good day.

Mom who never let us see her without her teeth, reacted like a champion player going for a fly ball. Faster than I ever saw her move, she dove after it, her chenille robe flapping around her, and caught the little pink and white half-moon mid-air. Before it even touched the floor. Then made a sharp side dash into the hall door and into the bathroom. The door slammed behind her.

Brew and I looked at each other. Both of us had our mouths open. Me, I was standing there by the windows through all this but my knees gave way and I fell on the floor laughing. Brew was howling like Laddy did sometimes at fire engines and I rolled on the floor with tears coming out of my eyes. By this time, Brew was almost laying in his chair making sounds like he couldn't stop laughing but wanted to and holding his sides. I laughed until my stomach hurt too bad to laugh anymore.

Mom came out of the bathroom then and stood in the doorway.

"I suppose you two thought that was very funny," she said.

Brew and me started laughing all over again.

61

Indian Summer

Those first months of school living in the new house, the weather was still like summer. Mom said it was what they call Indian Summer. The sun was warm during the day. Slanting down through the trees. The warm fresh air blowing across the field next door had a neat smell in it that was like Aunt Pearl's farm in the old days. Like a hay smell. It made your mouth water.

Brew said, " Why don't we go visit Eva at the coast?"

Brew's sister, my Aunt Eva that owned the bike Billy taught me to ride on, moved to Bay City at the beach and had a little farm there on a hill above the Tillamook Bay.

"Can I invite Billy?" I said.

"Well, sure," Brew said right away. He dipped his brush into the bucket of white paint he was using to repaint the storm windows on the new house right over where I was pulling weeds. "He helped us move, didn't he? He wanted to see the house anyway." Brew held the tip of his tongue between his teeth getting paint in the corner of the storm window. There were two drops of white in his widow's peak like planets at night and the peak scrunched down concentrating. "He can spend the night over here Saturday and we'll go to the beach on Sunday."

Well, that's Brew with his surprises. I could hardly wait for Saturday. Having Billy over was almost more exciting than singing a solo. I was gonna have a sleep-over. I never even went to one. Not like a lot of kids I knew. I hadn't even asked anybody over to watch our new TV yet. Now I was gonna have a sleep-over with Billy.

When I asked him, he said he had to ask his mom and dad. He never went to a sleep-over before. I told him I didn't either.

We were having lunch together in the cafetorium. We still didn't have class together. In all the time he had been at Multnomah, we never had class together.

"This'll be fun," I said. "I really wanna show you our new house. It's really nice. I don't like the neighborhood very much. None of my friends are there. But the house is nice. We can watch TV. Maybe Omnibus or something."

He was just kind of looking down at his plate. Pushing his macaroni around.

"Yeah," he said quiet.

"What's the matter, don't you want to?"

He looked up right away. "Sure I do. It's just my folks. They're kind of funny. I don't know if they'll let me." He took a big breath and his shoulders came up. Then he sighed and let them down again. "But I'll ask them."

I must of looked disappointed 'cause right away he said, "I'll ask 'em tonight. I really would like to come over."

So I got worried.

What if they wouldn't let him come?

Brew asked that night at dinner if Billy was coming over on Saturday. So I told him Billy was gonna ask his folks.

"Okay," he said. "We'll plan on going to see Eva on Sunday then."

But it was hard going to sleep that night. Things just weren't that easy. Parents were always a problem. Things would be so much better when I got to high school next year. When Billy and me were grown up and we could do what we wanted.

I was kind of sleepy in school next day. My teacher Mrs. Pyle with the red eagle claws on her hands didn't like it when I couldn't answer her question about Guatemala.

But all I wanted to do was go to lunch with Billy and find out if he could come over on Saturday night.

I met him outside his class. He ran out almost before anybody else. Jumping in the air and laughing. "YES," is all he said and we raced each other to the cafetorium.

On Thursday morning, I looked into the guest room and saw it was still full of unpacked boxes. The bed frame and mattress were leaning against the wall and there was no room to even move in there.

Parents.

I only had a little bed. We had to have a bed for Billy.

At breakfast, I asked Brew how Billy was gonna sleep in the guest room 'cause of all the boxes and stuff. He said he'd get it all taken care of that night. But that night, I saw Mom heating up some Chun King canned Chinese food. We always had that on nights that Brew had to work late 'cause he didn't like Chinese food.

"Isn't Brew coming home?"

Mom was busy getting dishes down for dinner and, with her face in the cupboard, she said, "No he has to work late." Her voice echoed in there like in a science fiction program or maybe the Grand Wizard in the Wizard of Oz.

Yeah, the Grand Wizard. Man, why are parents always such a problem? You expect them to be in control of things and it turns out they're just regular people hiding behind the curtains pretending they're in charge.

"But he said he'd get the guest room set up for Billy."

Mom shrugged her shoulders on the way to the table with the dishes.

"Well, maybe he forgot. You'll have to ask him. If you're still up when he gets home."

I went up and looked in the room after dinner. There were too many boxes in there to move them somewhere else and if I unpacked them, I wouldn't know where to put anything. I tried to wait up for Brew but I fell asleep before he got home. In the morning at breakfast I asked Brew where Billy was gonna sleep.

Brew looked surprised. His eyebrows went up like he forgot all about it.

"Well, maybe we'll just have to pick him up on Sunday before we go down to the coast."

That rock hit me in the chest again.

"But I already asked him and he asked his mom and dad and they said yes and I can't tell him not to come over now after we asked him to come over and spend the night 'cause he'll think we don't want him to come over here."

"Oh," Brew said and his widow's peak came down on his forehead. "Well, how about if we just take the mattress from the guest room and put it on the floor of your room for him?"

"Aw, geez," I said.

"It'll be like camping out." Big smile.

Yeah, camping out with the poor people who can't afford a bed for the people they invite over.

So on Saturday Brew drove the new Hudson, we called the Upside-down Bathtub, over to Billy's to get him for dinner and to have our first sleep-over.

I took him upstairs with his little back pack and told him I was sorry about the mattress on the floor.

"You can have my bed if you want," I said.

He laughed and said, "No, this is swell," and plopped down on the mattress we made up for him. "Anyway, it's just for tonight." He sat there; eyes sliding over everything in my new bedroom. "This is neat."

My new bedroom was all wood. Wood paneled walls and ceiling with a wood floor and a built-in desk and dresser. Out the two windows, you could see the open field down below. The really low sun as it was going down slanting across the tall moving dry grass making it look like it was made of gold. It was like being in a cabin far away from the city somewhere. Like out in the wheat country.

"Let me show you the yard," I said. He jumped up and both of us pounded down the wooden stairs. In that enclosed stairway, it sounded like the house was coming down.

Later Mom called us in after that and we washed up and ate a really great dinner in the dining room. At least Mom knew how important my first sleep-over was. After that, I wasn't so embarrassed having Billy sleep on the floor like we were poor people or something.

We went down the basement where Laddy was after dinner and watched the TV.

Ever since before Fair Weather, I was always going to ask Billy why sometimes we were almost like brothers and other times like we hardly didn't know each other at all. But then I got nervous or embarrassed about asking him. Sometimes I told myself it wasn't true. That it was only in my head. That we were always good friends. Then Billy'd start acting like somebody I didn't know. So there was no way I could talk to him about it.

But this day we were having so much fun. We were laughing and kidding each other. Talking and playing jokes on each other. It was the best. So when we were finally in bed, me in my little bed and Billy on his mattress, and we were joking about Mrs. Pyle's name—my teacher with the blood red eagle claws and red plastic jewelry—I was finally going to ask him about why sometimes we were friends and sometimes it was like he didn't want to be friends at all.

It was dark in the room except for a little light from the moon coming in the window. By that time, I had my eyes closed anyway. Just lying there feeling the warm bed and listening to Billy's soft, familiar voice telling me how the kids in his class called my teacher Mrs. Piles. I laughed and said that I knew that. Then I laid there in the quiet for a minute. Just getting myself to say what I wanted to say for so long. Listened to a dog bark way off somewhere.

Then there was no more thinking.

I was asleep.

~

When I woke up in the morning, the room was just a little bit gray with light coming in the windows. Right away there was something happy in me. Like a smile. Maybe even a laugh. I pushed up on my elbows. In me, it was like it used to be on Christmas morning or something. But there was something else too. Something sad. Then I looked across my little wood room and there was Billy's dark shadow asleep on the mattress. That's why there was that happy thing in me. Like when we went out to Gramma Brugger's farm and I sat by his bed waiting for him to wake up. That was like a long time ago, but it was like last week too.

The something else—the something sad—was that when I had the chance to talk to Billy last night, I fell asleep.

I scrunched down in the warm covers and turned on my side. My face on the edge of my mattress watching his dark shape. I couldn't really see him though. There was no chair beside his bed to sit on like at Gramma's. Pretty soon my eyes got tired and they closed. I fell asleep again.

Billy turned over then and my eyes opened again. Sitting and watching him sleep at Gramma's was nice. It made that happy thing last. Maybe I could sit on the floor beside his mattress. Then later when he woke up, we could talk. Quiet, my legs slid out from the covers. My feet on the bare wood floor. Cold.

I sat there for a minute. My arms wrapped around me to keep warm. The room was chilly in just my underpants but I got used to it a little, just sitting there. There was a scatter rug on the floor beside Billy. Under my desk that was folded into the wall. I stood up and my feet crossed the cold floor to the scatter rug. I sat down on it. Pulled my knees up. Still keeping myself warm with my arms around them.

There was more light in the room now and Billy was lying on his back. Those little blond moth wings resting on his cheeks. Covers pulled up under his chin. Soft breathing.

That dog from last night, somewhere way off, barked again.

Billy took a big breath of air.

Before I could move—to get up and get back in bed before he caught me watching him sleep—Billy's eyes opened. He looked at me sitting there beside him.

My face got really warm in the chilly room. I bit my knee and looked back at him.

Then he smiled, his eye lashes fluttering and he yawned.

"You look kind of cold," he said in the middle of his yawn. "Why don't you come under here?" he lifted the covers and scooted to the other side.

All of a sudden, I was really cold and couldn't say anything. If I did my teeth would rattle.

It was like I was in the Arctic or Alaska or somewhere like that and a really friendly Eskimo was inviting me into his igloo to get warm. I just slid in between his covers next to him.

Now it was the strange that made my teeth want to chatter. This was really strange. I was under the warm covers in bed next to Billy. Billy had a little brother. Maybe this was not strange to Billy. But I didn't live with a brother. I was never in bed with anybody ever.

Now I was in bed with Billy.

My jaw was getting sore from holding it still and I couldn't get myself to breathe right. My underpants were getting tight and I was really warm all over. From really cold to really warm.

The dog barked again far off. Coming in the window the sun was warming my old colored snowflake quilt on top of us.

Indian summer.

Billy and me just lay there staring at the wood ceiling of my little room. Then Billy moved a little. The sheets made a soft zipper sound and his arm brushed against mine. Skin. It was like an electric shock. Sharp at first. Then it buzzed all the way up to my neck and down to my feet, making my body hum like a transformer on a telephone pole.

"I'm getting pretty warm now," I said. "Maybe I better—"

"Me too," Billy said and pushed the covers down to the top of our legs.

My whole body shook and I closed my eyes. A big hard boner was right there in my underpants for him to see and I didn't want to see what he could see 'cause I was so embarrassed.

"Wow," Billy said.

The way he said it though was like he must be looking at something else. Like he just saw something really cool in my room he didn't see yesterday. I opened my eyes to see what he was looking at and he was looking right at my boner.

"Geez, I'm sorry," I said. "I-"

"Oh, it's okay, Davey. It's morning. Happens to all of us."

I looked over next to me and there was his too. About as big as mine was.

I was holding all my muscles tight like a fist. He kind of chuckled then and my legs and arms softened up a little. But that vibration that started with the feel of Billy's skin on mine was still there—a warm buzz humming inside me.

I looked down at the mound in his underpants again. It was beautiful. Like when you see big white clouds in a really blue sky. His underpants snow white, curved over his boner and against his creamy tan skin. Not white skin like mine. The little blond hairs on his stomach glistening in the sun like the fool's gold Scotty showed me in our creek in California.

"I never did show you where I had my operation," Billy said.

The buzz got louder in my head.

I tried to say, "No," but it came out all dry and scratchy. Not like a word at all.

"Do you still wanna see?"

This time I swallowed first and then said, "Yeah." But like a question too. Like, did he really want to show me?

But Billy just lifted his hips up and pushed his underpants down to where the covers were. For some reason all of Billy's old shyness was gone. I guess I was the shy one now.

His hard penis was just laying there against his belly. My eyes were stuck there again like inside the tent that night at Fair Weather but this time it wasn't scary. That happy thing inside me was there again. Looking made me warm and happy all over. It was Billy's most private place and he was showing it to me. There was no reason anymore to ask if we were really friends.

Underneath, where mine had a kind of bigger sack to hold my testicles, Billy's was smaller was all.

"It doesn't look funny," I said.

"Well, thanks," he said with a little kind of laugh. Like he didn't think that was a very nice thing to say.

My face got hot.

"No, I mean, you told me it looked funny. It's not funny. It's really nice."

"Umm. Well. Now it's your turn," he said. "Yours looks bigger."

My face was getting hot again.

"My turn?" I said.

His blue eyes looked up at me then.

"Well, I showed you mine, didn't I?"

Boy this was something. First I was in bed with somebody. Something I never did before and now I was gonna have to show Billy my weener. Something I never even thought about doing. Except when I was a little kid running around in the woods. I mean, looking is one thing. Showing is something else.

But we were friends. It wouldn't be right for just Billy to show me his.

I took a big breath and started to lift up my hips.

Then I said, "Mine isn't any bigger."

"Oh yeah?" he said. "Let's see."

So I lifted my hips and shoved my underpants down. My heart started to beat so hard, I could feel it all over me. When I put my hips back down and tried to relax, my boner lifted up off my stomach and was pulsing like it was keeping the beat to some music.

Billy and me, we just watched it. Then Billy's started doing the same thing. We both kind of laughed.

"See mine's about the same as yours. I mean, the same size." I said. It came out in a whisper like we were in the library or something.

"Yeah, you're right," he said and his voice was all gravely.

Both of us just watched.

The warm sun was shining on us and a little bit of stuff was coming out of both of us. Catching the sun like clear little tear drops.

Something was happening in my stomach too that was making my hand want to reach out and touch his. The skin looked so smooth. Like it would feel silky like the drapes in our old house. Like his belly did when I tickled him that time.

But Billy wasn't reaching out to touch mine and something was telling me that touching his boner would be wrong. My stomach was saying just the opposite though. It wanted me to touch him so bad it was starting to ache. Watching our two hard penises beating a rhythm together was starting to make me shake too. The hum and buzz and now trembling. If I didn't touch his soon, my stomach was gonna cramp big time.

Then Mom's voice came up the stairs. Loud in the closed up stairway.

"Hey, you guys. Breakfast."

My stomach all of a sudden let go and took in a big gasp of air. I jumped up pulling my underpants over my boner and so did Billy. My legs started to run for my pants but Billy grabbed my hand. I turned and looked at Billy. His blue eyes just below mine. Moth wings fluttering. He squeezed my hand and smiled. Not a big white teeth smile. Just a little soft one. And I was swimming in that blue below my eyes.

62

Holding Hands

Billy and me got in the back seat of the car after breakfast. All packed and ready for the beach. As Mom was getting in the front, Brew turned on the radio and put his arm over the back of the seat looking out the back window.

"Off like a herd of turtles," he said and one dark brown eye winked at us as he backed the Hudson out of the driveway.

A prickle went up my neck 'cause he might think Billy and me were sitting awful close together. But Brew was busy. His face didn't notice.

Back when we were having breakfast that morning, Billy kept looking at me every once in a while with a grin in his eyes and I grinned back. Then he quick looked down at his plate so nobody saw. When that happened, there was a catch in my chest. Like when you're running and you get a hitch in your side. But this one felt good. So good I had to hang onto the edge of the dining room table 'cause it made me dizzy. Like when you wind up the ropes on a swing and then you let it go and you spin out with the ropes.

Now we were sitting next to each other the first time since in my bedroom. *The High and the Mighty* was playing on the radio with the guy whistling and the big fields and farms in Beaverton going by outside the windows.

You had to step down into the Hudson and the floor in back had a big bump in the middle. If you didn't want to straddle the bump in the middle with your feet, you had to sit on one side of the car or the other. Billy was sitting all the way over by the window when I got in, so I slid over close to him. His hand was on the seat and when I slid over, my hand touched his. There was that kind of electric shock again. Sharp at first. Then just tingly when Billy's hand took a hold of mine. There was that grin in his eyes again. After Brew backed out, I snuck my hand behind my back and Billy reached around me so we could hold hands behind my back in case Brew looked in his mirror or Mom turned around. Guys weren't supposed to hold hands. Or people thought we shouldn't.

Billy wanted to. That was so neat 'cause so did I.

It just felt right.

People were nuts. There's a whole list of things they were always saying you shouldn't do. But there's nothing wrong with holding someone's hand when you like them. Little boys do. Little girls. People don't think it's wrong when little kids do it. They think it's sweet. So why shouldn't big kids hold hands? If it feels right.

Billy's hand was kind of rough. But nice. His knuckles were kind of big too, especially in his thumb, since his hand wasn't really so big. Probably from cracking his thumbs like he always did. His hand was warm too. He held on to my hand tight like he really wanted to hold on. Sometimes, he squeezed. Like a little hug. It made me want to holler, Yes! It was so right. But all I could do was squeeze back and sit there quiet. The happy thing in me flowing over.

Outside the windows then there were gray stumps and tall broken black half-trees looming like giant ghosts along the highway. Brew was driving down Highway Six through the Tillamook Burn where the big fire burned all the trees just before I was born. It was a curvy road. Like when we used to go up to visit Robby and Joey. When we went fast around a curve, Billy's whole body pressed against me. He was warm and that bread baking smell of his was strong. His body felt so good and smelled so good my eyes had to close then 'cause I'd melt or something. But when I closed my eyes, the meltiness got even more. Through his shirt, I could feel the muscles in his shoulder against me and his knee pressing against mine. Then we curved the other way and I leaned against Billy. He smiled soft and squeezed but didn't look at me. His blue eyes just looked straight ahead or at the gray/black ghosts that stood on the hills waiting for somebody. Like forgotten old people.

That was something sad about the Tillamook Burn. All those tree ghosts there. But something else sad in my head too. How I could never be like what Brew wanted me to be like. It was that time that Brew's brother Lloyd (one of my favorite uncles, the one who gave me so many great rocks and crystals for my collection) and Brew and me were together there, all three of us "hunting." Or that's what we said we were doing, tramping around with rifles in between the ghosts. We came to an old log trestle where trains used to go. But now just gray logs over a deep ravine about 200 feet down. Brew just started walking across one of the logs. But I took two steps out and looked down. It was like that old cracked sidewalk in Gary's backyard that came up and hit me in the face during the earthquake and I went down on my knees on that log I was so scared. Then I started to crawl.

Brew looked back at me and was laughing, "If you fall off and break your leg," he said, "I'll just have to shoot you like a horse and leave you there."

I wanted to die, I felt like such a stupid weakling.

Lloyd wasn't laughing at me though.

~

And today riding through there in the Hudson, I was with my best friend.

~

That day was the first time we ever went to my Aunt Eva and Uncle Fred's house in Bay City. The house was small. Like a little cabin. But there was a lot of property. The little house grabbed the side of the steep hill above the Tillamook Bay like it thought it might slide into the bay.

Uncle Fred took Billy and me out and showed us all his gardens. He had a vegetable garden and a melon garden. There was one just for cucumbers that they used for pickles and flower gardens were spread all over the side of the steep hill. One for roses. One for rhododendrons and hydrangeas. And one for just wild flowers. They weren't planted for decoration, though, like they were in people's yards in the city. They were gardens just to grow things. Probably because Uncle Fred had been a farmer all his life.

Gray clouds started clumping in the sky over us while we were out in his gardens and a wind was beginning to blow from the ocean. Way out, you could see white caps and even the bay was starting to churn up.

"Looks like our Indian Summer'll end soon," Uncle Fred was saying and there was a splat of rain on my arm. Then two more. By the time we got back up the hill to the house, the rain was getting us really wet. Aunt Eva met us inside with towels and the three of us dried our hair. Then she told us all to come to the table for "lunch."

Eva was definitely Gramma Brugger's daughter. On the big round oak table was dinner not lunch. Bowls of all kinds of vegetables, potatoes and sweet potatoes and a creamy coleslaw all from Uncle Fred's gardens. She even baked a pork roast and made delicious thick gravy for the mashed potatoes. And there was Royal Crown cola for Billy and me. Like at Gramma's.

Eva was short like Gramma but not wide like her. She laughed a little laugh deep in her throat when she saw my mouth go open and said, "No one goes away hungry from my house."

The rain kept Billy and me in the house. Even if it wasn't raining, there wasn't any reason to get away from all the grown-ups. The beach was too far away and there wasn't hardly any town at Bay City. So we had to sit in the living room, too hot from the wood stove, and listen to them talk their boring talk all afternoon. Then we got back in the car to go home.

But that was the best part. We got to sit close to each other and hold hands behind our backs all the way home. We were so groggy though from all the food and the wood stove and being close now, we both fell asleep in the back seat and weren't awake until Brew pulled up in front of Billy's house.

When he was gone, though, and we were driving away, something was empty. Something was empty where it was never empty before. When we got home the house was empty. And, oh boy, my room. There was something missing. There was his mattress on the floor with the messed up sheets and blankets. My colored snowflake quilt. It was like Billy had always been there. Now he was gone.

This empty thing was in me too. It was not a good thing. That happy thing that was in me all day was gone. It was something that was never in me before but now that it had been there, I couldn't be without it. That was scary.

63

The Empty

Since we lived on the opposite side of Multnomah now, I came into school the next morning from the other side of the building and was walking down the hallway to my classroom. I passed the big double glass doors out into the playground across from the water fountain where Miss Wilson first heard me sing. That seemed so long ago.

Billy was in the playground right outside the doors.

That happy thing did a little hop inside me.

But he was standing there talking to the echo kid, Thomas Thomason.

Mr. Magnificent with his big arms crossed. Legs spread. Like he owned the playground. Both of them laughing big at something.

It was like a flash bulb went off in my face. Then like I was falling eight floors down really fast zooming down in the old elevator inside me. My feet stumbled and I was running down the hallway so I wouldn't fall down. I got to my classroom. There was nobody else there. I sat down at my seat and put my head down on the desk. It was like when you hold your breath to make your face turn red, goofing around, and you feel like you're gonna faint. I didn't know Billy knew Thomas. But then of course he did. They were in the same class.

I was cold all over. And, not just because there was nobody else in the classroom, I mean, my eyes were closed and my head on my desk, but I was never so alone before. Even inside me.

That's when I saw his face. Inside my head. Our principal, Mr. Halverson's face.

Red and sweaty. Ugly.

"It is a disease, a sickness," his twangy voice said. "None of you wants to be thought of as…"

I jumped up and ran out into the hallway. The door handles to the double doors were right there in front of me. I pushed and there was Billy. No Thomas.

"Hi Davey," Billy said. He was smiling that soft smile but all I could see was Mr. Halverson. His ugly face.

"Billy, please don't say anything."

"What?"

Billy's face scrunched up like he didn't know what I was talking about.

"Please don't tell anybody about yesterday," I said.

" Wha... What about yesterday?"

His blue eyes were wide open. His eyebrows up. Like he still didn't know what I was talking about.

The bell rang.

My tongue didn't want to work again. I was still like I was gonna faint or maybe throw up.

Billy shrugged and his face scrunched again.

He said, "I gotta go to class."

~

That night, I didn't sleep much. Or a lota nights after that. I didn't have to go to sleep to have nightmares. My brain was full of them. When I was alone with Billy, nothing else mattered. It was wonderful. I felt so happy just being there and Billy seemed that way too. But when I was alone by myself there was that empty thing, I missed Billy.

Then, there were these nightmare things. They started to be there too when we weren't together but other people were around. I would think of Billy and I could hear Mr. Halverson's twangy voice saying…"It is when a man wants to be with another man instead of a woman."

Just because I missed my best friend?

"It is a disease, a sickness." The scrunched up ugly face right in front of me and I buried my face in the pillow, trying to make it to go away. What would Scotty think if he knew how much I liked Billy? Or, Brew, if he knew I wanted more than to shake his hand? Was I sick because I liked Billy? That I wanted to be with him? I know I'm weird. I want to sing, not look stupid trying to catch a ball. I know I'm different, does that mean I'm sick?

And Mr. Magnificent, Thomas Thomason, what if he knew? It is our secret. Our secret, Billy's and mine. Billy wouldn't tell anybody, would he? It's a secret that is making me hate myself...how much I like Billy.

64

Sail Inn

I couldn't be what Mr. Halverson was talking about. I just wouldn't let myself be. Men shake hands. They don't hold other guys' hands. And they don't go around wanting to look at other guys' penises.

I was a weird kid who liked to sing but I wasn't gonna be that weird.

I stopped going to Scout meetings. And other places I might see Billy.

Instead, I started going to the square dances they were having on Friday nights at school. Sunny Lea went to those. Maybe I'd meet some girls there. The dances were fun too. Sometimes we did folk dances where one couple just danced together. But most times we danced in a square. Four couples.

The only trouble with those dances was that Thomas Thomason went there too.

One Friday night we were learning a new square dance and the echo kid was in our square. When the caller said, "Allemande left with your left hand," I went right by mistake.

Old know-it-all T.T. said in a loud voice so everybody could hear, "No, Davey. Your other left hand."

I would of got on that down elevator inside me right then if I could of and kept on going through the floor and all the way to China. My face got all hot. I felt it turn red. And not just because I was embarrassed but because he made me so mad. He was always so much better than me. And right away I thought about Billy and him laughing together. What were they laughing about?

After that when we were having a break, I went outside the gym and sat on a bench in the cool air. It was a nice night. Black sky out over the ball field. Lots of stars. The kind of sky that makes you feel so small. I didn't need to feel any smaller.

Bent over with my face in my hands, I was still mad about Mister Magnificent—Thomason—when I smelled cigarette smoke. I looked up and there was Arlene standing looking at me. Smoking a cigarette.

"Don't feel so bad about it. He's just a dumb shit," she said.

Arlene was in our square when Thomason said that about my other left hand. She was the loose girl in our eighth grade class. She was pretty. Long billowy reddish brown movie star hair and kind of green eyes. But everybody said she "put out." She was new in school that year from some big city somewhere and her parents owned the Sail Inn Tavern where she lived. We all called it "The Sail Inn, Stagger Out."

Arlene dropped the cigarette in the pebbles of the ball field and twisted her foot around on it a couple times. Grinding it out in the crunchy gravel.

"Besides, I don't think he really meant anything by it," she said. Then sat down beside me on the bench.

I was still leaning over with my chin in my hands and her hand came down on the back of my neck. Her hand was cool and she started rubbing my neck there. It was really nice. Her long cool fingers loosening my neck muscles. That was something. I mean, that she knew my neck was so tight. She seemed to know a lot of things other girls didn't know.

She was being so nice it almost made me feel worse. It made tears in my eyes and I was ashamed she knew how that guy could get to me.

"Feel good?" she said.

"Yeah," I said with my eyes closed. "I guess. You know, I didn't even know my neck hurt until you started rubbing it."

"Yeah," she said. "We hide a lot of things from ourselves that hurt. Not just a pain in the neck. Like Thomas."

That made us both laugh. But I didn't look up 'cause my nose was running. I didn't want her to see.

When we had a couples dance later that night, I asked Arlene to dance with me. She was really warm against me when we danced and there was this different kind of smell coming up from between her big breasts. A hot smell like body and perfume all mixed together. Kind of good and bad at the same time. Good like perfume but scary too like animal. Where my arm went around her she was small but her chest against mine was really big. Her big boobs were the main reason all the guys talked about her.

She was really easy to talk to and she was so nice to me out on the bench that I asked her if she'd like to go to Al Call's Soda Shop on Wednesday after school. She said she would.

I asked the sexiest girl in school if she'd go out with me and she said yes. Wow.

~

That week I saw Billy in the cafetorium at lunch so I sat down with him and told him that I invited Arlene to the soda shop. He didn't believe me. So I told him to come over Friday night to watch TV with me and I'd tell him all about our date at the soda shop on Wednesday, if he didn't believe me.

On Wednesday, nothing happened. Nothing like what I thought might anyway.

We just sat at Al Call's and talked. Arlene had a chocolate malt and I had a root beer float. Still had a problem with anything close to a black walnut milkshake. Even the noise from the mixer for Arlene's malt made my stomach turn over. While we talked, I told her how nice I thought it was for her to cheer me up at the square dance. She said it was nothing. But I started thinking of where I could invite her on a real date so we could be alone. Maybe even do some necking. That'd be neat to tell Billy about.

The movie theatre had a balcony that everybody talked about. I sat up there once but I felt kind of weird sitting up there on a Saturday night by myself. Everybody else were couples. There must of been some really serious petting going on but it was so dark up there I couldn't really see. And it made me feel like such a dip trying to see other people necking. That was the place I decided to ask Arlene to.

When Billy came over on Friday night Mom and Brew and me were really excited. Brew had gone and traded our Hudson for a brand new Pontiac. Somebody Brew didn't even know—his granddad's stepson— died in a shack somewhere and left a bunch of people in the family a lot of money and Brew's part was enough to buy a new car with the Hudson as a trade-in.

The Pontiac was super gorgeous. White with big fins in the back with panels of what people called Kelly green inside the fins and a green stripe that went all the way up to the head lights. It had so much glass for windows, it almost didn't look like anything was holding up the green roof.

After dinner Billy and me, we went down the basement and into the garage. I got in the driver's seat and he got in the passenger side. It was kind of like when I was a little kid and used to sit behind the wheel and pretend I was driving. This time, I didn't pretend I was driving though. Billy and me just sat and talked. I told him about Arlene and me—the date we had at the soda shop. How we just talked.

"I really like her though," I said. "I think I'm gonna ask her out to the movie theatre next Saturday night."

It felt pretty cool to tell him that. I had started combing my hair in a duck-tail too. If I was gonna be going with Arlene, I had to have a certain look. So all in all, I was feeling pretty cool. Sitting there in a sporty new car in my duck-tail telling Billy about dating the loose girl in school.

"No way," Billy said. "You and Arlene?"

He kicked back in the seat and blew air out though his lips.

"Yup," I said sliding down in the seat so my head rested kind of easy-like on the back of the green and white seat. It would have been great to have a cigarette in my mouth. I could have taken a really cool drag on it right then.

Billy turned himself in the car seat. Knees up. Blue eyes looking at me squinty. Cheek resting on the seat back.

"That's pretty hard to believe, Davey. I mean, she's not exactly your kind of girl."

There was heat around my neck then which was definitely not cool. First he didn't believe we were going to Al Call's. Now the movies. And what's he think is my kind of girl?

"Well, you better believe it, Billy," I said. "We're gonna be in that balcony next Saturday night."

Of course, I hadn't even asked her yet but I was sure we were going and I was gonna get in Arlene's panties.

~

That week-end I decided I was gonna buy her a present. Then when I gave her the present, I'd ask her on a date to the movies. That way she'd almost have to go out with me.

In the Variety Store there was always so much to choose from. On Monday after school, I wandered around like I was sleep walking again. It was so hard to make up my mind about what to buy Arlene. She was so pretty, it had to be special.

Then I saw it. The perfect present. An emerald necklace. Well, not exactly emerald. Probably rhinestones. But the stones were green. It was the perfect thing to go with her reddish hair and green eyes.

I still had some money saved from my paper route although I didn't have the route anymore. Enough money to buy it. Even if it was kind of expensive. It came in a neat grey velvet box and the sales lady put a ribbon around it after she took the price tag off.

This was the present that would make Arlene really happy.

I was all set.

~

The little alley beside the Sail Inn was kind of dark that night. It wasn't any wider than a sidewalk between the two buildings. But there was a light bulb hanging over the door at the end where Arlene lived. My heart was beating awful strong and my hand was making the gray velvet on the box in my hand kind of damp. So I switched it to the other hand.

When I got to the one and only door in the narrow walk, I put the little gray box in my jacket pocket for a minute while I got out my comb and combed my duck tail. Made my hair neat for Arlene. Then buffed off the toes of my new brogues—what we called the new classy mahogany colored shoes I got for my date. Brushed them off one toe at a time on the back of my pant legs. Put my comb away and with the velvet box in my hand again and whistling *The High and the Mighty* trying to be cool, pushed the little cracked plastic button sticking out of the cement wall of the building beside the screen door. It made a really weird sound like the old electric sander we had in shop class when it hit a nail.

I waited a minute. Nothing happened.

So I pushed the electric sander button again.

That's when I heard feet clumping down some stairs on the other side of the door. The door creaked open. 'Cause the light bulb was on the outside of the door, through the screen was just the outline of what looked like Arlene.

"Davey?" her voice said.

"Yeah," I said back and smiled, even though the screen door was all I was smiling at.

Then it opened and Arlene was holding the screen door open. Her hair was up in a scarf. Probably in pin curls. And she was wearing a sweat shirt over her famous boobs and she had on jeans and pink bedroom slippers.

"How come you're here?"

My tongue was stuck again. I didn't plan it this way. In my head I was thinking square dance skirt with ankle strap shoes or skirt and sweater like at school and at least the movie star hair.

"I—well, I wanted to ask you something."

"Oh." She stepped out of the screen door and it slammed behind her. Echoing between the buildings. "You just surprised me. No one ever comes here. I mean, nobody ever comes to this door. And of course nobody from school comes to the tavern," she said with a little laugh. Kind of embarrassed.

"No. I guess not." And I tried to laugh a little too. "Oh, I almost forgot. I brought you something."

I put the gray velvet box in front of her with both hands.

She backed away a little. Her face under her pin curl scarf wrinkled up. Like I was holding a snake or something.

"Wha-? I mean, why'd you bring me something?"

Somehow this was not going at all like I planned it in my head. I never planned on having to explain it to her. She was just supposed to know and be really happy I brought something.

But then her face relaxed when she saw the velvet box.

"Well, I just wanted to and I thought maybe on Saturday night we could go to the movies," I said.

By this time her long pretty fingers had the ribbon off and were open-ing the lid of the neat little box. There was a flash of green. The overhead bulb caught the green stones as the lid opened and they glittered and sparkled from their little nest in the velvet box.

"Oh, Davey," she said on her breath. "It's beautiful."

When she looked up at me from the box, her eyes were so watery they didn't have any color. Just glittery in the electric light.

"But I can't take this."

My body was like somebody poured ice cold water on me. I just froze looking at her.

In her eyes there was a new look looking at me. It was a sad look but it was hurt too. Like when Laddy looked at me with something stuck in his foot. A thorn or something that he couldn't do anything about.

"Oh, Davey. I'm so sorry."

"What?"

"I think you got the wrong idea."

She was closing the little box and handing it back to me.

"I can't go out with you," she said.

She was looking down at the box but I could barely feel the box in my hand. Like it might not even be there. Or like it was made of tissue paper.

"You can't? Why not?"

"Oh, Davey. You're such a good boy."

Did she say "boy?" A good boy?

"Really. Way too good for me."

What she was saying was so different than the way I pictured what was going to happen, the words didn't make any sense.

I looked down at the box. Maybe it wasn't the velvet box after all and I had handed her something else by mistake.

"And besides. Well. Davey, I'm sorry. I'm seeing someone."

In my head, I saw some handsome college guy.

It was the velvet box in my hand. It was damp. But I couldn't switch hands. Both my hands were damp.

She was still looking down at it in my hands. Then her eyes looked up. Green.

"Al Summers."

"So you can't go to the movies," I said.

It was really stupid that I said that.

She leaned forward and kissed my cheek. Her breasts were warm against me. Her lips were soft. Like something had just brushed my cheek. A flower. There was that smell again. More perfume than animal this time.

Al Summers. He's that kid that lives along the way I used to go home from school. About where I swallowed the dime that time. The guy with the Mom from England.

So why him? He's in eighth grade. Same as me.

Isn't he a "good boy?"

He seems nice to me.

I looked back down at the box in my hand and put it back in my jacket pocket. Then her arms went around my shoulders. Both my hands in my pockets. It was like a hug Mom would give me.

"Davey, I'm so sorry."

I didn't look up. I just said, "Yeah. That's okay."

"See you at school?" she said.

"Yup."

The screen door opened then. I looked up and she smiled sad at me and went inside.

I staggered down the sidewalk.

Sail in. Stagger out.

~

I made it home thinking of Arlene, trying hard not to think of Billy. I got up to my room still holding the velvet box that I took out of my pocket on the way home, sat down on the bed and the tears started to come. I didn't want to cry but I couldn't stop them. Why is this so hard? Do all guys have to go through this? Why can't I just love someone and be with them? Then I was sobbing. Oh, for cryin' out loud!...Yup, that's what I was doing—crying out loud.

Then I heard Mom, "Davey, are you all right?" and the door opened. Mom just stood there looking at me. That's when it happened. A sound from down inside me came out, first like a moan, then like a yell and I couldn't see from all the tears coming out, my mouth slobbered. Then my teeth crashed down.

Mom ran into the room, "Oh, Davey!" She sat down hard on the bed beside me and pulled my head down on her chest. "Oh, my Davey Boy!" and she rocked me.

Through all the noise I was making, there was a tune in my head— *Danny Boy*—that she sang to her "Davey Boy" when I was little after I fell down or something...skinned my knee maybe.

She just rocked me and I felt her cool hands smoothing my hair and my neck.

Finally the tears stopped and I sat back up. My eyes felt like little puffy slits.

~

I told Mom about Arlene.

I didn't tell her about Billy...but that was really what this was about.

She smiled a very soft smile at me and her sky cloud eyes looked like she was remembering, "Davey, you are very young right now." She reached out and took my hand in hers. "You will probably fall in love lots of times from now on. I know this won't help right now, but when it doesn't work out, it won't be the end of the world. There will be other times." Her hand on top of mine felt like silk smoothing mine.

There was such an awful pain in me somewhere inside my chest and my throat ached. That's when I asked her if she knew right away when she was in love.

"Well, you know, it wasn't really like that with your dad. I've told you already about that. I really wanted to write. I wanted to be a journalist, but my family didn't have that kind of money, to send me to school. Because of the 'depression.' And other girls were just getting married, so that's what I did. BUT...when I met John, that was entirely different. I did know." She looked down at her hand smoothing mine, thinking.

I looked down too. Her ruby engagement ring glittered. Eight carat French cut.

"And I broke all the rules so we could be together."

After Word

I was waiting at those floor-to-ceiling windows in our house on the hill. Across the road, the valley from there to Barbur Boulevard was getting filled in with new construction. Duplexes. Triplexes. Pretty crappy looking stuff. Through the red and rust leaves of the few trees left, whitish bare lumber was going up. There was the whack, whack of hammers putting up the walls. Wrecking the view the windows used to have when Mom and Brew bought the house years ago.

But looking at the view now, my head was filled with how things had been in high school. Patti. Across Barbur there at the drive-in. Becky.

After Arlene, I did have dates. Even sexual ones with girls. But I was never able to brag to Billy. We hardly ever saw each other. In high school, Billy was more involved in sports. I wasn't. The choir, the band and the drama club were what I was doing.

Of course, necking with Patti right over there on the other side of Barbur turned me on too. Under a blanket on the side of the hill by the drive-in-movie. And feeling Becky's soft little breasts one night riding home on the bus from the choir concert. But with all the girls I dated, it was like it had been with Arlene. Never as romantic as I planned in my head beforehand. Something was still missing. That "happy thing." That thing I shared with Billy.

The first year at Portland State I went steady with a pretty blond girl. The aunt and uncle she lived with were both doctors on a college medical campus. Every time I went to see her, they spent the evening with her grandmother. Even told her they would get her protection, if we wanted it. Made it pretty easy to get it on together.

But, really, I was more attracted to her best friend's boyfriend that we double-dated with than my blond girlfriend. That was always disturbing to me. Not to mention, to my girlfriend. So we finally broke up before I went off to San Francisco State for my second year of college.

In San Francisco, I finally stopped trying to prove something to myself or anybody else. There, I wasn't alone. The Bay Area had plenty of men who accepted the fact that they were different. One night in a gay bar, a dark haired Italian guy came up to me. Asked if he could buy me a beer. But his eyes said all the rest.

I went home with him.

Stayed for several weeks.

But again, it turned out that it was not like I planned it in my head.

Mom had said way back there when she told me about sex, "This is only possible between two people who love each other very much." And then Cyril Bibby said the same thing in the book Crazy Lady Faely read to us in the fifth grade. The wonderful sex Dino and I were having must mean only one thing. We were very much in love.

After a couple of weeks though, my boyfriend told me that he was not in love with me.

That old rock slugged me in the chest again. I couldn't sleep at night. I didn't want to eat. After a few weeks, my skinny body got even skinnier. And aside from the pain, I was really confused.

He didn't love me back.

But something good came out of that time. Something of a miracle. It ended the bad dreams. Those horrible continuing sleep-walking hallucinations I'd had for years were gone. I had my last daymare a week before I met Dino. After that, they were only a bad memory. Maybe it was because with him I found the antidote. A magic potion. Love. For me, anyway. And sex. Together for the first time. How sweet life with someone would be if we both felt the same way. I would be willing to break all the rules for us to be together. No matter what the rest of the world said.

There it was again, the feeling of Billy, the old ache inside of me.

~

A year after my Italian, I decided to attend The Royal Music Conservatory in Stockholm and returned to Multnomah to say goodbye to Mom and Brew. Before leaving for Sweden while I was in our house on the hill, I invited Billy over for the afternoon.

So there I am standing by the floor-to-ceiling windows of the front room when this handsome young man with curly blond hair, sky blue eyes, and what could be described even at a distance as moth wing eyelashes, came walking up the winding sidewalk to our front door. My friend Billy had changed. His little boy face was gone. The soft features: hardened, leaner, more sculptured. His short body was taller now. More filled out and muscular. But when he smiled up at me, there was the same thing between us there had always been. It was like a private and perpetual electric current. An invisible beam of energy that tied us together.

A phrase from Rogers and Hammerstein went through my head. Like in one of those sappy Saturday afternoon movies I used to sit through in the Multnomah theatre, "across a crowded room." What the connection was, for the first time, was unmistakable.

"This is only possible between two people who…"

It had been there all the time. But I had been too busy hearing the other things—that what I felt was "a disease, a sickness," and the biggy—shaking hands was the limit of emotion men shared.

I bought into these.

As kids, we are taught what to believe, and we believe it to be true.

No one ever told me that you could fall in love with a friend.

I opened the door to my old friend with a hope that what we were both taught wasn't true. That maybe it wasn't too late for us after all. That he might feel the same way I did.

Billy and I sat over coffee that afternoon and talked. Talked like we used to over lousy macaroni and cheese casserole in the cafetorium. I filled Billy in on stuff I had been doing for years. Except for my new sex life. Waited for a loop hole in the conversation. Just a hint to go in that direction.

Billy told me what he had done in high school that I didn't know about. What he'd been up to since.

We finished our third cup of coffee. His cup sat on our old robin's egg blue table in front of him. Those eyes that always surprised me with their blueness looked at me and a little smile twitched in the corners of his mouth. Like he wasn't sure he should ask what he wanted to.

"You know," he said. "I never asked you what happened with you and Arlene back in the eighth grade."

"Oh," I said and tried to laugh off what came up for me.

Laughing had taken quite a while. It was too painful for years. But now I could almost laugh about it.

"It was a fiasco. She turned me down flat."

"Well, I knew she was going with Al Summers after that."

There was a little twinge of regret in my gut.

"Yup," I said.

Billy looked straight at me then. Held my eyes in his, like he wanted to say something.

I waited.

"Sorry, I know how much you wanted that to happen." Then his eyes dropped down at his coffee cup.

It sounded for all the world like an apology.

My eyes went down to the cup too. His hand wrapped around the warm coffee cup. The warm hand I held in the back seat of our Hudson.

A big empty hole yawned in my belly. I swallowed hard…

Finally, "Water under the bridge," I said. Trying to get out of my feelings, out of my memories. "How about you? Did you ever make it to the balcony on a Saturday night?"

Billy's eyebrows shot up and he laughed a little too loud. Maybe at himself. His face was red, but he looked relieved.

"Me? No. I'm a really late bloomer."

"Oh, yeah?" I said.

"Yeah, I guess maybe I was interested earlier but I was just too shy to do anything about it."

There it was again—hope. It was an ache in my stomach like the one I had on the mattress we put down for him on the floor of my bedroom. An ache that made me want to reach out to him. Put my arms around him. Feel his head on my chest. The warmth of him fold into me. I could show him what I had learned about loving, if he'd let me. If he'd let me in. Like that time when he lifted the covers. Invited me into his igloo. Billy could be the one. The one that could love back.

His blue eyes looked down again at the coffee cup. The fingers of his left hand fumbled with the handle.

A lump grew in my throat. There on the handle were those swollen knuckles.

"Well, you know I never had a girlfriend," he said.

This was not news. I was always thinking of that when I was talking to him about girls. Arlene. Telling him about making out with Gary's cousin, Alicia. Kind of sorry for him but hoping at the same time. Maybe now he had finally come to the same place I had. Maybe. My heart was pounding so hard in my ears I stopped breathing so I wouldn't miss it when he told me what I was dying to hear. Maybe this was the loop hole.

Then Billy said, "But I do think maybe I've met her."

I felt the muscles change in my face. Every nerve end tightened.

"Yeah," he said. "She might just be the one I ask to marry me."

His blue eyes darted up to mine again like this time there might really be apology in them.

It was like the chair went out from under me and I ended up sprawled on the floor. My stony face just looking up at him. Another one of those moments when things just don't work out like you hope or plan them in your head.

Billy went on to tell me the odd way he met this young nurse while he was finishing college. His eyes were down looking at his cup again all the time he was telling me. His hand playing with the handle. How his mother wanted to set up his younger brother with a nurse who worked with her in a doctor's office. It had to be a double-date to get the nurse to date his brother. So a double-date was set up for Billy to go out with the nurse's best friend, Jennifer. Jennifer just happened to be a nurse as well.

I sat there trying to look happy for him. All the time inside the upright posture and pleasant smile a power mower was shredding my innards.

"You know," he was saying, "I've always been so shy about that stuff. It took my mom to fix me up with a date. If it hadn't been for her, I probably wouldn't 've ever met anybody."

His eyes finally looked up at me.

How could I have been so dumb to wait so long? Taken so long to wake up?

"But we've been going together ever since," he said with a smile now. Like one you practice in the mirror. A smile he was just trying out on me.

I lifted my cup. Took a sip. The coffee was cold. An acid muddy taste in my mouth.

There was no point in me telling him where my journey had taken me. No point sharing with him what I felt for him when I saw him coming up our walk.

He was clearly not going there. We were headed in different directions. I wondered if we had ever been on the same path. But, it was clear, there wasn't going to be a loop hole. No hint in the conversation.

To him, his nurse was the perfect life partner. He was glad he'd bloomed late and not gotten involved with anyone before he met her.

I made some noises that he could take for approval. Tried to hide that my throat was raw and burning and my mind was telling me to scream.

As he talked, a numbness came over me. It was harder and harder to respond. My smile muscles hurt.

At about four thirty, he looked at his watch. Jennifer asked him to pick her up from work. He was afraid he might be late.

We stood up.

Somebody must've snuck up behind me and hit me in the head with a hammer.

I walked him through the living room.

My head ached. The carpet under my feet was unsteady. My feet were trying to walk a tight rope. With every step, my legs were shaking. Not sure where to put my feet.

The person I had loved for a good part of my life was stepping out of it. Oh, we'd call each other. Send each other Christmas cards. Birthday cards. But he was leaving. Compared with what I had hoped, he would be gone from my life.

At the front door, he smiled that soft smile and the moth wings fluttered but he didn't stop. He moved through the door.

And was gone.

After Afterword

Stockholm, Copenhagen, Paris, London, Vienna, Rome. By the mid-sixties, I had been to most of the capitols of Europe. But not like I dreamed I would back in Multnomah Grade School after meeting Mr. Nichols. I did become a professional singer. But the only performance I did outside the U.S. by then was for the ship's audience on the way to school in Sweden. My visits to these cities had been either as a student or tourist.

After school in Sweden, I returned to San Francisco and sang with a non-professional theatre company for a couple of years. Then, determined to pursue a singing career, I moved across the U.S. to New York City.

The country was going through a social revolution. Making love not war. In a few years San Francisco would have its summer of love.

Back home in Oregon, the most loving men of my childhood were gone. My wonderful Pop. He'd gone off to dance with his beloved Belle in a place where the dancing never stops. My Uncle Lloyd of the agate shop succumbed to MS and was gone. Who knew where my brother, Scott, was? Probably somewhere in the jungles of Micronesia. But, here in New York, I did have new love in my life. Ironic as it was, his name was Bill. But this Bill could love back.

Making a living at singing had come pretty easily in New York. A permanent position as the assistant soloist for a church that met at Carnegie Hall. Then a job as a soloist at Radio City Music Hall. There, I could come and go. When a show closed at the Hall, I could sign on again. Or go on tour in the chorus of one of the many new musicals.

Mom and Brew came through town from a trip to Europe when I was singing in one of the old ones, off Broadway—the title role in The Student Prince. Most likely I was doing it because of my infatuation with Mario Lanza as a kid. Mr. Nichols would have been proud.

Mom and Brew were staying at the Mansfield on West 44th Street off 5th Avenue. A little hotel listed in their guide book, New York on $5 a Day. Just one night and they'd be on their way back home to Oregon. Since it'd been a couple of years, I was looking forward to seeing them. Mom and I had been writing. We never ran out of things to talk about. But that might not be the case now for me and Brew. I hadn't said three words to him in over a year.

There would be one thing though.

A month before their visit, I went with friends to Coney Island on the Fourth of July. After finding a couple beach-towel size spots on the beach between all the other sunbathers, we headed for the waves. Right after diving into the water I remembered I was wearing my watch. It was a Bulova I'd had for years. Since high school graduation. It was the last gift Earl, my father, ever sent me. Probably the last time I ever heard from him.

Since Brew and my dad, Earl were both in the jewelry business, I knew enough to get out of the salty water. I jumped out onto the beach and headed for my beach towel. Then popped open the watch and set the pieces gently on the towel to dry in the sun. By the time my folks arrived in New York, it still wasn't running. It would be the perfect thing to talk about with Dad. After all these years, that's what I was trying to call Brew: "Dad." If nothing else, he at least hadn't rejected me for who I was. Like a lot of gay men's fathers had.

When Brew opened the door to their hotel room, he looked a lot older. There was grey in the black wavy hair and wrinkles around his eyes. He was wearing one of those polyester leisure suits and it just looked kind of out of place on him. He always looked more comfortable in work clothes anyway, but this one was a pretty vivid rust color.

Mom was weathering a lot better. But she said they were both tired from their trip. They were anxious to get home. When Mom wrote to me about their trip to the British Isles, it was kind of a surprise. Brew was pretty much a stay-at-home kind of guy.

Mom looked different though. She had begun her new era of fashion. Pants. These were pale beige. Skirts and dresses were now a thing of the past in her wardrobe. And her glasses were no longer swooped up but more round and over-sized. Like Audrey Hepburn sunglasses.

We went down to the hotel restaurant and had lunch. I didn't need the watch story though. They both had stories of their trip they wanted to tell me. How they'd made friends with an English couple. Planned to stay in touch. Had seen palm trees in southern England. And how surprised Brew was that Mom didn't want to see much of Ireland. Mom wanted me to tell her all about Student Prince. She said she was really sorry they'd arrived on a Sunday night. She didn't know we were dark on Mondays. But Dad was grinning into his highball of scotch and water all the time she was telling how sorry they both were that they couldn't see the show.

There was a lull in the conversation though when we got back to their room. Mom was busy rattling coat hangers, piling stuff in suit cases and closing up cosmetics. Brew and I were just sitting on the beds with nothing much to do. It was kind of left up to the two of us to talk to each other. So I brought up the Bulova.

"Dad," I said, "I was wondering if you thought this was worth fixing."

I held out the watch to him in my hand.

"I went swimming in the ocean and-"

I got that far and he took it from my hand and with a quick flick of his wrist, flipped it into the near-by waste basket. *Klunk*.

Then, always the man of few words, he just looked at me with a kind of unreadable grin on his face.

The machinery in my head just stopped. Like the watch. And my mouth fell open.

That was from my dad…Earl.

Then the machinery started to whir double time.

He must have remembered Earl gave me that. Maybe not. Maybe he just thought the watch was a lost cause. Maybe he thought Earl was. Pretty true. Could have been a weird way he was showing affection—I'm here, Earl's not.

In my head, there was a picture of Brew with that same expression. It was when I had come back from Sweden and found that my uncle Lloyd had died. I asked Brew where my rock collection was and he told me with that same unreadable expression and a shrug that he'd given it away. Never asked or told me, just gave it away. The same happened to my collection of old 78 Caruso recordings.

Had he wanted to remove all traces of me from their life like stuffing Teddy into the closet or did he just get rid of things he considered useless?

My mind slowed a little.

A breath of air brought in Mom's powder smells, like I was just learning to breathe. Then, hotel air freshener.

Something had lifted off my chest.

Well, that was the last of Earl. With a final flip what was left of him in my life went into the waste basket.

Downstairs, I flagged an airport cab for them on the corner of 5th Avenue. The driver got their luggage and Mom jumped in. Dad was about to. Then he turned with his hand out to shake.

There was this hand in front of me. Worn and rough from a lot of work. Callused fingers. Broken nails. A hand that one time had been tanned and smooth. Held out the same way back then. But this wasn't the nineteen forties now. We were in the nineteen sixties. Men had learned to do more than shake hands, for God sakes. Forget the hand. It was now or never. I was going to give old Brew a hug.

My arms spread out like I was about to take off flying. Like I was standing again at the top of the Moo-Cow Hill.

A look of panic was on Brew's face. The graying widow's peak came down and the fading brown eyes opened wide. My arms closed in and around him standing paralyzed on that street corner. The sensation was that I was standing on a corner in the middle of Manhattan hugging a telephone pole. His body was as rigid as a tree rooted to the pavement. But the body in my arms was clearly made of flesh. At least of blood. His face was a dark blood red. And it wasn't wood against me. It was overheated polyester.

But I held on.

As a child, I had lost my best friend without a goodbye. I had lost Uncle Herb early on too. The man who made me feel I was a man while I was still a boy. I lost a father before I even knew what a father was. The remnants of that relationship ended up just now in a hotel waste basket. My beloved Pop was gone. Uncle Lloyd. So was Billy. And I had lost my brother years ago.

This was my chance to hang onto the only remaining male figure of my childhood and I was not about to let go until I got an indication that this man was capable of some sort of emotional response. After all, the whole country was going through a change. Love Now. Could this man be the only one not affected by it?

Cars moved by on Fifth Avenue like part of a glacier flow.

A cab horn blared at the intersection. A siren sounded somewhere uptown.

And still his body was as dense as wood.

The light changed and the traffic on Fifth Avenue bolted like horses at a starting gate. The street was empty.

What was that?

I felt something on my back.

Was that a pat?

Brew's body was easing up. Softening. Less rigid. He was responding.

I looked down at his face.

When did he get to be so short?

He always towered over me. But now I was looking down at him.

His face was a normal color. No longer red. And there was a smile trying to form on his face.

Then he actually squeezed.

I was so surprised, I let go. As soon as I did, he ducked into the cab and it took off down 5th Avenue to Chambers on the way to La Guardia.

~

My eyes followed the cab darting from one lane to another until the dot it became was lost in traffic.

"You son of a gun," I thought. I wanted so much for that to have meant something.

I almost believe it did.

Acknowledgements

This book might never have been written at all if it had not been for Kate Gray and her encouragement and support and for her unwavering faith that Davey Brugger had something to say. It is with many thanks also to Portland State University's summer writing program, Haystack, at Cannon Beach, Oregon and Tom Spanbauer's Dangerous Writers where Kate and I met, and the first page of this book was written. From that first page to the completion of *Men Shake Hands*, Kate offered her skillful help and steadfast assurance that it was necessary to tell Davey's story.

The book, because of two major illnesses, took an inordinate time to come into being. Through these times I had an amazing number of friends and family helping me to recover and giving their time and encouragement to get well and to keep writing. In particular, I would like to thank my lifelong friend, Sunny Graham whose friendship and enthusiasm about writing has been a torch leading the way. That group of friends also includes the members of my beloved Light Opera of Portland. Not "a little," but "a lotta help from my friends" got me here today. Thank you, David and Linda Smith, and especially the five people who gathered weekly in the later stages of development of the book to read together and help get *Men Shake Hands* on its feet, Lindsey Lefler, Bill Wuertz, Kevin Lay, Beth Kahlen and Michael Harvey.

And finally, my editor extraordinaire, Ginna BB Gordon, thank you for believing in Davey Brugger so much to sit with him and really listen.

To all these loving and generous souls, I give my heartfelt thanks.

About the Author

A lifelong man of the theater, Dennis Britten began as a musician, study-ing composition and developing as a singer. He became a member of Actor's Equity and began to perform at an early age. After years of perform-ing opera and musical theatre in New York City, nationally and abroad, he returned to school where he obtained an undergraduate degree, summa cum laude with departmental honors, in theater direction at SUNY Stony Brook and then continued on there to hold a master's degree in creative writing. His first novel was his master's thesis, *To Value Both*.

While still in NY, he collaborated with Kenneth Fuchs in writing the book and lyrics to their Off off-Broadway musical, *If Wishes Were Horses*. Later, as an Asst. Professor at Arizona State University, he founded his first theatre company, Phoenix Show Space Theatre where he acted as Artistic Director and manager.

Back in his home state of Oregon, he founded and became Artistic Director of Light Opera of Portland - Absurdity Done in Complete Sincerity, where his second musical, *We Met in Moscow*, written in col-laboration with composer, Kevin Bryant Lay was produced.

Dennis is also the author of one collection of poetry, *Made in Oregon*.

CPSIA information can be obtained
at www.ICGtesting.com
Printed in the USA
FSHW011736240122
87855FS